RIO NEGRO, RICH LIFE IN POOR WATER

RIO NEGRO, RICH LIFE IN POOR WATER

Amazonian Diversity and Foodchain Ecology
as Seen Through Fish Communities

Michael Goulding, Mirian Leal Carvalho
and Efrem G. Ferreira

SPB Academic Publishing bv 1988

CIP-DATA KONINKLIJKE BIBLIOTHEEK, DEN HAAG

Goulding, Michael

Rio Negro : rich life in poor water : Amazonian diversity
and foodchain ecology as seen through fish communities /
Michael Goulding, Mirian Leal Carvalho and Efrem G.
Ferreira. – The Hague : SPB Academic Publishing. – Ill.
With ref.
  ISBN 90-5103-016-9
SISO 573.3 UDC 574.2/.3(81) (282) NUGI 823
Subject heading: ecology ; Rio Negro.

ISBN 90-5103-016-9

CONTENTS

Part II: Trophic interactions and organization

Part III: Diversity and community development

Appendices

PREFACE

The Rio Negro is the Amazon's largest tributary. It is also either the second or third largest river in the world. This work offers an ecological view of the Rio Negro as focused through fish life. Following the Introduction, the book is divided into four parts. Part I provides a geographical overview of the Rio Negro basin, including its physical features, the origins of its blackwaters and the nature of the plant life on which the ecology of the system is based. Part II examines herbivory, detritivory, carnivory on invertebrates and piscivory in the framework of the diversity of terrestrial, arboreal and aquatic life with which Rio Negro fish life interacts. Theoretical aspects of the trophic ecology are also discussed. Part III presents an analysis of Rio Negro fish diversity, habitat use and community organization, followed by the major conclusions of the book. The Appendices contain summaries of the quantitative data on which the study is based.

ACKNOWLEDGEMENTS

The research on which this book is based was made possible through financing from Brazil's Conselho Nacional de Desenvolvimento Científico e Tecnológico (CNPq) -in conjunction with its Amazonian research institutions, the Museu Paraense Emilio Goeldi (Belém) and the Instituto Nacional de Pesquisas da Amazônia (INPA, Manaus) – and World Wildlife Fund US. The Rio Negro project was further supported by the Secretaria Especial do Meio Ambiente (SEMA – Brazil's Environmental Protection Agency). The Museu de Zoologia of the Universidade de São Paulo (MZUSP) provided logistical and identification support for the large fish collections that were made. Sharp do Brasil provided free transportation for much of the fish collection.

The following people are thanked:

Administrative and scientific support: Thomas E. Lovejoy (Executive Vice President, World Wildlife Fund US), Paulo Nogueira Neto (former Director, Secretaria Especial do Meio Ambiente), Guilherme de la Penha (Director, Museu Paraense Emilio Goeldi), José Seixas Lourenço (former Director, Museu Paraense Emilio Goeldi), Nancy Hammond (Vice President, World Wildlife Fund US), Fernando Novaes (Chairman, Zoology Department, Museu Paraense Emilio Goeldi), Heraldo Britski (Chairman, Fish Division, Museu de Zoologia da Universidade de São Paulo), Paulo Vanzolini (Director, Museu de Zoologia da Universidade de São Paulo), Enéas Salati (former Director, Instituto Nacional de Pesquisas da Amazônia), Henrique Bergamin (former Director, Instituto Nacional de Pesquisas da Amazônia), Russel Mittermeier (Vice President, World Wildlife Fund US), Pieter Oyens (Brazil Project Director, World Wildlife Fund US), Mark Plotkin (Plant Conservation Director, World Wildlife Fund US), Herbert Schubart (Director, Instituto Nacional de Pesquisas da Amazônia), Gelso Vazzoler (former chairman, Ichthyology Department, Instituto Nacional de Pesquisas da Amazônia).
Laboratory, field or fishing assistance: Nisa S. M. Gonçalves, Raimundo Aragão Serrão, Raimundo Sotero da Silva, Anazildo Mateus da Sena, George Nakamura, Graça Overal, Tereza Lobão, Guilherme Borges, Carlos Sotero da Silva, Raimundo Nonnato (Lola), João Pena, Aderson de Souza dos Santos, Antônio Torquato de Oliveira, Agenor Negrão da Silva, Gentil Alves da Rocha, Abacaxi, Manoel Sotero da Silva, Umbelino Jorge de Oliveira, Dorval dos Santos, José Umbelino da Silva, Chico de Tefé, Raimundo Laredo Smith, Jurandir Pina do Nascimento, Raimundo de Tefé, Sebastião, Estácio Gomes, Pedro Makayama, Walkiria da Conceição, Rosa Makayama, Valter dos Santos Dias, Raimundo (SEMA raft), José Edson de Rezende, Joaldo Bezerra, João, Márcia Motta Maués, Ivan Rebelo Porto, Walmecy da Silva Miranda.

Computer assistance: Sid Cowles (Lawrence Livermore Laboratory, University of California) and Barry Lewis (IBM consultant).
Drawings: Sandoval Ferreira Martins Neto and Antônio Carlos Seabra Martins.
General help: William L. Overal, Anthony Anderson, Chris Seamans, Charles F. Bennett, Carole Bennett, Bob Waste, Kathy Lemke Waste.
Advice on Rio Negro blackwater chemistry: Jerry A. Leenheer.
Fish identifications: Sven Kullander (Cichlidae), Richard Vari (Curimatidae), Luis Paulo Stockler Portugal (various small characin groups), Naércio Menezes (various predatory characin groups) Stanley Weitzman (Gasteropelecinae, Lebiasinidae, various small characins), Heraldo Britski, (various catfish groups), William L. Fink (initial separation of piranhas), Sara Fink (initial separation of piranhas), José Lima Figueiredo (separation of various loricariid genera), Jaques Gery (various small characins), Horst Schwassmann (Gymnotiform electric fishes), Gareth Nelson (Engraulidae), Marilyn Weitzman (Lebiasinidae and various small characins), Júlio Garavello (various Anostomidae), Bruce Collette (Belonidae), Lucia Py-Daniel (separation of Loricariidae), Labbish Chao (separation of Sciaenidae).
Plant identifications: Ione Bemerguy (organization of plant collection in the Museu Goeldi), Nelson Rosa (various taxa), M. E. Fallen (Apocynaceae), A. Gentry (Bignoniaceae), G. T. Prance (Chrysobalanaceae), D. F. Austin (Convolvulaceae), C. A. Stace (Combretaceae), E. Forero (Connaraceae), C. Jeffrey (Cucurbitaceae), K. Kubitski (Dilleniaceae), M. J. Huft (Euphorbiaceae), J. Rohwer (Lauraceae), S. Mori (Lecythidaceae), R. Barneby (Leguminosae), G. P. Lewis (Leguminosae), M. G. A. Lobo (Leguminosae), A. S. L. Silva (Leguminosae), R. Cowan (Leguminosae), W. R. Anderson (Malpighiaceae), J. Wurdack (Melastomataceae), C. C. Berg (Moraceae), W. Rodrigues (Myristicaceae), J. H. Kirkbride (Rubiaceae), J. M. Pires (Sapotaceae, Quiinaceae), P. Cavalcante (Gnetaceae, Simarubaceae).
Arthropod identifications: William Overal, Bento Mascarenhas, Innocêncio Gorayeb and the Entomology Department of the Museu Paraense Emilio Goeldi (insects); Brian Kensley (Smithsonian Institution) and Célio Ubirajara Magalhães Filho (INPA) (decapods).
Criticisms of the manuscript: Rosemary Lowe-McConnell, Stanley Weitzman, Sven Kullander and Marilyn Weitzman.

1. INTRODUCTION

PURPOSE OF INVESTIGATION AND STUDY SITE

The choice of the Rio Negro for the present investigation springs from an intellectual curiosity about the nature of life in the world's largest blackwater river and an interest in developing generalizations about Amazon ecology that can be used for management and conservation theory. In terms of natural history exploration, the Rio Negro represents one of the great fluvial frontiers left on earth. The only previous general accounts of Rio Negro natural history are Alfred Russel Wallace's (1853) *Narrative of Travels on the Amazon and Rio Negro* and Richard Spruce's (1908) *Notes of a Botanist on the Amazon and Andes*, the two works that, along with Sir Arthur Conan Doyle's (1912) *The Lost World*, ushered the giant blackwater river into the scientific and literary theater. In this work we attempt to outline the ecological play of the Rio Negro as revealed through fish life and its interactions with habitats and food organisms in the blackwater environment.

FIELD METHODS

Time Period

The study was conducted during various periods between 1979 and 1987 as part of a larger project designed to elucidate ecological and distributional patterns of Amazonian fishes. Subsequent to the main field work period (1979-1982) in the Rio Negro basin, the delay in publishing the results was due mostly to the great amount of time that was needed to separate specimens into species groups and to obtain the best identifications available in the present state of knowledge. Two to three full-time laboratory assistants were employed to help separate and measure specimens, and the assistance of about a dozen systematists and taxonomists was needed to arrive at the present identifications of species [see below for problems associated with identifications].

The investigation was initiated in 1979 with a two month (May and June) surface reconnaissance by boat of the Rio Negro from its mouth to the first major cataracts, located about 1200 km upstream at São Gabriel da Cachoeira (Fig. 1.1 and Fig. 1.2). The middle and upper Rio Negro, that is, above the mouth of the Rio Branco, was studied on four different occasions: May and June, 1979 represented the high water period; October and November, 1979 represented intermediate water levels, and; February and March 1980 embraced the dry season with low river levels. The last excursion was undertaken in January and February, 1987 to photograph fishes and to gather more information on the aquarium trade [the latter data to be published elsewhere]. Taken together, the four excursions to the upper Rio Negro sum to about

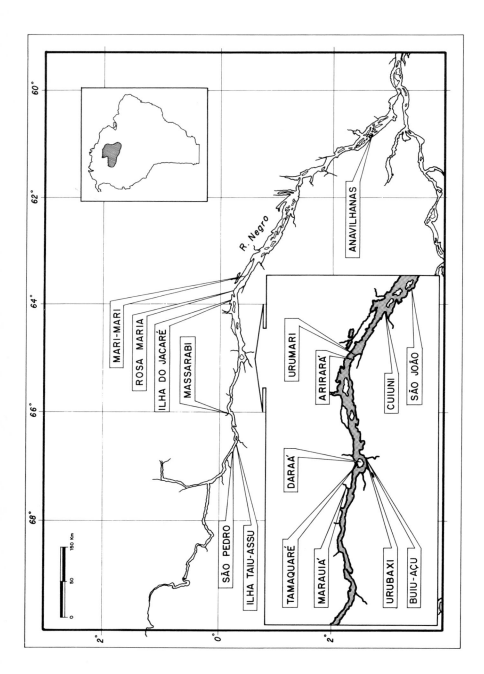

Fig. 1.1. Collecting sites of the Rio Negro study.

2

Fig. 1.2. Type of boat used during Rio Negro excursions.

seven months, which provided sufficient time to collect large numbers of specimens and to witness the seasonality of this part of the river.

Since the late 1970's, Brazil's Environmental Protection Agency, known under the acronym of SEMA, has maintained a vigilance and research raft in the federal government's ecological reserve that embraces the huge river archipelago, called the Anavilhanas, in the lower Rio Negro (Fig. 1.3). Between February 1980 and February 1981, we were given permission to collect fishes and other organisms in the SEMA reserve. A site near the middle of the archipelago was chosen for the study, and it was fished in every month for a one year period.

Choice of Habitats for Study

Surface reconnaissance, Landsat satellite imagery and natural history folklore gleaned from the local residents were considered when dividing the Rio Negro into its principal habitat types and to choose sampling sites. For the purposes of this study, the Rio Negro was divided into the seven major habitat types outlined below [cataracts, including those of clearwater tributaries, were also studied, but they will be considered elsewhere]. The development of Rio Negro habitats in relation to geology, water level, stream morphology and vegetation is found in Chapters 2 and 3. The habitat characteristics of the collection sites are presented in Appendix 1. See Fig. 1.1 for schematic distribution of the habitats sampled.

1. *Inundation Forest:* Forest subject to seasonal inundation by the river is found

3

Fig. 1.3 Research raft used in the Anavilhanas Ecological Reserve of the lower Rio Negro.

the length of the Rio Negro, though most extensive in the lower and middle reaches. Nearly all of the numerous islands in the Rio Negro are covered mostly by inundation forest. Ecologically, island inundation forest is here considered the same thing as floodplain forest.

2. *Isolated Island Lakes:* These waterbodies are found nearly the length of the Rio Negro wherever there are islands. Most are isolated from the river channel for 5-8 months each year. Fishes either retreat to them or become trapped therein with falling water level. During the floods they are joined to the river by waters inundating the intervening forest that surrounds them. They were sampled only after they had become completely isolated from river channels, that is, during the low water season.

3. *Woody Shore Areas:* These are defined here as the edges of inundation forests, including those of islands, during the low water period. There are also extensive woody shores along *terra firme* banks, but these account for less shoreline in the Rio Negro than the total contributed by islands.

4. *Beaches:* Most Rio Negro beaches are sandy, though some are clayey. Near the confluences of leftbank clearwater tributaries of the middle and upper Rio Negro there are also pebble beaches. All but one of the beaches sampled were sandy, the one exception being composed of silt. Beaches are emerged mostly during the low water period, at which time they can be seen intermittently the length of the Rio Negro.

5. *Confluence Swamps*: Large swamps are characteristic of the areas near the confluences of middle Rio Negro tributaries with the main trunk. These swamps have a complex network of interdigitating channels that are divided by small islands, on

4

Fig. 1.4 Seine fishing method.

which palm communities are often the dominant plant formation. The one confluence swamp studied was collected only during the low water period.

6. *Floating Meadows*: These habitats are only found in the lower Rio Negro, where they are most developed adjacent to inundation forest.

7. *Rocky Pools*: Rocky substrates are only common in the upper Rio Negro region, especially near and above the Rio Daraá. The one rocky pool studied was fished during the low water period.

Sampling Techniques

All of our analyses are based, spatially and temporally, on individual sites. All together, 40 individual sites embracing seven habitat types were sampled for this study; only 10 of these sites, however, were sampled intensively (site locations are shown in Fig. 1.1 and summary information can be found in Appendices 1 and 2). The sites were distributed along a 1200 km transect. Sampling and collecting a river as diverse in species as is the Rio Negro presents difficult problems in an initial survey, especially when you are trying to deal with all of the taxa. There is no one fishing method that is adequate for all habitats. Our principal collecting goal was to attempt

Fig. 1.5 The preparation of *Derris* sp. root to be used as piscicide. The root is beaten with clubs so that the toxic compounds will be released more freely into the water.

Fig. 1.6 Piscicide fishing is commonly practiced in the middle and upper Rio Negro in the manner shown in the photograph.

Fig. 1.7. Schematic illustration of how flooded forest habitat was sampled

to detect the community species diversity in various habitats and to gather sufficient numbers of specimens for stomach content analyses. No attempt was made to measure biomass and we doubt that there is any practical and reliable method for measuring it in a meaningful way in most Rio Negro habitats.

A 30 m seine was the principal gear used on beaches (Fig. 1.4). Beach waters are relatively easy to sample because, during the low water period, the fishes are usually schooling and found in dense concentrations in these shallow habitats. Island lakes and the one rocky pool studied were sampled with locally grown *Derris* sp. (Leguminosae), a piscicidal plant used by Amerindians in the middle and upper Rio Negro region (Figs. 1.5 and 1.6). Woody shore areas were sampled with the 30 m seine and with dipnets and gillnets. Fishes from flooded forests were collected with gillnets, line – and – pole and dipnets (Fig. 1.7). The habitat that requires the most amount of time to sample is the flooded forest. This is because the annual inundations greatly increase the aquatic environment and the fishes are able to disperse over many kilometers of floodplain, thus much more time is needed to catch them.

COLLECTIONS AND ANALYSES

The total sample for the Rio Negro included approximately 108,000 specimens em-

Tab. 1.1. Summary of Rio Negro fish collection and the specimens studied.

	N Sites Samples	N Species Captured	N Specimens Captured	N Species Examined for food	N Specimens Examined for food
HIGH WATER					
Flooded Forests	8	183	6775	97	1808
LOW WATER					
Woody Shores	9	201	11106	83	1282
Beaches	15	268	35890	121	2144
Island Lakes	4	163	15417	91	1360
Floating Meadows	2	56	1695	17	163
Rocky Pool	1	107	1388	46	308
Confluence Swamp	1	148	35960	80	1498
Totals	40	450	108231	250	8563

bracing at least 450 species (Tab. 1.1 and Appendices 1,2 and 3). Over 95 percent of the collection was studied, that is, all specimens that were not too damaged to be recognized. All specimens were separated into their respective species, either by ourselves or by specialists listed in the acknowledgments. All specimens were measured for standard length, which was taken from the snout to the posterior bones of the caudal peduncle. Most of the Rio Negro fish collection was incorporated into the Museu de Zoologia of the Universidade de São Paulo, the registration numbers of which can be found in the Appendices and in Goulding, Carvalho & Ferreira (no date). The plant collection was registered with the Herbarium of the Museu Paraense Emilio Goeldi (Belém), from which specimens were sent to specialists for verification or correction of identifications [plant registration numbers are found in Appendix 7].

IDENTIFICATIONS AND NOMENCLATURE

A stable nomenclature is an annoying problem for scientific studies of the Amazon fish fauna. The present classifications of most Amazonian fish groups do not reflect evolutionary relationships below the family level, as most of the genera, and the species that are grouped in them, have not been subjected to rigorous systematic analyses (Bohlke, Weitzman & Menezes, 1978; Weitzman & Fink, 1983). It should be expected that at least 50 percent of the Latin binomials now used for Amazonian fishes will be changed once systematists have done the necessary revisions. This point is demonstrated by Kullander's (1983, 1986) recent reclassification of South American cichlids, where most of the binomials have been changed in accordance with new generic and specific definitions embracing modern systematic concepts. Since our study deals with aspects of life histories, community diversity and broad-scale interactions, and not with hypothetical relationships of taxa related to evolutionary ecology, nomenclatural changes should not taint our general conclusions. By registering our specimens at the Museu de Zoologia of the Universidade de São Paulo, the assigned voucher numbers will serve as well as Latin names until such time that a stable nomenclature is available, and this will probably be decades for most genera.

There is undoubtedly misidentification - splitting and lumping -of some taxa in this study. Also, ichthyological taxonomists working with the South American fish fauna do not follow a uniform splitting and lumping pattern, each taxonomist using a slightly different, and often subjective, criterion to define species. Overall, however, we believe that the species are separated accurately enough for the community analyses we present herein. We suspect that at least another 50 species, especially 'cryptic' forms that are rare but closely resemble common taxa, could be culled from the Rio Negro collection if enough taxonomic knowledge, time and money were available. Our fish collection, then, probably contains around 500 species from the blackwaters of the Rio Negro.

ANALYSES OF DIETS

The stomach and/or intestine content analyses used for this study were based on three main factors:
1) the food item;
2) the number of species that fed on each food item;
3) mean volume of each food item for each population studied.
The absolute and relative occurrences of individual food items were also measured, but this factor is more important for the study of individual species than for community analyses. Occurrence values of individual food items are presented in Goulding, Carvalho & Ferreira (no date).

Potential food items for fishes are theoretically as numerous as the total number of plant and animal species present. Because of obvious identification problems, we only recognized 68 types of food items. The number of plant and animal species used by Rio Negro fishes as food probably exceeds 5000 species. Our choice of the food items recognized was based on our own ability, or that of specialists consulted, to identify the organisms.

Volumetric measurements were based on total stomach fullness and the relative contribution of each food item. This measurement is somewhat subjective because of the great elasticity of most fish stomachs, but nevertheless it is accurate enough for evaluating general food habits derived from non-experimental data (Hynes, 1950; Hyslop, 1980). Furthermore, our analyses are based on individual populations of individual species, thus the degree of elasticity, which to some extent appears to be influenced by seasonal factors for the larger taxa, would not appear to bias the overall analyses. Size class disparity could also bias volumetric measurements but, overall, the standard deviations of the populations we studied were not so great to suggest that this might be a serious problem. In other words, few young fish were examined as they were not captured.

Stomach fullness was estimated at one of the following intervals: empty, 10%, 25%, 50%, 75% or 100%. To measure the relative contribution of each food item in a stomach, we first estimated its volume as a percentage of the total food present. Each of these food item percentages was then multiplied by the fullness value for each specimen examined; the resulting product is the absolute volume of each food item for each specimen. The absolute volumes of each food item from all specimens examined from each individual population at each individual site were then summed. The sums for individual food items were then converted into percentages, that is, the volumetric percentage that each food item represented in the population sample of each species that we studied. An evaluation of trophic tendencies was gleaned from these percentages, and the method is discussed in more detail in Chapter 9.

PART I
THE RIO NEGRO

2. PHYSICAL ASPECTS OF THE RIO NEGRO

SITE AND SITUATION

The Rio Negro is situated in northern South America, in the Amazon Basin and un-evenly astride the equator (Fig 2.1). The river basin of the Rio Negro, including its tributaries, is shaped, as seen on a map, like a deformed and inverted teardrop. The Rio Negro encompasses about four degrees of latitude and ten degrees of longitude. The large river flows within three degrees, either north or south, of the equator but, meteorologically, it embraces both equatorial and tropical climatic patterns, a fact, as will be seen later, that plays heavily in the aquatic ecology of the region.

The Amazon Basin drains about 7 million km^2, of which the Rio Negro contrib-utes .75 million km^2, or a little over 10 percent. Although not larger in total annual discharge of water, several of the Amazon's southern tributaries, such as the Xingu and Tapajós, are longer than the Rio Negro. The Guiana Shield slopes mostly north-wards to the Orinoco system, thus the Rio Negro to the south of the highlands, drains only about 30% of the area of the ancient massif. The length of the Rio Negro, from its mouth to its northwestern headwaters in pre-Andean Colombia, is at least 1,700 km. From the Rio Negro's confluence with the Rio Solimões-Amazonas (Amazon River) to its headwaters on the high Guiana Shield, via the Rio Branco and Rio Ura-ricoera, the drainage length is about 1,500 km. The Rio Negro basin is connected fluvially to river systems to the north, west, east and northeast. The most famous connection, the Casiquiare, links the upper Rio Negro with the Orinoco system [see Fig 2.1]. The Casiquiare was made a famous geographical word through the studies of Alexander von Humboldt, whose travels to the equinoctial regions of South America were undertaken, in part, to investigate the concept of stream capture, that is, of a river, when viewed on a map, that appears to defy the laws of gravity and flow in two directions. Humboldt's investigations demonstrated that the Casiquiare region was not a headwater swamp of the two large river systems − the Negro and Orinoco − but rather a relatively swift moving waterbody that easily qualified as a 'rio', as it is often now labeled on maps (Humboldt, 1852). The Canal Casiquiare, or Rio Casiquiare, presents no technical problems for explaining its existence. Geo-morphologically, it is a tributary of the Orinoco, but fluvially, an affluent of the Negro which in recent geological history has *captured* it because relative elevational changes have favored the Casiquiare's flow to the south instead of north to its parent trunk (Stern, 1970; Edwards & Thornes, 1970).

The Guiana Shield is a swaybacked formation trending southeast to northwest and, for the most part, the ancient massif separates the coastal areas of the Guianas from the Amazon Basin. In the low-lying region between the Guiana Shield's two up-land formations, headwaters (Rio Tacatu) of the Rio Branco meet with streams flow-ing into the Essequibo-Rupununi rivers of Guyana. Aerial photography also suggests that the Rio Negro is linked, during high water, with the Rio Uatumã to the east and to the Rio Japurá to the west. Historical documents indicate that Amerindians, at

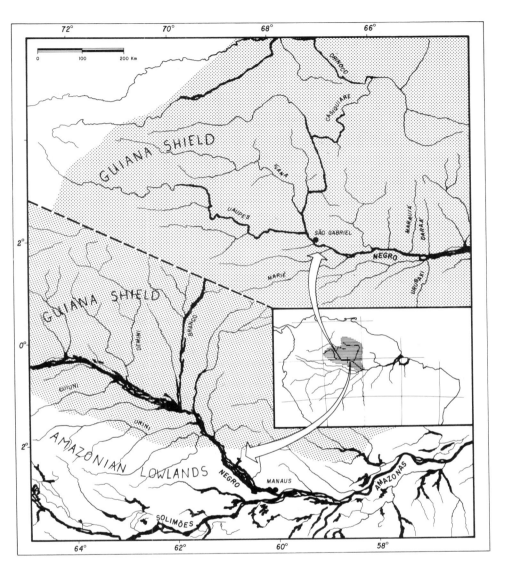

Fig. 2.1 The Rio Negro basin and its general geological features.

the time of the arrival of Portuguese conquerors in the sixteenth century, were canoe-ing between the Rio Negro and Rio Japurá systems for the purpose of trading feathers and other products (Sweet, 1974). The Rio Urubaxi and Rio Cuiuini, right-bank tributaries of the upper and middle Rio Negro, are mentioned, and satellite im-agery and local information strongly suggest that these two affluents, and probably several others as well, link the Japurá and Negro rivers.

DISCHARGE

In terms of total annual discharge, the Rio Negro appears to be the second largest river in the world, that is, slightly surpassing the Zaire of Africa but, of course, well behind the Amazon river of which it is the major contributor. The Rio Negro contributes about 15 percent of the water that the Rio Amazonas delivers to the Atlantic (Meade et al., 1979). At its confluence with the Rio Solimões, which then becomes nominally the Rio Amazonas, the Rio Negro, by volume comparison, is about one-fourth the size of the main trunk. The following comparisons can be made: the Rio Negro discharges over three times the volume of water that the Mississippi annually delivers to the Gulf of Mexico, and its annual flow exceeds that of all the rivers of Europe combined. Its absolute annual discharge has been estimated to be about 1.4 x $10^{12}/m^3$/yr (Gibbs, 1967).

SEASONAL RISE AND FALL OF THE RIO NEGRO

The Rio Negro is a seasonal river in the sense that it has fairly predictable seasonal fluctuations in water level during most years. The Manaus Harbour Authority began recording daily Rio Negro water levels in 1902 at a site about 12 km upstream. River level data has continued to be collected for the Rio Negro since 1902, though the task is now handled by Portobras, Brazil's Port Authority. Within the last decade, Portobras has also located staff gauges at about a dozen sites in the Rio Negro drainage, and hired local school teachers or other literate people to record data daily. Climatic data for the Rio Negro basin are more precarious, and often questionable because of faulty equipment and carelessness, though much improvement has been made in the last decade. Some authors accept data recorded as early as the 1930's, but care must be taken. For the purposes of aquatic studies, the river level data appear to be the most accurate and dependable.

Rio Negro basin isohyets suggest that most of the region receives an annual average precipitation of 2,000-2,200 mm, though this increases to over 3,500 mm in the Northwest Amazon near the equator in the area of the Rio Uaupés, or Vaupes as it is called in Colombia (SUDAM, 1984). In nearly all parts of the Rio Negro basin, monthly total precipitation values show highly seasonal patterns. In general, it begins raining earlier in the lower Rio Negro drainage than in its upper reaches. The rainiest months in the lower Rio Negro are between December and May, whereas in the middle course they are between March and July, and apparently March to August in the Rio Uaupés area. The lower Rio Negro experiences a pronounced dry season, with monthly totals falling below 50 mm. Near Barcelos and Tapuruquara (Santa Izabel)* in the middle course, monthly precipitation averages appear to exceed 100 mm. In the high rainfall area of the Rio Uaupés, the monthly average recorded exceeds 225 mm (Salati & Marques, 1984).

The temporal and spatial distribution of rainfall in the Rio Negro basin is not the only factor that influences river levels. Other than seasonal distribution of rainfall, the rise and fall of the lower Rio Negro, to about its confluence with the Rio Branco, 300 km upstream, is largely controlled by the Rio Solimões-Amazonas. This is impor-

---

*Place name geography of the Rio Negro can be confusing because Salesian missionaries have attempted to substitute religious names for what they perceive to be the more vulgar indigenous appellations. Thus some of the villages and towns are referred to by two names.

14

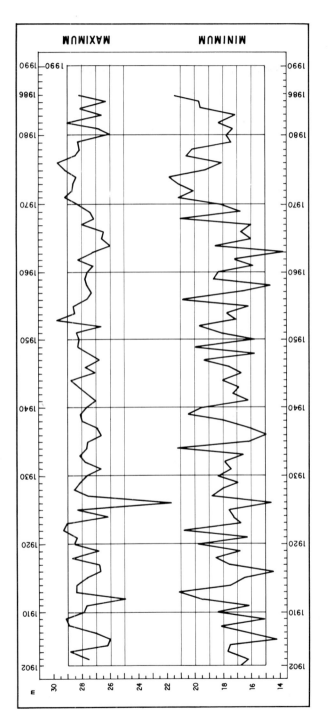

Fig. 2.2 Annual fluctuation of the Rio Negro between 1902-1985. Data provided by Portobras, Manaus office.

15

tant to keep in mind because river level data recorded at Manaus are more a reflection of the fluctuations of the Rio Solimões-Amazonas than of most of the Rio Negro. Between November and February, the upper Rio Negro is usually falling, whereas the lower course is rising because it is being dammed back by the Rio Solimões-Amazonas that, due to the earlier floods of its numerous southern tributaries, is on the rise. The impounding effect of the main trunk on the lower Rio Negro increases the latter's flooding season, and this does not correlate with climatic data. The lower Rio Negro is still at the height of its floods when, climatically, the region is entering its dry season. Though the lower Rio Negro region experiences a much more pronounced dry season than felt in the middle and upper reaches, this is not manifested in the aquatic environment because of impoundment in the months of June, July and August. In fact, in three of the six months for which monthly average rainfall totals are lowest at Manaus, the Rio Negro is in its highest flood level.

The annual fluctuation of the Rio Negro varies between about 9-12 m (Figs. 2.2 and 2.3). At Manaus, near the mouth of the Rio Negro, the annual average since 1902 has been 9.8 m. The absolute highs each year are usually reached in June or July at all of the stations for which data are available. If we use the inundation of floodplain forest as the principal biological marker of floods, then the lower Rio Negro experiences about seven months of high water each year, in contrast to only 4-5 months for most of the middle and upper course. The lower Rio Negro rises for eight or nine months each year, and then falls very rapidly. On the other hand, the upper Rio Negro shows a more equitable annual rise and fall, though there are years, for example 1979 and 1980, when at least eight months of falling river levels have been recorded during an annual cycle. Because data are not available for most of the Rio Negro except for a short period of time, it is difficult to judge the annual stability or instability of river level fluctuation of most of the Rio Negro. The Manaus data indicate that about once every decade there is an extremely low water period, and likewise, and usually subsequently, relatively large floods. The maximum levels of floods show less variability than do the minimum levels of the low water periods. Extremes, in fact, have almost attained the same levels for weak floods and exceedingly high low-water levels. In 1926, for example, the maximum flood level at Manaus was only about one meter higher than the minimum low-water point in 1934. The largest flood recorded was in 1953 and much of downtown Manaus was inundated.

There are not enough data to know whether the extremes experienced in the lower Rio Negro are also characteristic of the middle and upper reaches. The botanist Richard Spruce (1908), speaking of the Rio Uaupés in June, 1853, stated that the river was so far from attaining the ebb of former years that the Indians said the summer passed without any low water so-called. The naturalist also reported that local residents stated that in other years the river dried so much that scattered rocks peeped out all across in front of the village of São Jeronymo. Unlike the lower Rio Negro, the upper course of the river experiences bimodal rises in river level during most years. One of these rises represents the main floods, whereas the other, which usually comes in November or December, is slight and ephemeral. During the small floods, the river rises very rapidly, usually within a few days, for a meter or so, and then falls again until the main inundation comes in March or April [all river level data was supplied by the Portobras regional office in Manaus, Amazonas].

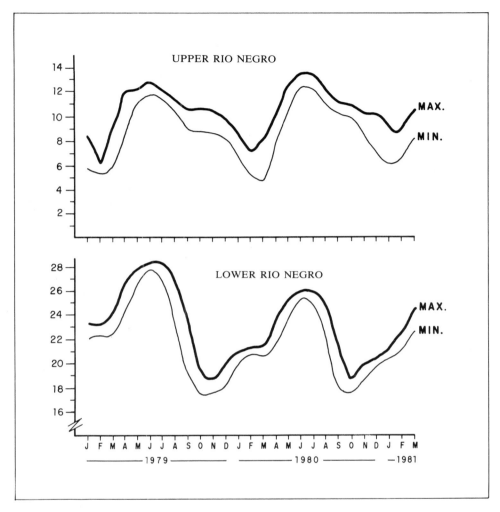

Fig. 2.3 Seasonal fluctuation of the lower and upper Rio Negro during the principal field study period. Data provided by Portobras, Manaus office.

GEOLOGY

Rio Negro hydrography drains three principal geological formations, that is, the ancient Guiana Shield, late Cretaceous to early Tertiary Lowlands and Quaternary Lowlands [see Fig 2.1]. In general the rocks, and derived soils, of the Rio Negro basin are acidic and extremely poor in chemicals associated with nutrients, this being clearly reflected in the waters which act as a chemical telltale of the geology they drain (Sioli, 1968).

Rio Negro headwaters drain a southern arc of the Guiana Shield that lies between the main river and the Rio Branco to the west. The Guiana Shield is composed mostly of ancient rocks, such as highly metamorphic gneiss, migmatites, intrusive granites,

Fig. 2.4. Granite dome that abuts the upper Rio Negro.

acid volcanics and meta-sediments such as quartzite and crystalline schists. Strong leveling and denudation of the ancient platform took place more than two billion years ago, and these processes resulted in huge fans of pebbles, gravels and sands that have been cut into by rivers draining the ancient peneplain. The consequent beds of these ancient geological materials appear never to have been drastically folded or metamorphosed, though dikes of diabase have cut and intruded into them. The old tableland, known as the Roraima Series, has been dissected by erosion and today is characterized by flat-topped formations called inselbergs or *tepuis* (Petri and Fulfaro, 1983; Schobbenhaus, 1984).

The main watershed divide of the northwestern Guiana Shield consists of a serpentine-like low-lying mountain range that geographers usually divide into four segments, from southwest to northeast these being the Serra Imeri, Serra Tapirapeco, Serra Parimi and Serra Paciraima. The highest elevation (3,014 m) is found on Pico da Neblina, a part of the Serra Imeri geological complex. South of its mountainous backbone, the Guiana Shield descends abruptly into the lowlands and extends across most of the upper Rio Negro. In the upper Rio Negro region, in fact, the western extension of the Guiana Shield is so eroded and leveled that it forms a peneplain that seldom rises above 100 m elevation and, superficially, it appears to be a continuation of the younger Tertiary Lowlands that make up much of Central Amazonia. The presence of the underlying Guiana Shield in the upper Rio Negro, however, is clearly revealed by cataracts flowing over ancient rocks and sugarloaf-like remnants, or hills of resistant granite, that project high above the rainforest (Fig. 2.4). The Serra do Curicuriari, for example, which lies between the Rio Curicuriari and Rio Marié, rises to over 400 m.

18

Most of the lowlands of the Rio Negro drainage lie on Tertiary and Quaternary unconsolidated, fluvial deposits that are now seen as clays, silts, sands and soft sandstones. These materials are derived from the ancient Guiana Shield and, because of eons of weathering, they are extremely poor in basic salts. The Quaternary-Tertiary Lowlands form a roughly triangular space in the Rio Negro drainage, with the base west of the main river and the apex reaching well up the Rio Branco. Most of the lower Rio Negro is abutted by older clastic (unconsolidated) sediments and sandstones. Red and white sandstones are easily seen along the shores of the lower Rio Negro where they are quarried during the low water period to supply construction stone for Manaus. The Tertiary-Quaternary Lowlands in the Rio Negro drainage are usually undulating as a result of erosion cycles that took place in recent geological history during Pleistocene dry periods (Klammer, 1984; Irion, 1984). Minor tectonic activity has also been suggested as a factor inducing the undulating topography of part of the region and its very complex stream network (Sternberg, 1950,1953).

RIO NEGRO MORPHOLOGY

Too little is known about the historical geology of the Rio Negro to permit a discussion of the river's origins and development. The Rio Negro, as seen today, is a relatively channelized river with few meanders and a stream gradient, for most of its length, of less than 2m/100km. Near Manaus the surface current speed of the Rio Negro in mid-river usually exceeds one meter/second, that is, 3.6 km/hour (Gessner, 1962; Meade et al., 1979). Though data are not available for the middle and upper Rio Negro, but assuming that current velocity is faster in these reaches than in the lower course, water passing São Gabriel da Cachoeira, 1200 km upstream, would still take about a month to reach the Rio Amazonas.

In great contrast to the Rio Solimões-Amazonas, the Rio Negro transports a very minimal sediment load. Calculations suggest that the Rio Negro transports only about 2-3 percent of the amount of suspended solids, per liter of water, that the Rio Solimões does at the point where the two rivers meet (Fisher, 1978; Meade et al., 1979). Whereas sediments, and their shifting by current activity, constantly modify the bank morphology of the Rio Solimões-Amazonas, the Rio Negro shoreline is much more stable and not greatly affected by annual sedimentation processes. The Rio Branco is the main supplier of lower Rio Negro sediments, but these are not sufficient to greatly affect the water color of the blackwater trunk. Rio Branco sediments, however, as will be seen below, are the foundation of island development in the lower Rio Negro.

For the purposes of this discussion, the morphology of the Rio Negro will be presented with a view to habitat development for aquatic communities. The principal morphological features of the Rio Negro are 1) channels, 2) floodplains, 3) river archipelagoes, 4) beaches, 5) cataracts and rocky substrates, 6) rias or mouth-lakes, and 7) *terra firme* banks.

Channels

The width of the Rio Negro channel, where not interrupted by islands, averages

Fig. 2.5 Aerial view of the lower Rio Negro.

about 1-3 km, though it is considerably larger than this in the lower course (Figs. 2.5 and 2.6). Channel depths in the Rio Negro vary greatly because of the nature of the river bed and the seasonal fluctuation of water level. During low water, the river channel of the middle Rio Negro is often choked with shifting sand deposits which reduce depths to less than one meter and make boat travel difficult. The average depths during low water, however, appear to range between about 5-20 m and increase to 15-35 m at the height of the floods. The mouth-bay is the deepest part of the Rio Negro, and perhaps of the Amazon, and soundings of nearly 100 m having been recorded (Sioli, 1967). If there are fishes in the deepest part of the Rio Negro mouth-bay, then they are 40 m below sea level [the deep parts of the mouth-bay have not been fished, thus it is not known if there are fishes there].

Though the Rio Negro does not meander, its channel often appears to do so within the main riverbed. Furthermore, the channel is often split into arms by the numerous islands that stud the river. Other than striking color differences, the Rio Negro contrasts sharply with the Rio Sollimões-Amazonas because the former transports only minimal quantities of trees, herbaceous plants and other large plant debris. Floating and submerged trees present a danger to small boats traveling the Rio Solimões-Amazonas, but little if any to navigation of the Rio Negro. The bank landscape of the Rio Negro also contrasts strikingly with counterparts in silt-laden rivers, such as the Rio Solimões-Amazonas and Rio Madeira. The bank cave-ins, which usually occur during falling river levels, that are characteristic of the silt-laden rivers are seldom encountered in the Rio Negro.

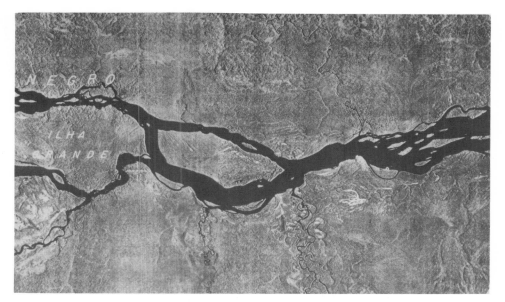

Fig. 2.6 Aerial view of the middle Rio Negro.

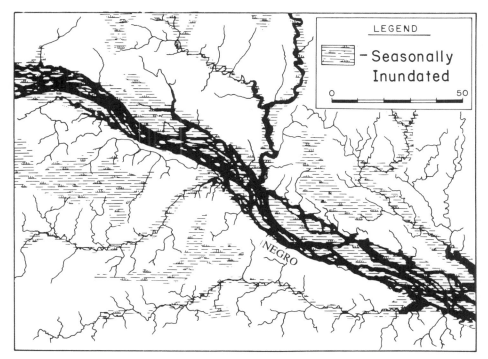

Fig. 2.7 The extensive floodplain area of the middle Rio Negro.

Fig. 2.8 Aerial view of the Anavilhanas Archipelago of the lower Rio Negro

Floodplains

Although the Rio Negro is a relatively channelized river, it nevertheless has extensive areas of floodplain, especially in its middle course and along many of its tributaries (Fig. 2.7). The numerous islands are also equivalent to floodplain, since they are inundated seasonally, and they will be discussed in more detail below. The middle Rio Negro is a low-lying area with extensive floodplain covered with Quaternary sands. The rightbank drainage of the middle and upper Rio Negro contains at least a dozen tributaries that have very extensive floodplains.

River Archipelagoes

The Rio Negro has two major archipelagoes, the Anavilhanas in the lower course and an unnamed complex beginning above the mouth of the Rio Branco and extending upriver past the town of Barcelos (Figs. 2.8 and 2.9). All together, the Rio Negro is studded with over 1,000 islands, some of which exceed 30 km in length. Islands greatly increase the shoreline coefficient − the amount of shoreline versus river length − and, in the case of the Rio Negro, this is probably by a factor of hundreds. The two large archipelagoes mentioned above represent deposition zones for sediments transported out of the Guiana Shield by, respectively, the Rio Branco and Rio Padauari/Rio Demini.

Most islands in Amazonian rivers have the general shape of a double-convex lens,

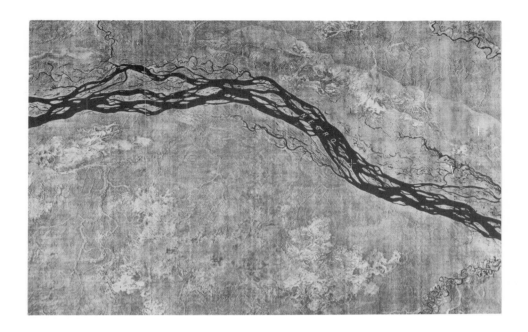

Fig. 2.9 Aerial view of the archipelago that begins upriver of the Rio Branco

whereas in the Rio Negro they are usually more elongate. The Rio Negro archipelagoes are built from alluvial silt, which is mostly caolinite. The upstream and lateral sides of the islands are usually vertical and, within the archipelagic complexes there are few sandbanks. Vertical cuts along the islands show that there is no obvious stratification of sediments, but that the complete profile is unconsolidated fine silt and clay. Leenheer and Santos (1980) have shown that the low pH and high content of humic acids in the Rio Negro result in a flocculation of the fine silt that is injected into the main trunk by the Rio Branco. Flocculation leads to greater particle size, which in turn increases sedimentation potential. The sedimentation zone for Rio Branco suspensoids is the Archipelago de Anavilhanas, that is, just upstream of the wide and deep mouth-bay. The island banks remain fairly stable because the particles are not deflocculated during most of the year, though in August, September and October the relative discharge of the Rio Branco can increase sufficiently to raise slightly the pH of the Rio Negro, hence causing silt particles to be resuspended in the water column. With increased pH, the deflocculation process literally eats away at the islands and is thought to be responsible for their peculiar shapes.

A characteristic feature of Rio Negro islands, especially in the two archipelagoes, is the lake-like waterbodies that are found in the centers of many of the islands. These lakes usually have inlets and outlets through which they fill and drain with river channel fluctuations. In the Anavilhanas complex, we have measured lake depths greater than 20 m, though averages, depending on the time of year, and exact site, appear to range between 1-20 m. Nearly all of the islands are subject to annual inundations

23

Fig. 2.10 Beach of the middle Rio Negro.

to some degree. Only in relatively large floods, however, do the majority of islands become completely covered with water.

Beaches

Sandy substrates are found intermittently the length of the Rio Negro (Fig 2.10). Both physical and biological factors appear to be involved in Rio Negro beach development. The Guiana Shield is the main source of quartz sand found on Rio Negro beaches. The very extensive sandbanks found along the Rio Branco and some of the other rivers draining the southern Guiana Shield suggest that most of the larger particles are deposited out before reaching the Rio Negro. Leenheer and Santos (1980) state that much of the channel sand of the lower Rio Negro is not quartz, as might be expected, but silica spicules of the sponge genera *Spongilla* and *Myenia*, thus some beaches may have a partial to largely biogenic origin. Our own observations, however, suggest that most beaches of the Rio Negro consist of quartz. The sandy beaches of the Rio Negro are not stable, but are constantly being eroded, resuspended and redeposited during the annual floods. Many beaches, and especially in the middle Rio Negro stretch, are over 20 km in length during their exposed period. Beaches are occasionally found in island lakes, but in these cases they usually consist of fine silt rather than larger sand particles, the latter being deposited out before they reach the inner waterbodies.

During the low water period, beaches provide thousands of km of habitat for aquatic communities. In the middle and upper Rio Negro, beach habitat is extensive for about 4-7 months each year, but only 3-5 months in the lower course because of longer flooding. Most Rio Negro beaches appear to have fairly smooth gradients, thus providing much space for aquatic organisms.

Cataracts and Rocky Substrates

Cataracts are only found in the upper course of the Rio Negro. The first rapids, which are minor, are encountered at Tapuruquara, about 900 km upstream. This is usually as far as large boats travel upriver in the low water period because of the danger of running aground on submerged rocks. The first major cataracts, however, are 1,200 km upstream between the Cachoeira de Camanau and the Cachoeira de São Gabriel. The Camanau-São Gabriel stretch can be negotiated by motor boat, though experienced local pilots are needed. There is also a portage around these cataracts. Above São Gabriel de Cachoeira there are many cataracts in the Rio Uaupés, Rio Tiquié and Rio Içana. Cataracts are confronted within 20-30 km of the mouths of the leftbank tributaries of the upper Rio Negro, and they indicate the presence of the Guiana Shield.

The first major cataracts of the Rio Branco are located at Caracaraí, about 500 km from the tributary's confluence with the Rio Negro. Affluents of the lower Rio Negro often have sandstone cataracts, and even small waterfalls, though the main trunk has none. Sandstone formations just upriver of the Rio Negro's deep mouth-bay, and underlying the main riverbed, however, may have formed a large waterfall during Pleistocene Ice Ages. When sea levels were lower than today, the rivers excavated their beds because of increased stream gradients [see below]. The more resistant sandstone crossing the lower Rio Negro would have provided ideal conditions for the formation of a large waterfall, as only the area downstream of these formations would have been deeply excavated (Fittkau, 1974). Detailed geological surveys of the Rio Negro riverbed could lend evidence to test this hypothesis, which would appear to have biogeographic implications because of a possible faunal barrier.

Rocky outcroppings of any size are first met near the mouth of the Rio Branco, and these are the same as those from which the naturalist Alfred Russel Wallace copied Amerindian pictorial writings (Wallace, 1853). Above about the Rio Paduari, where the underlying Guiana Shield is fully met, the Rio Negro riverbed is studded with rocky outcroppings, though these are often fully submerged during the floods.

Mouth-Bay or Rias

Ria − not to be confused with the Portuguese and Spanish word for river, or *rio* − is the name limnologists give to the lake-like mouth-bays of Amazonian tributaries that resemble fjords (Rai & Hill, 1981a,1981b). Amazonian rias, which are very numerous, were formed when sea levels were lowered during the Pleistocene Ice Ages. With lowered sea levels, stream gradients increased, and consequently riverbeds that were built of soft materials were excavated. The lower Rio Negro, and many of its affluents, have the appearance of fjords because sedimentation has been insufficient to fill them (see Fig 2.6). The widest part of the lower Rio Negro ria is about 15 km and, as mentioned above, depths of nearly 100 m have been recorded near Manaus. Most of the lower Rio Negro, however, is less than 50 m in depth.

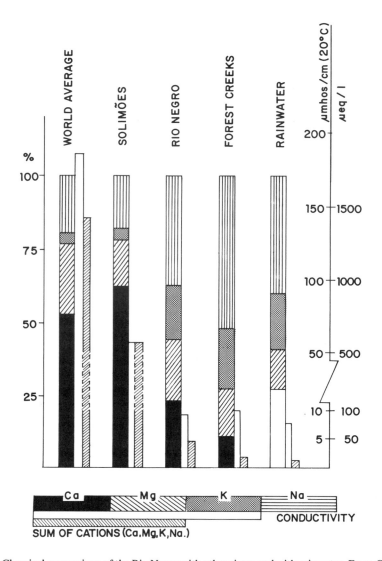

Fig. 2.11 Chemical comparison of the Rio Negro with other rivers and with rainwater. From Gibbs (1972).

Terra Firme Banks

High banks abutting the main channels are commoner in the lower than in the middle and upper Rio Negro. Consequently, as mentioned above, the lower Rio Negro, other than the Anavilhanas island complex, has little floodplain. The *terra firme* banks of the lower Rio Negro usually consist of several meters of latosols underlain by soft sandstones. In a few places, Rio Negro *terra firme* banks tower 30-40 m above the water.

The Rio Negro is chemically one of the poorest rivers in the world (Figs. 2.11). Sioli (1967) succinctly summarized Rio Negro hydrochemistry when he referred to it as

r. In the absolute concentrations of major ele-
to rainwater (Gibbs, 1971). The blackwater river
ents because the geology it drains has very im-
drochemistry and its relation to primary produc-
hich nutrients limit that production. Because the
the major elements (especially phosphorous, cal-
ated with aquatic primary production, a discus-
little use, and it will not be pursued here. Quan-
nt poverty and poor *in situ* primary production
ound in Anon (1972), Gibbs (1967,1972), Furch
l (1980, 1981a, 1981b, 1984), Santos, Bringel and
).
ls that color it, which will be discussed in the next
characteristic of the Rio Negro is its low pH or
ie to the low pH of the soils that the tributaries
: organic matter. The pH of the Rio Negro ranges
the exact site and time of year. Values increase
he clearwater tributaries, especially just down-
Demini, that drain the Guiana Shield, though in
main channel usually fall below 4.8. Low water
ugh more seasonal measurements for the river as
ssner, 1958; Sioli & Klinge, 1962; Schmidt, 1976;
Richey, Stallard & Edmond, 1981). For compari-
pH of the Rio Solimões-Amazonas ranges about
ch, 1984).

ERRATUM

M. Goulding, M. Leal Carvalho and E.G. Ferreira, **Rio Negro, Rich Life in Poor Water**

page 26

in figure caption reference from 'Gibbs (1972)' should read:

Furch, K. et al (Acta Cientifica Venezolana) 33:269–273

o, as measured by the depth at which a white Sec-
chi Disk disappears from sight, ranges between about 0.9-1.5 m (Sioli, 1956; Schmidt, 1976; Fisher, 1978; and pers. obser.). The relatively poor transparency of the river is due to the organic plant compounds that color the water, hence preventing better light penetration. Because the Rio Negro is darker in color than turbid and clearwater rivers of the Amazon, it absorbs more solar radiation and is thus slightly warmer. This is clearly seen where the Rio Negro meets the Rio Solimões-Amazonas, as the former, being warmer and thus less dense, rides on top of the latter for many km downstream until turbulent intercourse mixes and makes them one and the same.

Rio Negro water temperatures in the lower course are usually above 28 degrees and only occasionally exceed 31 degrees (Gessner, 1962; Schmidt, 1976; Fonseca, Salem & Guarim, 1982; Wissmar, Richey, Stallard & Edmond, 1981). Lake-like waterbodies of the Rio Negro are usually stratified due to decreasing temperatures from the surface to the bottom (Rai & Hill, 1981a; Alves, 1983). Though these temperature differences are slight, compared to temperate latitude systems, the stratifications are nevertheless maintained, unless disturbed by wind action. This is due to the fact that thermal resistance, or stability, increases progressively with increasing temperature above 4 degrees. During the low water period, when many lakes and pools become very shallow, super-heating can take place and we have recorded temperatures in excess of 35 degrees.

Rio Negro waters can become very deoxygenated due to thermal stratification, decomposition of organic matter and, in shallow lakes and pools, because of superheating (Gessner, 1962; Irmler, 1975; Schmidt, 1976; Rai & Hill, 1981a,1981b). Below about 2-3 m depth, and even in the river channel, Rio Negro dissolved oxygen levels decrease rapidly and fall below 40 percent saturation. The bottoms of lakes and flooded forests are often almost totally anoxic (Gessner, 1962; Rai & Hill, 1981b). Oxygen availability is perhaps one of the most important factors influencing the vertical and horizontal zonation of fishes and other animals at specific sites in Amazonian waters (Geisler, 1969; Junk, Soares & Carvalho, 1983).

3. BLACKWATERS

There has been much speculation on the causes of the production of blackwater in the Amazon Basin, the Rio Negro being the main focus of various hypotheses. This chapter presents a review of ideas concerning blackwater origins of the Rio Negro, followed by our own comments.

THE NAME RIO NEGRO AND AMERINDIAN PERCEPTIONS OF BLACKWATER

On June 3, 1542 the first European sponsored expedition down the Amazon, led by the Spaniard Francisco de Orellana, and recorded by the Dominican friar Gaspar de Carvajal, came upon a river that was, according to the scribe, 'as black as ink, and for this reason we gave it the name of Rio Negro' (Medina, 1934). Friar Carvajal mentions no ideas that the Orellana expedition might have had regarding the origins of the color of the Rio Negro. The local Amerindians must have had ideas as to the cause of the darkness of the Rio Negro, but the first explorers were unable to communicate with them. Even subsequent explorers and naturalists to the Rio Negro region have little to say about the natives' perceptions of blackwaters. The few observations that we have found, such as those recorded by Alexander von Humboldt (1852) in the early nineteenth century and by the German ethnologist, Theodore Koch-Grunberg (1909-1910), in the first decade of the twentieth century, strongly suggest that Amerindian groups familiar with the Rio Negro linked its color to byproducts of plant decomposition. Amerindians we interviewed in the middle and upper Rio Negro region reported that they felt the river was stained by plant compounds originating in areas of shrub vegetation growing on sandy soils. Migratory workers in the middle and upper Rio Negro region are very familiar with the shrub communities of the tributary systems because this is where the *Leopoldinia piassaba* palm is found, a tree whose fibers are cut and shipped downstream for the broom market in Manaus [see Chapter 4 for more comments on Rio Negro shrub communities]. The blackest waters of the Rio Negro basin are reported to issue from the sandy soil regions where *L. piassaba* is found. The ecology of these areas has yet to be investigated.

FIRST REPORTS TO PORTUGUESE CROWN ON ORIGIN OF RIO NEGRO BLACKWATERS

Alexandre Rodrigues Ferreira was the first naturalist to inventory parts of the Amazon in any detail for the Portuguese Crown. Between 1783 and 1792 Ferreira was dispatched to reconnoiter the natural history of what were then the captaincies of

Grão Pará, Rio Negro, Matto Grosso and Cuiabá (Goeldi, 1895; Carvalho, 1983). His studies resulted in a series of reports that have recently been collated and published (Ferreira, 1972,1983). While on the Rio Negro, Ferreira was based mostly in Barcelos, 400 km upstream, which was then the capital of the Captaincy of Rio Negro, but he also investigated parts of the upper Rio Negro as well.

Viewed as a whole, Ferreira's comments on blackwater origins do not seem coherent, this probably due mostly to the fact that he never edited his reports as he apparently had intended to do. His reports suggest three different blackwater hypotheses. In one report he writes that the real color is not black but amber, as one realizes when taking up a cup of water. The naturalist then hypothesizes that the amber color is due to bitumens that are probably found in the numerous rocky outcroppings that stud the course of the Rio Negro. He was probably referring to the ferruginous residue that is often seen in rocky areas and along some shores, but this material is not at all related to bitumen. In another account he states emphatically that the amber water color is due to iron derived from beaches, mineralized schist fragments and from the ferrous-rich vegetation that is laved by Rio Negro waters. It is difficult to understand how he arrived at this conclusion, as the degraded plant materials in Rio Negro waters are easily seen even with the naked eye, and these do not at all resemble ferrous compounds. Ferreira also reported, however, that others whom he interviewed believed that the dark color was derived from the decomposition of the bordering vegetation, thus he appears to be the first to state that plant extracts might account for Rio Negro blackwaters.

ALEXANDER VON HUMBOLDT'S EXPLORATION OF SOUTH AMERICAN BLACKWATERS

One of the highlighted events in Humboldt's travels in northern South America was his exploration of the Casiquiare region, where headwaters of the Negro and Orinoco systems meet. Unfortunately, for science, Humboldt, and his companion, Aime Bonpland, did not descend the Rio Negro for fear of being arrested by authorities in Brazil. His investigations of blackwaters were confined to the southwestern Orinoco system, including headwater areas of the Rio Negro in the Casiquiare region (Humboldt, 1852).

Humboldt noted that, of the areas he reconnoitered in Venezuela, blackwaters were found mostly near the equator. He was confounded to find black and turbid water rivers rising very close to each other in the same forest or savanna area. The local missionaries reported to him that blackwater had its origin in the roots of certain plants, especially sarsaparilla (*Smilax*) vines. Humboldt stated in his narrative that, 'The Smilacaceae no doubt abound on the banks of the Rio Negro, the Pacimony and Cababury; their roots, macerated in the water, yield an extractive matter that is brown, bitter and mucilaginous; but how many tufts of *Smilax* have we seen in places, where the waters were entirely white. In the marshy forest which we traversed, to convey our canoe from the Rio Tuamini to the Cano Pimichin and the Rio Negro, why, in the same soil, did we ford alternatively rivulets of black and white water? . . . Although, on account of the abundance of rain, vegetation is more vigorous close to the equator than eight or ten degrees north or south, it cannot be affirmed that the rivers with blackwaters rise principally in the most shady and thickest forests. On the contrary, a great number of the *aguas negras* come from the open savannahs.' Humboldt then concludes that the blackwaters are colored by a carburet of hydrogen that is analogous to the dunghill-waters prepared by gardeners or to the waters that issue from bogs. 'May we not also admit,' he concludes 'that it is a mixture of carbon and hydrogen, an extractive vegetable matter, that colors the blackwater rivers. . .'

ALFRED RUSSEL WALLACE'S CLASSIFICATION OF AMAZON RIVER TYPES

Alfred Russel Wallace (1853) was the first naturalist to divide Amazon limnology systematically into three major water types: whitewater, clearwater (or bluewater) and blackwater rivers. Wallace's travels in the Amazon placed him in intimate contact with all three water types. The reasons for the colors of the first two river types could be deduced directly from the nature of the geologies of their drainage basins. Whitewater rivers, Wallace noted, obtained their heavy sediment loads and muddy color from headwaters tapping the Andes, whereas clearwater rivers drained the eroded shields or Amazonian Lowlands where few sediments found their way into the streams. Blackwater rivers were more problematic because they often drained areas in close proximity to clearwater streams.

'The causes of the peculiar color of these rivers [blackwater rivers] are not,' he stated, 'very obscure; it appears to be produced by the solution of decaying leaves, roots and other vegetable matter. In the virgin forests, in which most of these streams have their source, the little brooks and rivulets are half choked up with dead leaves and rotten branches, giving various brown tinges to the water. When these rivulets meet together and accumulate into the river, they of course have a deep brown hue, very similar to that of our bog or peat water, if there are no other circumstances to modify it. But if the streams flow through a district of soft alluvial clay, the color will of course be modified, and the brown completely overpowered; and I think this will account for the anomalies observed, of streams in the same districts being of different colors. Those whose sources are pretty well known are seen to agree with this view.' Years later, writing in his autobiographical *My Life*, Wallace (1905) stated his perceptions of the origins of Rio Negro blackwaters in a slightly different way. The blackwaters of the Rio Negro are, he said, 'due, no doubt, to the greater part of the river's basin being an enormous forest-covered plain, and its chief tributaries flowing over granite rocks. It is, in fact, of the same nature as the coffee-colored waters of our Welsh and Highland streams, which have their sources among peat-bogs.' Wallace's ideas expressed in his travel account are closer to the truth than his bog hypothesis expressed in the autobiography.

FLOODED FOREST AS BLACKWATER PRODUCER

Huber (1909), a botanist who worked during the rubber boom at what is now the Goeldi Museum in Belém, speculated that blackwater originated in the contiguous and seasonally inundated floodplain forests of rivers. He did not, however, develop this hypothesis any further. Sioli (1951, 1956) viewed the flooded forest hypothesis within the context of historical fluvial morphology. He stated that as rivers develop in time they eventually are unable to fill their valleys with alluvia, and that, in

Amazonia, the floodplains are then colonized by forest communities subject to annual inundation. In these flooded forest communities the contact and intercourse of water and dead organic plant matter leads to the production of dissolved and colloidal humic substances. Furthermore, blackwaters only develop in flooded forests whose soils and/or waters are very low in calcium.

BLACKWATER PRODUCTION UNDERWATER DUE TO INCOMPLETE DECOMPOSITION PROCESSES DOMINATED BY BACTERIA

Stark and Holley (1975) attempted to determine whether Amazonian blackwater is generated on land and/or underwater, and furthermore, what were the major decomposer groups in the oxisolic and spodosolic soils that dominate the drainage surface of most of the Central Amazon region. Oxisols are soils high in iron and aluminum, with the silica leached out; spodosols, now generally called podzols, are highly leached sands where the iron and aluminum have been removed. Three sites were selected for investigation: *terra firme* producing blackwater, flooded forest with blackwater and *terra firme* adjacent to turbid or whitewater but not producing blackwater. The study revealed that litter from all three sites required a softening period of several weeks before it is readily attacked by either fungi or animals. Submerged litter of the blackwater flooded forest was shown to be decomposed, while submerged, mostly by bacteria adapted to low pH (about 3.5) and anaerobic conditions. The abundance of bacteria discovered in the decomposition process of inundated forest litter was thought to result in the high output of organic compounds that produce blackwaters. Blackwater production, it was hypothesized, probably takes place mostly underwater, as during the dry season invertebrates invade the flooded forest substrate and, along with fungi, function more effectively as decomposers in breaking down the organic molecules.

The conclusions as to how blackwater might be produced on *terra firme*, in relation to nutrient recycling, were inconclusive. They found that spodosolic *terra firme* litter was decomposed mainly by fungi and saprophytic animals (especially ants), but they did not elucidate why decomposition was incomplete thus leading to blackwater production in podzolic areas. Their general conclusions suggested that blackwaters can be produced either underwater or in *terra firme* soils if decomposition, for whatever reasons, is dominated by bacteria instead of animals and fungi. The dominance of bacteria was associated with high acidity and anaerobic conditions.

INCOMPLETE OXIDATION OF HUMIC MATTER DUE TO LOW DISSOLVED OXYGEN LEVELS

Foldats (1962) made observations of blackwater rivers in Venezuela near the headwaters of the Rio Negro. He stated that the blackwaters in this region are colored by the accumulation of humic acids of plant origin. The accumulation only takes place, however, because of the incomplete oxidation of organic matter in the water, and this is the result of the small amount of free oxygen. Foldats stated that the suggested lack of oxygen in blackwaters was due to high temperatures and lack of atmospheric turbulence. Many clearwater rivers have temperature, oxygen and turbulence patterns similar to the Rio Negro (pers. obser.), thus Foldats' hypothesis is rendered *non sequitur* since large quantities of humic compounds are not found in the former.

PODZOLIC SOILS AND THEIR GROUND WATER AS BLACKWATER PRODUCERS

Sioli (1955) traced clearwater and humic-stained streams to their sources in the upper Rio Negro region. He found that clearwater streams of the Rio Negro always had their headwaters within the high *terra firme* forest, whereas the blackwater creeks rose in stunted, almost shrub-like plant communities growing on extremely sandy soils. There are no adequate English translations for these stunted plant communities, but in Portuguese they are variously called *caatingas, campinas* and *campinaranas* [discussed in Chapter 4]. The pedology and limnology associated with Rio Negro blackwater origins led to the hypothesis that the large quantity of humic compounds was derived mostly from podzolic soil areas in the Rio Negro drainage (Sioli & Klinge, 1961,1962, 1965; Klinge, 1965,1966,1967,1976). The exact biological and/or physical mechanisms producing blackwaters, however, were uncertain.

Leenheer (1980), a chemist, made observations of blackwater sources in the sandy areas of the leftbank drainage of the lower Rio Negro. He also conducted laboratory experiments with Rio Negro blackwater. He states that the source of Rio Negro blackwater is found in lateral ground water drainage from podzolic soils developed on alluvial sand deposits. Leenheer found, however, that not all podzolic soils of the region produce blackwater. If the vegetation cover of the podzolic soil is too sparse, then too little organic material is produced to supply sufficient degraded humic substances to stain the runoff water. This usually occurs when the albic horizon, or upper bleached sandy layer, of the soil is greater than three meters depth. Streams draining deep podzols of the lower Rio Negro were shown to be crystalline in transparency.

In the podzolic soil profiles with an albic horizon less than about three meters, Leenheer found an underlying layer of humic material (spodic horizon), and this rested on a clay lens or clayey parent material. Plant roots tap this organic horizon if it lies less than about three meters below the surface. The organic layer provides nutrients to the vegetation, thus the plants whose roots reach down to it are taller and form denser communities than those growing on podzols thicker than three-meters. With increased nutrients available, the podzolic communities produce more litter, which in turn leads to a greater input of organic matter into the ground water.

The humic substances remain relatively stable in the ground water of podzolic soils because of a lack of nutrients, absence of light, no clay to remove humic substances through sorption and a relatively anaerobic subterranean environment which inhibits oxidation, compared to decay processes in the litter. In the shallower podzolic soils, the underlying clay becomes saturated at active sorption sites with humic substances, thus diverting overload to the ground water. Furthermore, the underlying clay pan also acts as a hydrologic barrier to the downward mobility of organic compounds. Leenheer also noted that the thick organic layer that accumulates on Rio Negro podzolic soils suggests slow decay, and consequently the litter, in conjunction with the other factors mentioned above, provides a continuous source of soluble humic substances, which then move through the ground water and are responsible for the coloration of the Rio Negro.

33

In addition to the above observations and experimental evidence, Leenheer also found that the soluble humic substances that give the Rio Negro its color represent only about one-half of the soluble organic matter in the river. The other half consists of colorless organic acids. Chromatography suggested that blackwater humic solutes are made up of many chromorphic groups, which he described as aromatic nuclii, quinone or free-radical classes. The nuclii of organic residues in Rio Negro blackwaters also indicated that the humic solutes are the end products of the humification process of decay.

HIGH CONCENTRATIONS OF DEFENSIVE PLANT COMPOUNDS IN PODZOLIC SOIL VEGETATION, OR POTENTIAL HERBIVORES LEADING TO BLACKWATER PRODUCTION

Janzen's (1974) review of the literature convinced him that Rio Negro blackwater had its origin in the extremely poor sandy soil areas because of the presence there of plant taxa that had evolved high levels of defensive organic compounds as protection against potential herbivores. Hypothetically, these secondary compounds should also have a negative effect on the degradation communities living in the litter, thus decreasing decomposition rates and increasing the amount of organic matter that is carried into the streams. Furthermore, he hypothesized, these negative effects would be enhanced by 1) the initial low nutrient content of the sandy soils, thus making the decomposers more dependent on the organic litter itself for their sustenance, 2) the high acidity of the soil would exclude nitrifying bacteria, thus reducing the input of nitrogen, 3) the initial low nutrient quality of the litter itself as a food source for micro-organisms and arthropods, 4) proteinaceous nutrients would be removed from potential decomposer use by complexing with phenols (extremely toxic compounds), 5) the low input of litter owing to low primary productivity, and 6) the high water content of the soils minimizes the chances for aerobic metabolism. Janzen concluded that, 'It is ironic that the soil [podzols] least able to deal with a high input of toxic phenolic compounds should be the one to receive the highest input of them' [see below for measurements of secondary compounds].

FUNGI AND COMPETITIVE EXCLUSION OF SAPROPHYTES LEADING TO BLACKWATER PRODUCTION

Singer (1978,1979,1984) was the first scientist to discover ectomycorrhizae in the Amazonian rainforest. He defines ectomycorrhizal relationships as symbiotic associations between cormophytes [plants with roots, stems and foliage] and fungi, the latter mostly of the class Basidiomycetes, whereby the plant rootlets are penetrated by fungal hyphae in a reticulating pattern. The relationship represents symbiotic mutualism because fungi provide the higher plants with mineral nutrition, and likewise, the tree supplies the fungi with simple carbohydrates which the latter are unable to attain since they lack the capacity of enzymatic reduction of polysaccharides, or at least they have a much reduced capacity to do so in comparison to non-mycorrhizal fungi. The ectomycorrhizal relationship described above was found by Singer to be confined to plant communities growing on podzolic soils of the Rio Negro region, including those also of floodplains. The adjacent *terra firme* forests also have mycorrhizae but these are different in class and function from those found in sandy soil communities.

Singer states that the evidence gathered during his investigations of the Rio Negro region, and by others elsewhere in the world, strongly indicates that the litter decomposing fungi are unable to compete with ectomycorrhizae, whose mycelia [branching, thread-like filaments] are combative weapons against other potential saprophytes. He goes on to suggest that the plant communities growing on Rio Negro podzolic soils have evolved in close association with their ectomycorrhizae, and these fungi, in turn, have prevented saprophytic fungi from establishing themselves to any significant degree (Singer & Araujo, 1979). Because podzolic communities lack saprophytic fungi, and other organisms associated with them, there develops a thick layer of raw humus from which organic compounds are constantly supplied to streams, thus rendering them dark in color. This is in great contrast to the adjacent forest growing on latosols where ectomycorrhizae are rare but saprophytic fungi abundant. The presence of saprophytic fungi explains why most *terra firme* forests have only a thin layer of humus, and why the streams issuing from them are generally clear in color.

TOWARDS A GENERAL HYPOTHESIS OF THE ORIGINS OF RIO NEGRO BLACKWATERS

Blackwater as a limnological term is a description of color and should not be interpreted as a water type derived from a single process. There appear to be several kinds of blackwater in the Amazon Basin, in the sense that each is produced by different combinations of physical and/or biological mechanisms. There is still no quantitative analysis of the humic acids in Amazonian blackwater rivers and floodplain lakes, thus chemical comparisons cannot be made. In general, it can be stated that blackwater can be formed wherever the rate of carbon fixation (photosynthesis) and its partial decay to soluble organic acids exceeds the rate of complete decay to carbon dioxide (oxidation). This phenomenon can take place on land, in ground water or in streams, rivers and lakes.

Because the Rio Negro is now known to be colored by humic acids, the role of inorganic matter, such as the iron hypothesized by Alexandre Rodrigues Ferreira, can be dismissed without any further comment. From Alexander von Humboldt onward, scientists have agreed that the Rio Negro is stained by humic compounds, and this has led to the hypotheses outlined above. At this time we believe that it would be premature to accept any single factor as the sole explanation of the origins of Rio Negro blackwater. Several of the hypotheses presented earlier still need to be tested, though the present evidence seems to favor ideas linking the water color mostly with podzolic soil drainage, and this may take place in upland areas and probably in some sandy floodplain areas as well.

Experimental work carried out by St. John and Anderson (1982) in the podzolic areas of the lower Rio Negro suggests that the stunted plant communities associated with the sandy soils do not contain extraordinary quantities of secondary compounds, as was hypothesized by Janzen (1974). In other words, the plant communities growing on podzolic sands are no more toxic than their adjacent *terra firme* counterparts. It is worth remembering, however, that Janzen (1974) hypothesized that toxicity would be enhanced by a series of other negative effects, such as poor soils and low primary production, and his synergistic argument, even if high levels of secondary compounds are not found, would appear to deserve more attention. St. John's and Anderson's (1982) data confirm Leenheer's (1980) hypothesis that clay acts as a filter in removing humic acids. Thus the absence of clay, or its burial beneath several meters of sand, eliminates the filtering effect in podzolic soil profiles, causing the humic acids to be removed by runoff and ground water. This still does not explain, however, why there is so much litter in the first place in the podzolic areas. Only Singer's (1980) ectomycorrhizal hypothesis offers a testable alternative to Janzen's (1974) toxicity arguments.

Other than the biological and physical mechanisms that produce blackwater, the total area in which they operate is also important. Leenheer's (1980) observation that Rio Negro blackwater is produced mostly in areas where the upper sandy horizon is less than three meters would appear to have implications as to the nature of the soil profiles in individual tributary watersheds. The blackest, or most acidic, affluents may drain areas of relatively shallow sands, whereas the clearwater tributaries either rise mostly on non-podzolic *terra firme* or on deep sandy soils.

4. PLANT LIFE IN THE RIO NEGRO BASIN

This chapter is designed to present an overview of the terrestrial and aquatic plant life of the Rio Negro system. The Rio Negro drainage, lying mostly in low relief, embraces four principal vegetation types: *terra firme* rainforest, relatively open shrub-like communities, savannas and rainforest subject to seasonal inundation. At present Rio Negro botanical studies are mostly in the phase of collection, identification and description of species, though a few investigations are available that shed light on aspects of physiognomy, diversity and ecology. Though Rio Negro waters support very limited primary production, they nevertheless sustain an impressive algal flora.

TERRA FIRME RAINFOREST

The average height of rainforest in the Rio Negro basin is less than that found in most of the Central Amazon region (Ducke & Black, 1953; Takeuchi, 1961a,1961b, 1962a,1962b,1962c; Rodrigues, 1960; Williams, Loomis & Alvim, 1967; Prance, 1978,1979; Cardenas, 1981). As far as is known and indicated on maps drawn from aerial photography and ground reconnaissance, Rio Negro *terra firme* rainforest grows mostly on latosols, and is replaced by other vegetation types on sandy soils. The RADAM (1976-1978) phytogeographical maps, which are necessarily highly generalized, strongly indicate that Rio Negro *terra firme* rainforest is taller and more robust in the Tertiary region (clays and latosols) of its southern drainage than in the northern area (middle and upper Rio Negro) that is underlain by the western extension of the Guiana Shield. North of a parallel running through about the mouth of the Rio Branco, relatively high rainforest interdigitates with shrub-like communities, which suggests a large region of floristic, physiognomic and ecological complexity.

Recent studies indicate that around 50 percent of all precipitation that falls on the Amazon Basin is returned to the atmosphere as water vapor through evapotranspiration (Salati, Marques & Molion, 1978; Salati & Marques, 1984; Jordan & Heuveldop, 1981). Each river basin has its own potential evapotranspiration rate and, in rainforest systems, this is mostly a function of average temperatures, relative humidity and vegetation densities. The fact that the upper Rio Negro region has relatively high rainfall and temperatures throughout the year, but nevertheless a pronounced low water period in the rivers, suggests to us that the evapotranspiration potential of the upper course drainage is the main factor that controls the amount of water that reaches the streams and tributaries. The evapotranspiration rate must increase during the low-water months, otherwise the tributaries would evidence less seasonal fluctuation than they do.

STUNTED PLANT COMMUNITIES CALLED CAATINGA, CAMPINA AND CAMPINARANA

Studding Rio Negro *terra firme* rainforests are clusters, islands and peninsulas of relatively open shrub communities. As far as is known, these communities are always found on sandy soils (podzolics), which were originally alluvial in origin and derived from degraded granites of the Guiana Shield. The podzolics, as mentioned earlier, are highly leached, usually white in color and extremely poor in nutrients. The presence of podzolics appears to represent the sediment remains of ancient rivers and perhaps lakes.

Open plant communities, forming 'islands' in the rainforest, are found from the headwaters of the Rio Negro in Colombia and Venezuela to Manaus near the Rio Solimões-Amazonas. In both the Portuguese and English scientific literature, the open plant communities of the Rio Negro are referred to as *caatingas*, *campinas* and *campinaranas*. Although the term *caatinga* is often used by local inhabitants, botanists have suggested its elimination as a technical term in the context of Rio Negro vegetation because the word is also employed for a large plant community type found in arid Northeastern Brazil. Both Portuguese and English writing botanists have adopted *campina* and *campinarana* as the most appropriate terms to describe the shrub-like vegetation of the Rio Negro basin. *Campina* is the accepted generic term for the communities in general, and it will be employed herein (Pires & Rodrigues, 1964; Pires & Prance, 1978; Anderson, 1981).

Campina communities owe their stunted stature to sandy soils that, in comparison to adjacent rainforest pedology, represent zones of nutrient and water stress for plants. Overall plant diversity in *campinas* is reduced in comparison to contiguous rainforest, and many endemic species are found. Recent studies indicate that *campina* plant endemicity is not particularly local, but more characteristic of the Rio Negro shrub communities in general (Macedo, 1975; Macedo & Prance, 1978).

Some *campina* communities are very open, with almost full sunlight reaching the substrate (Fig. 4.1). The taller *campina* communities reach 20 m or more, with one or two dominant tree species, but still the vegetation is too sparse to cut out most of the sunlight. Epiphytes, such as bromeliads and orchids, are often abundant in *campinas*. The *campina* forests of the upper Rio Negro show greater species diversity than those transects that have been analyzed in the lower course drainage near Manaus. Prance and Schubart (1977) hypothesize that the greater plant diversity of the upper Rio Negro region is due to the older formation of the white sands on which they grow, the overall wetter climate with a less pronounced dry season and less disturbance by pre-Columbian man. It should be kept in mind, however, that there are many transitions between the taller, more diverse *campinas* of the upper Rio Negro and their more meager counterparts near Manaus.

Campina vegetation, as discussed in Chapter 3, appears to be the principal source of the humic compounds found in the Rio Negro. Unfortunately, there are no accurate estimates of the total area of the Rio Negro basin occupied by this forest type.

SAVANNAS

Within the Rio Negro drainage, large savannas are only found in the Rio Branco

Fig. 4.1. A shrub formation growing on podzolic soils of the middle Rio Negro region.

basin in the Territory of Roraima. The Roraima savannas occupy at least 100,000 km^2, though their area is increasing rapidly because of deforestation of adjacent rainforest for pasture development. These savannas, in addition to adjacent felled forest, are set afire annually and it is probable that this process results in slightly increased nutrient levels in the Rio Branco and lower Rio Negro. The suggested additional nutrient input might be partially responsible for the recent increase in herbaceous plant communities of the lower Rio Negro [an alternative hypothesis is presented later in the chapter].

Smaller savannas, associated with sandy soils and adjacent shrub vegetation, are found in the middle and upper Rio Negro area, and occasionally these are on floodplains where they are annually inundated (Fig 4.2). Many of the small savannas of the middle and upper Rio Negro that lie on the floodplains or near to them are also fired annually or every few years. This appears to be mostly the result of burning adjacent shrub communities to clear the vegetation to facilitate turtle egg hunts. Riparian folk of the region also report that burned-off areas attract nesting turtles in subsequent years. We have also witnessed what might be called recreational fires, that is, pyromania.

INUNDATION FORESTS

Flooded forests are, as Alfred Russel Wallace (1853) observed, the most singular feature of the Amazon (Figs 4.3 and 4.4). It is usually assumed by botanists that flooded forest species must have special adaptations to tolerate long periods of inundation,

Fig. 4.2. Savanna of the middle Rio Negro floodplain.

Fig. 4.3. Flooded forest of the lower Rio Negro.

Fig. 4.4. Flooded forest of the Rio Negro.

but little experimental work in the Amazon has been carried out in this research area (Scholander & Perez, 1968; Garcia-Novo & Crawford, 1973). No universal adaptation has been detected, such as seasonal leaf fall, and the physiological responses are probably many and diverse, depending on the plant group.

One of the main ecological questions to be answered is how do inundated plants survive in the absence of oxygen in the root zone? Some species have aerial roots, or pneumatophores, that originate above the floodline and thus transport oxygen from the atmosphere down to the rhizosphere. This adaptation, however, is found only in a minority of Rio Negro flooded forest plant species. It has been hypothesized that some species, subjected to the anaerobic conditions of flooding, accumulate malate (related to the malic acid in green apples and other fruits) rather than ethanol (a type of alcohol), the latter of which is the usual compound produced by plants in anoxic conditions. It also appears that flood tolerant species may use nitrate more effectively as an electron acceptor to overcome a lack of oxygen (Keel & Prance, 1979). Whatever the physiological adaptations are, they allow most flooded forest species to maintain their foliage even while the roots are inundated. Furthermore, the foliage of many, if not most, seedlings, saplings and shrubs, appears to remain intact even during the flooding period.

A floodplain flora is not yet available for the Rio Negro. Combining all of the lists that are available, and our own collections, the inundation forests of the lower Rio Negro alone have at least 250 angiosperm woody plant species, and the total is certainly much larger than this. Rio Negro floodplain forest is less diverse than its *terra firme* counterpart, but has more species than the *campina* communities discussed

41

above (Takeuchi, 1961a,1961b,1962a,1962b,1962c; Prance, 1978; Cardenas, 1981). Floristically, Rio Negro inundation forest is distinct from *terra firme* communities, but nevertheless some species are shared. Rio Negro flooded forests also share many species with inundation communities of clearwater and whitewater rivers. Richard Spruce (1908), who spent over two years collecting the Rio Negro, thought that its floodplain floristics and physiognomy were similar to comparable communities he investigated in clearwater systems. Spruce stated that the flooded forest vegetation of the Rio Tapajós, a clearwater river, had quite the same character as that of the Rio Negro, with identical species being shared in some cases. Botanical reports, and floodplain plant collections made by the first author, suggest that the Rio Negro shares more common taxa with clearwater than with turbid water rivers. Clearwater affluents, however, share many species with whitewater rivers, and these taxa are often missing from the blackwater river floodplains. The distribution of one of the tallest and most majestic Amazon floodplain species, the kapok tree (*Ceiba pentandra*, Bombacaceae), exemplifies the above observation. The kapok tree is found along the Rio Solimões-Amazonas, disappears along the Rio Negro, but reappears on the floodplains of its leftbank clearwater tributaries, such as the Rio Branco and Rio Marauiá.

In stature, Rio Negro flooded forest is shorter than its clearwater and whitewater counterparts and, because it is no denser, it is also less in biomass (Prance, 1978). Flooded forests show distinct floristic and physiognomic zonation. The lowest areas colonized by woody plants lie at the edge of the river channel or border lakes. These zones are subjected to long periods of inundation, often in excess of 7-10 months. Beaches and low-lying banks support shrub communities that are usually dominated by 1-3 species. On higher ground, that is, moving up the levees and onto the floodplain slope behind them, species diversity increases. Cardenas (1981) studied plant diversity and zonation in the Anavilhanas islands of the lower Rio Negro where he recorded 111 species/hectare. Most of the taxa he encountered were trees and vines, with shrubs, epiphytes and hemi-parasites being represented by only a few species. The tallest trees are generally found on the highest ground, that is, on the best drained soils.

Middle and upper Rio Negro inundation forests, especially on many islands, are sometimes dominated by the *Astrocaryum jauary* palm (Fig. 4.5). These palms are among of the first colonizers of newly-formed sandy islands. Their seeds are common along beach areas as a result of large-scale downstream dispersal. Within the palm communities, seeds are also dispersed by fishes. Near middle and upper Rio Negro tributary confluences, and in the low parts of some islands, are also found large communities of the *Leopoldinia pulchra* (Fig 4.6). These palms appear to be adapted to long periods of inundation and this apparently explains why they are so dominant in low-lying, often boggy areas.

A few generalizations can be made about the phenology of Rio Negro inundation forests. The most obvious seasonal event is that inundation forests fruit mostly during the high water period. This means that most of the fruit falls into the water where it can be dispersed aquatically or by animals, the latter mostly fishes (Gottsberger, 1978; Goulding, 1980,1983a,1985; Kubitzki, 1985). Adis (1984) reported late fruit fall in the flooding season for a small floodplain of a tributary of the lower Rio Negro, though our own personal observations and those of Cardenas (1981) suggest

Fig. 4.5. The *Astrocaryum jauary* palm is commonly found in nearly pure stands on many islands of the middle Rio Negro.

Fig. 4.6. *Leopoldinia pulchra* palms are often the dominant trees in the swampy areas of confluences of the middle and upper Rio Negro.

43

a more staggered pattern for the Rio Negro in general, depending on the species and type of biotope (eg, beach or levee). Spruce (1908) and Cardenas (1981) noted that most of the trees of the Rio Negro do not begin to flower until the water begins to recede from the flooded forest. In a detailed study of the phenology of the *Astrocaryum jauary* palm in the lower Rio Negro inundation forest, Piedade (1985) found that the species flowers mostly in August and September, and consequently requires about nine months for the fruits to mature, which then fall in large part into the water in May and June at the height of the floods.

The shore shrub communities, which are flooded for extensive periods each year, must flower and fruit rapidly during the emerged months, within weeks in some cases. It is not known whether these shrubs, such as wild guavas, are able to use water level as a signal for flowering and fruiting. We have observed individuals of the same species, one of which was flooded, the other not, but both flowering and/or fruiting at the same time. Other environmental signals may be involved that trigger reproductive behavior.

Leaf fall in Rio Negro flooded forests can be witnessed throughout the year. Cardenas (1981) recognized three patterns of leaf phenology: 1) species that produce a small quantity of leaves throughout the year, but which do not present a marked seasonal fall; 2) species which present an alternating cycle of marked leaf production and fall and another period of low production, and; 3) species that show a marked period of leaf production and a subsequent one of foliage fall. The majority of species studied in the lower Rio Negro fell into the third pattern with intense leaf fall 2-3 months before flowering, that is, after the end of the floods.

Most of the inundation forest of the Rio Negro may be characterized as *seasonally flooded forest* [see Prance (1978, 1980) and Irmler (1977,1978b) for inundation forest types]. The lower Rio Negro inundates its floodplain forests for about 5-7 months each year, and this usually happens between January and August. Ten meter water depths in flooded forests are common, but the average is somewhat less than this. Middle and upper Rio Negro flooded forests appear to be inundated, on the average, based on observation and local information, for about 3-5 months annually.

Most flooded forest tree and shrub species appear to require an emersed period to guarantee their survival. Based on field observations, we believe that the emersed period need not necessarily be annual, but must not exceed 2-3 years for most species. River level data clearly reveal that since the early 1970's there have been relatively high low-water periods in the Central Amazon. This phenomenon may also be referred to as prolonged floods (Junk, 1984). Consequently, shrub and tree communities growing in low-lying areas were inundated without respite for several years. This phenomenon apparently explains the large amount of dead vegetation that can be witnessed in the lower courses of many tributaries, of which the Rio Negro is an example (Fig. 4.7).

Other than *seasonally flooded forest*, the Rio Negro also has many areas of *irregularly flooded forest*. This latter type is found mostly along small streams where local rains can raise water level sufficiently to inundate a limited strip of forest. *Swamp forests* appear in low-lying areas, usually along streams or the confluence areas of middle and upper Rio Negro tributaries that are poorly drained, and these communities are often dominated by palms or one or two species of the family Lauraceae.

The total area occupied by Rio Negro flooded forest has not been surveyed but,

Fig. 4.7. Tree and shrub mortality of the lower Rio Negro as a result of 2-3 years of continuous flooding during the 1970's.

judging from surface reconnaissance and Landsat satellite imagery, it must exceed 1,000 km^2. If the tributary areas are added, then it probably exceeds 2,000 km^2. Inundated forest during high water is found the length of the Rio Negro, but is often limited to a narrow strip where *terra firme* banks abut the main channel. Most of the islands in the Rio Negro are covered with seasonally flooded forest. The largest areas of flooded forest, however, are found in the middle Rio Negro region and along the meandering tributaries of the rightbank drainage. There are also extensive flooded forests in the northwest drainage, especially along the Rio Tiquié (Chernela, 1983).

AQUATIC HERBACEOUS VEGETATION OF THE RIO NEGRO

Travelers have generally noted the absence, rather than the presence, of aquatic herbaceous vegetation in the Rio Negro. In the 1850's and 1860's, Spruce (1908) did not find aquatic grasses in the Rio Negro, and he noted how much different this situation was than the richly-clad shores of the Rio Solimões-Amazonas. Due to the prolonged floods in the 1971-1975 period, there have been die-offs of trees and shrubs, as mentioned above, in the lower Rio Negro (Fig. 4.7). Junk (1983,1984) correctly suggests, we believe, that the herbaceous vegetation that has recently colonized the Rio Negro is rooted, chemically, to the nutrients released from the relatively large amount of dead vegetation that is now in various stages of decomposition. In the Anavilhanas islands, however, there are also herbaceous communities along floodplain

Fig. 4.8. Herbaceous vegetation along the edge of the inundation forest of the lower Rio Negro.

plain forests where die-offs are not present (Fig. 4.8). These plant communities are not so easily explained by the nutrient recycling hypothesis outlined above. The principal grasses that have colonized the lower Rio Negro are *Paspalum repens*, *Luziola spruceana* and *Oryza perrenis*. Sedges (*Cyperus*) and water hyacinth (*Eichhornia crassipes*) are also now found in the lower Rio Negro region.

Aquatic herbaceous plants of the upper Rio Negro are confined mostly to cataract rocks, and these species belong to the family Podostemonaceae (Fig 4.9). These lithophilous plants form thick mats on the rocks during the high water period, but die back during the low-water season. It has been suggested that the Podostemonaceae require a high current speed to supply sufficient oxygen for photosynthesis (Sculthorpe, 1971). Fast currents may also improve the rate of nutrient supply, and this would be especially important in the Rio Negro if the plants are fed more by the river than by the rocky substrate on which they live (Junk, 1984). Podostemonaceous seeds germinate on emerged rock surfaces during the low water period.

ALGAE

Algal production is largely dependent on hydrochemistry and water transparency, both of which are unfavorable in the Rio Negro. Algal blooms in Rio Negro waters have neither been reported in the literature nor did the authors observe any. Although primary production is very low in the Rio Negro, the river nevertheless has a relatively rich algal flora (Uherkovich, 1976,1984; Uherkovich & Rai, 1979). Phytoplankton

Fig. 4.9. Plants of the family Podostemonaceae of the São Gabriel rapids of the upper Rio Negro

sampling in the Rio Negro has been carried out mostly in the large mouth-bay area and in the lake-like debouchures of some of the tributaries. Quantitative sampling in the river channel revealed that diatoms of the genera *Melosira* and *Tabellaria* were abundant in relative biomass, and that green algae of the order Chlorococcales and desmids of the family Conjugatophyceae were characteristic of most hauls. Also noteworthy were the extremely small, unicellular but motile algae of the crytomonad group and, though numerous, they represented a very minimal part of the biomass. Rai and Hill (1980) characterized the algal community in a lower Rio Negro tributary mouth-lake as consisting mostly of Chlorophyta (green algae) with 27 species, Cyanophyta (blue-green algae) with one species and Pyryophyta (dinoflagellates) with three species.

In terms of biomass, periphyton is probably more abundant in Rio Negro algal communities than phytoplankton. Periphyton consist of algae that grow attached to a substrate or very near to one. The extensive flooded forests of the Rio Negro provide enormous substrate areas for periphyton development, though shade is a limiting factor. Submerged vegetation, including live or dead stems, leaves and trunks, in Rio Negro flooded forests usually support a slimy layer of algae, which is often in conjunction with other micro-organisms and detritus. Periphyton production appears to be greatest at the edge of flooded forests where the light environment is best. This is especially important in island areas because of the high shore coefficient where relatively large areas receive nearly full sunlight. Based on the quantity of periphyton that can be observed in Rio Negro flooded forests, and the known poor primary productivity of the river, we hypothesize that the algal communities found in flooded forests derive most of their nutrients from live or dead woody vegetation. In the

47

Anavilhanas islands, masses of filamentous algae are often seen stringing from submerged vegetation. These algae, however, are never observed in large agglomerations in open water, as is the case in many other Amazonian rivers that have more favorable nutrient inputs and water transparencies.

PART II
TROPHIC INTERACTIONS AND ORGANIZATION

5. HERBIVORY

WOODY PLANTS

Due to extensive floodplain and riparian forests, Rio Negro fishes are in close contact with woody plants that provide cover, breeding sites and food. In general the consumption of woody plant parts by fishes is restricted by structural and chemical properties of the former and ingestion and digestion limitations of the latter. Despite the great diversity of Amazonian fishes, species have not evolved that can graze freely on the plant biomass, even that part which could be ingested if other factors were not involved. Live or fresh wood, leaves and flowers are relatively unimportant in fish diets, though the first two account for most of the floodplain and riparian plant production, and they are available in large quantities to piscine communities during the inundation period. Most of the plant biomass consumed by Rio Negro fishes enters the foodchain through the detritus cycle [see Chapter 7]. Of live plant material, fruits and seeds are the most important fresh components in herbivorous diets.

Leaves

HYPOTHESIS: Folivory by Amazonian fishes is limited by the toxicity of leaves.
    Although Amazonian inundation forests are correctly thought of as evergreen, there is nevertheless large-scale leaf-fall that results in major carbon flow from the forest canopies to the water (Franken, Irmler & Klinge, 1979; Bayley & Petrere, 1986). Litter-fall in Amazonian inundation forests has been estimated at about 3.5-7.5 dry tons/hectare/year; wood usually accounts for more of the standing litter biomass than does foliage (Klinge, Rodrigues, Brunig & Fittkau, 1975; Adis, Furch & Irmler, 1979). According to the last authors cited, most litter-fall in the lower Rio Negro takes place during the flooding season, and at this time of year the foliage shows lower concentrations of important elements, especially nitrogen and phosphorous, than during the low water period. Wood decomposition is much slower than that of leaves, but no comparative data area available for inundation forests. Breakdown of leaves, however, is also very slow and it is estimated that in many cases the foliage found in blackwater areas may take six years to reach 95 percent decomposition (Adis, Furch & Irmler, 1979).
    In flooded forests, leaves are available to potential folivorous fishes in three ways: as litter on the inundated substrate, as leaf-fall floating at the surface and as live leaves that remain attached to the trees, shrubs and other life forms. Thus litter alone cannot be used as the principal measure of the quantity of leaves that are available to potential folivorous fishes. Our impression is that live leaves probably represent a much greater biomass of foliage available to fishes than does litter.
    The evidence from this investigation strongly suggests that there are no specialized

Tab. 5.1. The numbers of fish species in various habitats that fed on angiosperm plant material.

	Beaches	Confluence Swamp	Floating Meadows	Flooded Forest	Island Lakes	Rocky Pool	Woody Shores	Total Species That Fed on Item
WOODY PLANTS								
Fruits/Seeds	43	35	11	41	9	3	35	79
Leaves/Flowers	6	5	-	9	3	2	5	22
HERBACEOUS PLANTS								
Herbaceous Plant Roots	2	4	-	6	-	-	4	8
Herbaceous Stems/Leaves	11	17	5	14	2	3	17	46

folivores amongst the herbivorous fishes of the Rio Negro, though many species feed occasionally on leaves (Tab. 5.1 and Appendix 8). The fishes that were found with relatively large quantities of leaves in their stomachs are mostly frugivores, and they only turn to foliage when fruits and seeds are not available, that is, at the end of the flooding season or during the low water period. This pattern was also observed elsewhere in the Amazon Basin (Goulding, 1980). Live leaves clipped by fishes can usually be observed in a survey of a Rio Negro flooded forest, but our reconnaissances revealed that these were mostly new, tender foliage. For example, rubber trees (*Hevea* spp.), subsequent to their fruiting period, which is during the floods, lose their leaves and a new crop appears immediately. If water level should rise subsequent to the peak of the floods, the new foliage often becomes inundated and is eaten by fishes of the genera *Myleus*, *Metynnis* and *Brycon*. New foliage in general, however, does not appear to be available in large quantities to flooded forest fishes.

Considering the great diversity of the Amazonian fish fauna, and the fact that the annual floods inundate huge quantities of dead and live leaves, it is somewhat surprising that folivory is not more common, especially in the periods when preferred foods are not available. We can think of only two testable hypotheses to explain this observation. First, leaves in general may be too toxic for fish food. The evidence compiled from a recent symposium on folivory suggests that herbivorous vertebrates and invertebrates face detoxification problems with leaf eating, and this is probably the reason why the habit is not more widespread (Montgomery, 1978).

Second, leaves may be too poor in nutritional values to serve as major fish food. There is little evidence to support this argument. Janzen's (1978) suggestion that toxicity and poor nutritional value should be considered together in experiments dealing with leaf eating ecology would appear to be more relevant.

Fruits and Seeds

HYPOTHESIS: Fruits and seeds represent an important nutritional source for many Rio Negro fish species. Fishes are major seed predators and seed dispersal agents in

Rio Negro flooded forests, the exact interaction depending on the plant and animal species involved. There is no way of knowing whether flooded forest plant species and fruit/seed eating fishes co-evolved, but the ecology of either, as seen today, cannot be understood without considering the other as well.

Fruits and seeds account for most of the terrestrial plant matter that is eaten *fresh* by Rio Negro fishes. All together fruits or seeds were found in the diets of 79 fish species, of which about a dozen of these Rio Negro taxa are mainly frugivorous, at least during the floods when the food item is most abundant (see Tab. 5.1 and Appendix 8). As mentioned in Chapter 3, plants in the flooded forests fruit mostly during the high water period. This being the case, most of the fruit production, at least in inundated areas, drops into water and thus fishes, migrating into the arboreal habitat, have access to it. Fruits and seeds are the only food item eaten by fishes where apparently there can be a mutualistic relationship between the consumer and the consumed. This is because many seeds pass viable through fishes and, subsequent to being defecated, they are potentially dispersed. Seed dispersal by fishes is now referred to as ichthyochory (Van der Pijl, 1982).

Fruit and seed production in Amazonian flooded forests has not been measured with any accuracy though, viewed superficially, it appears to be less than that of leaves, and this observation is confirmed by a relatively small-scale survey of a site on a tributary of the lower Rio Negro (Adis, Furch & Irmler, 1979). In general, it appears that fruits and seeds, or parts of them, of woody plants are more nutritional and less toxic than leaves (Janzen, 1976). This appears to be the main explanation why herbivorous fishes prefer fruits and seeds over leaves.

The interactions between fishes and fruits was first investigated in tributaries of the upper Rio Madeira region (Gottsberger, 1978; Goulding, 1980,1983b,1985). The observations presented below complement the first studies. Fruit and seed morphology tends to be very similar for species of the same genus and often even of the same family. First observations, including those from the Rio Negro, suggest that fishes select their preferred fruits and seeds at what taxonomically are referred to as genera. This is probably due to the presence of many sympatric plant species in Amazonian floodplains and the similar morphological, size and chemical properties of their fruits and seeds [see Appendix 7 for list of genera whose species are potentially dispersed by fishes]. The following discussion of fish and fruit/seed interactions is organized around plant families. Life forms indicate those whose fruits or seeds Rio Negro fishes are known to eat, and not necessarily all of those that are found in the respective plant families.

Annonaceae

Life Forms: trees and shrubs. Annonaceous fruits eaten by fishes are aggregates of berries. The berries usually coalesce with an edible, fleshy receptacle. The entire aggregate of berries can fall into the water as a single unit or, as happens in some species, the individual berries separate and fall into the water while the fruit is still attached to the tree. Fishes seldom masticate annonaceous seeds, but rather ingest them for the associated fleshy material.

Arecaceae or Palmae

The fruits of all palm species of the Rio Negro are probably eaten by fishes. Rio Negro palm fruits are drupes with a single, large seed. The fruit surface is usually smooth with a fleshy underlying mesocarp. Most of the energy in palm fruits is stored in the endocarp, and this structure is protected by a hard nut wall that allows the seed to pass undamaged through fish guts. Several of the larger fruit-eating characins are able to crush palm seeds, though even in these cases whole fruits are also usually found in stomach contents. Catfish species that eat palm fruits are never able to crush the seeds as they lack the dentition to do so. Large catfishes, such as those of the genera *Phractocephalus* and *Megaladoras*, have been captured that had more than 50 whole palm seeds in their stomachs and intestines. In many cases, seed dispersal through fishes is the only reasonable explanation for the distribution of individual palm plants in flooded forest, as has been shown quantitatively for *Astrocaryum jauary* in the lower Rio Negro (Piedade, 1985).

Bignoniaceae

Life Forms: trees and shrubs. Most of the species produce dehiscent capsules that, when ripe, liberate winged seeds that float and are consequently dispersed by water and wind. The floating seeds are taken at the water surface by fishes and dispersal never appears to be involved.

Chrysobalanaceae

Life Forms: trees and shrubs. The genera *Couepia* and *Licania* are particularly abundant in habitats near the edge of the river channel (Cardenas, 1981). Chrysobalanaceous fruits of the Rio Negro are fleshy drupes with bony endocarps. The fleshy material buoys the fruits, though the naked seeds sink. The fleshy material is often tart to nearly sweet. Fishes appear to be mostly interested in the fleshy covering of chrysobalanceous fruits, as the seeds are rarely masticated.

Combretaceae

Life Forms: trees. The tree *Buchenavia viridiflora*, and perhaps a few more species of its same genus, produce small drupes on which fishes were observed feeding. No fish specimens were captured, however, while feeding on combretaceous fruits, though we suspect that both predation and dispersal may be involved.

Euphorbiaceae

Life Forms: trees and shrubs. All of the euphorbiaceous fruits whose seeds are eaten by Rio Negro fishes are dehiscent capsules, many of which are explosive. Fishes are major predators of Rio Negro euphorb seeds. Only seeds that are invested with fleshy material (arillate appendages) are occasionally swallowed whole, and these include species in the genera *Alchornea* and *Amanoa*.

Gnetaceae

The family Gnetaceae belongs to the gymnosperms which, by definition, have no fruits. The seeds, however, are enveloped in a fleshy envelope that corresponds functionally to an angiosperm fruit wall. For convenience, the seeds are often referred to as fruits. The family is represented in the Rio Negro by two liana species of the genus *Gnetum*. The fruits are relatively large (3-5 cm), have fleshy coverings and hard seeds (one per fruit). Large characins were observed feeding on *Gnetum* sp. in the upper Rio Negro, and we assumed that the seeds were crushed. Fishermen also report that large catfishes swallow the fruits whole, and this observation is further corroborated by botanists (Cavalcante, 1978; Kubitski, 1985). Dispersal and predation appears to be involved.

Lauraceae

Life Forms: small and large trees. *Nectandra amazonum* is often found in dense, almost pure, stands in low-lying areas along the edges of channels and floodplain waterbodies. The first author has observed at least six fish species feeding on *N. amazonum* fruits in the same area. The fruits are usually swallowed whole, though seeds are occasionally crushed by some of the larger characins.

Lecythidaceae

Life Forms: trees. Rio Negro flooded forests have several species of the genus *Eschweilera* whose seeds are commonly eaten by fishes. These lecythidaceous plants are often common in the swampy areas of islands. The seeds are enveloped in a large capsule whose lid (pyxidium) usually opens while the fruit is still attached to the tree. The seeds are eaten by the larger frugivorous characins, and these fishes always masticate them.

Leguminosae

The Leguminosae is one of the most abundant families of trees and shrubs in Rio Negro flooded forests. Most of the species produce relatively large fruit crops. Our overall impression is that legume fruits and seeds are not eaten by fishes in large quantities as might be expected, judging from the large biomass of capsules that are easily seen on trees, floating in the water and along the shore. Rio Negro turtles, however, feed heavily on legume species and the reptiles may have better adaptations for digesting the seeds than do fishes.

Loranthaceae

The mistletoes are common parasites of many Rio Negro floodplain trees. Their fruits are adapted for dispersal by birds or bats flying from tree to tree. When the fruits fall into the water they are eaten by fishes. Although fishes often swallow the mistletoe fruits whole, these animals should not be considered dispersal agents because the seeds are adapted to germinate on branches above the floodline.

Malpighiaceae

Life Forms: trees and shrubs. There are at least four malpighiaceous genera and six species whose fruits (mostly seeds) are eaten by fishes in Rio Negro flooded forests. The seeds are usually masticated, though in some cases (*e.g.*, *Byrsonima*) the fruits appear to be eaten mostly for the fleshy material.

Melastomataceae

Life Forms: mostly shrubs but at least one tree species. Melastomataceous fruits found in flooded forests are berries, and they are heavily sought after by fishes. The shrubs are common along shores, and they are among the first plants to become inundated with the annual floods. They fruit at the beginning of the flooding period, that is, before they become completely inundated. The shrub fruits are often sweet to semi-tart, and the fleshy parts so heavily colored, usually purple or red, that they stain the stomach and intestines of the fishes that consume them. The seeds of these species are small and escape mastication, thus extensive dispersal by fishes is suggested. *Mouriri subumbellata* is a relatively common tree species in the Rio Negro flooded forests. The seeds in its sweet drupes often escape mastication by fishes.

Moraceae

Life Forms: trees, parasites and strangler vines. The genus *Ficus*, or figs, is the most commonly seen taxon, and its species may be tall trees, parasites or stranglers. All species of fig fruits are very similar in structure, and they are referred to botanically as syconia. Syconia are fleshy fruits with numerous, small seeds. Fishes eat figs for the fleshy material, and the small seeds escape mastication. Though the seeds of the parasitic species whose fruits fall into the water are eaten by fishes, dispersal is probably not involved because these plant taxa are mainly adapted for germination in bird or mammal feces that has been deposited on limbs. Some of the tree species, however, may have their seeds dispersed by fishes. The umbrella tree, *Cecropia latiloba*, is a colonizer that quickly invades, by dissemination of seeds via birds, disturbed areas in the floodplain forest of the Rio Negro. The seeds of *C. latiloba* germinate on the ground, and thus fishes, along with birds, bats and perhaps a few mammals, help disperse them.

Myristicaceae

Life Forms: Medium to large trees. *Virola elongata* is not only a common species but one of the most common emergents that defines the upper outline of Rio Negro inundation forests. Its fruits are dehiscent drupes that, upon maturity, split into three or four valves dislodging the relatively large seed. The seed is enveloped in orange colored tissue, referred to as an aril, and this material is heavily sought after by many fish species. In most cases seed dispersal appears to be involved.

Myrtaceae

Life Forms: Mostly shrubs but also small trees. Myrtaceous shrubs are often the dominant plants along the Rio Negro riverside and in the higher parts of beach habitats. The important genera are *Eugenia*, *Psidium*, *Myrcia* and *Myrciaria*, and there are perhaps a dozen species. Most of the species appear to fruit at the beginning of the floods, that is, just before they are completely inundated. Their fruits are fleshy berries, and some of the species are sweet enough to be edible by humans. Since myrtaceous shrubs are some the first plants to be inundated, at which time they are also fruiting, fishes are often found in large numbers snapping-up the fruits as they fall into the water. All of the species are probably dispersed to some extent by fishes.

Passifloraceae

Life Forms: vines. Their are at least 3-4 *Passiflora* species in Rio Negro flooded forests. Passion fruits are large berries whose seeds are surrounded by tart to almost sweet arils. It is the arillate material that interests fishes, as the seeds are usually swallowed whole. In flooded forests, fishes, along with arboreal birds and mammals, help disperse passion fruit seeds.

Polygonaceae

Life Forms: trees, shrubs and vines. The most common polygonaceous species, at least in the lower stretch of the river, is a riverside shrub that belongs to the genus *Coccoloba*. At the beginning of the floods, *Coccoloba* sp. produces a huge fruit crop that is heavily sought after by frugivorous fishes. The fruits are bright red berries with a relatively large nut. Seeds were found variously broken and whole in stomach contents, thus some dispersal via fishes probably takes place.

Quiinaceae

Life Forms: trees and shrubs. The only quiinaceous species commonly seen is *Quiina rhytiodopus*. This small tree produces berries with 3-4 seeds that are often swallowed whole by fishes. Extensive dispersal is suggested.

Rubiaceae

Life Forms: mostly shrubs or small trees. The only rubiaceous fruits that we observed fishes eating were from the shrubs of the genus *Psychotria*. These shrubs produce berries with small seeds, the latter of which are probably extensively dispersed by fishes.

Sapindaceae

Life Forms: trees and vines. The woody lianas of the genus *Paullinia* produce large fruit crops. Their fruits are capsules whose seeds are enveloped in fleshy arils. The seeds of *Paullinia* species can be masticated or swallowed whole, depending on the fish species that eats them. Fishes are also reported by fishermen to eat the drupes of the tree *Talisia* cf. *japurensis*.

Sapotaceae

Life Forms: medium and large trees. Sapotaceous fruits of the Rio Negro are berries with 3-4 large and very smooth seeds. The seeds are usually found unbroken in fish stomach contents.

Simarubaceae

Life Forms: medium trees. The fruits of *Simaba* spp. are oblong, flattened drupes; the single seed is also flattened. The fruits of *Simaba* species are heavily attacked by fishes, and both dispersal and predation appears to be involved.

Solanaceae

The only common solanaceous plant seen along the Rio Negro is the shrub *Solanum* cf. *juripeba*. It is often found in disturbed areas or in low-lying habitats of the flood-plains and islands. It produces yellow berries whose seeds are usually swallowed whole.

AQUATIC HERBACEOUS PLANTS

As discussed in Chapter 3, the production of aquatic herbaceous plants in the Rio Negro is very limited because of the poor nutrient quality of the river. The appearance of relatively large floating meadows is a recent phenomenon, and it is most closely correlated with die-offs of flooded forest vegetation. Fish communities are now found in the floating meadows of the Rio Negro, though we found no evidence of major grazing on herbaceous plants [similar observations reported by Araujo-Lima, Portugal & Ferreira, 1986]. We found at least 46 fish species that had fed to some extent on herbaceous plants in the Rio Negro, but none of these appears to specialize on this item.

Grass seeds and aquatic invertebrates are the main food items eaten by fishes inhabiting the floating meadows of the lower Rio Negro. The apparent avoidance of large-scale consumption of herbaceous roots, stems and leaves by fishes is not easily explained by any evidence available. Other Central Amazonian animals, such as manatees, capyvara rodents and domestic livestock, eat the same aquatic grass species that are found in the lower Rio Negro (Junk, 1979,1980,1983; Best, 1984). Grass-eating fishes - *e.g.*, anostomids of the genera *Schizodon* and *Rhytiodus* and the doradid catfish *Lithodoras dorsalis* - have been found in turbid water rivers of the Amazon Basin, but even there they do not graze the plant biomass to any detectable reduction (Goulding, 1980; Santos, 1981; Junk & Howard-Williams, 1977,1984).

The principal aquatic herbaceous plant families found in the Rio Negro region are Araceae, Lentibulareaceae, Pontederiaceae, Salviniaceae, Gramineae (Poaceae) and Podostemonaceae. Only the arums (Araceae) and grasses (Gramineae) will be discussed here, though it should be mentioned that podostemonaceous plants are impor-

Tab. 5.2. The numbers of fish species in various habitats that fed on algae.

	Beaches	Confluence Swamp	Floating Meadows	Flooded Forest	Island Lakes	Rocky Pool	Woody Shores	Total Species That Fed on Item
Filamentous Algae	43	39	7	21	36	18	39	101
Microalgae	24	22	4	9	22	7	22	65

tant fish food in cataract areas of the upper Rio Negro region. Cataract ecology will be presented elsewhere in another work.

Araceae

Most of the araceous plants found in Rio Negro flooded forests are epiphytes of the genus *Philodendron*. *Montrichardia arborescens*, on the other hand, is shrub-size (but not woody) in appearance and often found in patches in low-lying areas of the flooded forest. Its fruits are oblong heads of berries that turn yellow to yellow-brown when ripe. Fishermen state unequivocally that fishes eat these fruits, and at least one botanical work has also mentioned the interaction (Silva, Lisboa & Lisboa, 1977). It is highly possible that fishes disperse the seeds of *M. arborescens*.

Gramineae

The principal grass species of the Rio Negro are *Oryza perennis*, *Paspalum repens* and *Luziola spruceana*, and these are only found in any quantity in the lower course of the river. Fishes feed on their seeds, which they masticate, and occasionally on their roots, stems and leaves.

ALGAE

At least 107 species of algae have been identified from Rio Negro waters (Uherkovich & Rai, 1979). For the purposes of this investigation, algae were divided into two groups: filamentous algae and microalgae. Most of the microalgal species consumed by fishes were unicellular, in contrast to the multi-cellular form of filamentous taxa. No specialized phytoplanktivorous fish species were found in the Rio Negro, though at least 101 and 65 species had eaten filamentous and micro-algae, respectively, to some extent (Tab. 5.2 and Appendix 9).

Filamentous Algae

Over 75 percent of the filamentous algae found in fish stomach contents consisted of species belonging to two genera, but each of a different class. The green algae

58

(class Chlorophyta) were represented by one species of *Spirogyra*, which is commonly seen in Rio Negro waters in flooded forest and woody shore habitats. Small masses of this algae often trail from submerged trunks, limbs and leaves of woody plants. The filamentous blue-green algae from stomach contents were represented by several species of the genus *Oscillatoria*.

Microalgae

The majority of microalgal species eaten by Rio Negro fishes were diatoms (class Bacillariophyceae), and these were often found together with filamentous species from other groups. The diatom flora of the Rio Negro contains at least 15 recognized species (Uherkovich & Rai, 1979), and a large number of these was found in stomach contents. There was no evidence that Rio Negro fishes are as selective of diatom species as they are of filamentous algae taxa.

6. DETRITIVORY

Detritus is a general term used herein for fish stomach contents that consisted of fine-structured organic and inorganic matter found together, plant remains in an advanced stage of decomposition or coarse litter in the initial stages of decomposition. Detritus removed from fish stomachs usually contains varying quantities of fungi, bacteria, protozoans and algae. There are too few data to know if there are major differences between detritivorous fish groups in the quantities of different types of decomposer micro-organisms that are ingested. Of the three detritus components outlined above, fine-structured matter and plant remains in an advanced stage of decomposition are the most important. Coarse litter is probably not consumed in greater quantities because of leaf toxicity factors [see Chapter 6]. All together 132 fish species had fed on fine detritus and 100 species on plant remains, whereas only 37 species had eaten coarse litter (Tab. 6.1 and Appendix 10).

The energy that reaches fish communities through Rio Negro detritus is undoubtedly derived mostly from forest vegetation. The plant remains and coarse litter components show this clearly, and most of the organic fine-structured matter is derived mainly from these two sources. This aspect has also been emphasized in reference to invertebrate and detritus interactions in blackwaters of the lower Rio Negro system (Irmler, 1975,1976b; Irmler & Furch, 1980).

At least one of the three detritus components outlined above is found on almost any substrate of Rio Negro inundated habitats. The major saprophytic organisms involved in the decomposition of litter in the blackwater and clearwater streams of the lower Rio Negro region have been identified (Walker, 1978,1985; Walker & Franken, 1983). Foodchains in the above mentioned waterbodies begin essentially with saprophytic fungi that turn organic matter, which is mostly rainforest litter, into finer detritus. Foodchains are only secondarily based on algae and bacteria. It was suggested by the above authors that the so-called *detritus* feeders may in fact be feeding mostly on fungi. It is not yet known, however, whether this is the case for detritivorous fishes.

The role of saprophytic fungi in Rio Negro flooded forests may be different from the patterns detected in rainforest streams. Singer (1984) states that the thick litter layer reported for Rio Negro inundation forests is due to the repression of decomposing fungi. In flooded forest habitats, most of the litter decomposition evidently takes place during the emersed period, and the major decomposers involve arthropods, fungi and bacteria (Stark & Holley, 1975; Irmler, 1975,1982; Adis, Furch & Irmler, 1979; Irmler & Furch, 1980). Many more studies will be needed before reasonable generalizations can be made about the decomposition pathways in Rio Negro detritus. The above observations, however, indicate that fungi, bacteria and arthropod communities are probably all important, depending on the exact habitat and circumstances.

Tab. 6.1. The numbers of fish species in various habitats that fed on detritus.

	Beaches	Confluence Swamp	Floating Meadows	Flooded Forest	Island Lakes	Rocky Pool	Woody Shores	Total Species That Fed on Item
Coarse Litter	11	13	–	18	4	4	13	37
Fine Detritus	51	45	7	27	52	23	45	132
Plant Remains	49	36	6	35	33	9	36	100

The part of detritus that is used by fishes is not obvious without experimental tests. For example, recent studies of the South American detritivorous fish, *Prochilodus platensis*, have shown that over 98 percent of the organic matter eaten consists of material other than micro-organisms. Furthermore, experimental data suggested that the detritivore could not maintain itself by assimilating only the micro-organisms and not the organic matter (Bowen, 1984; Bowen, Bonetto & Ahlgren, 1984).

In striking contrast to the above study, another experiment, involving a loricariid grazer in Panama, suggested that the organic-rich sediment ingested by the catfish was of no nutritive value (Power, 1984b,1984c). Power concluded that 15-22 percent of the energy that the catfish consumes each day is used for the elimination of non-food detritus, or sediment as she referred to it. The sediment is consumed in the first place in order to swallow nutritious food items with which it is associated.

DETRITUS FEEDING ON RAINFOREST TREES

HYPOTHESIS: The lower Rio Negro's most important commercial fish species are detritivores whose major food source is found on living vegetation of the flooded forests. The trees of the flooded forest act as mesh that forms a large net that traps fine organic matter on the trunk, limb and leaf surfaces. The organic matter itself is derived mostly from floodplain forest litter in an advanced stage of decomposition. The trees themselves appear to supply additional nutrients and energy to their attached detritus communities. This additional input is thought to be derived from exudates or nutrients released from the live vegetation.

Over 90 percent of the commercial fish catch of the lower Rio Negro consists of two detritivorous species of the genus *Semaprochilodus* (Prochilodontidae). Their importance in the commercial fisheries is due mostly to their relatively large biomass (at least as indicated by fisheries), their seasonal migrations and the fact that they form large schools that are highly vulnerable to exploitation with seines. Observation in flooded forests reveals that *Semaprochilodus* species feed mostly on the fine detritus that accumulates on submerged trunks, limbs and leaves (Fig. 6.1). *Semaprochilodus* species have labial teeth, that is, on their lips and outside of the mouth. When they evert their lips, they are able to employ their minute teeth, along with sucking movements, to remove fine detritus from substrates. It is not known how selective

Fig. 6.1. Schematic illustration of the manner in which detritivorous fishes of the genus *Semaprochilodus* obtain their food from trunks, limbs and leaves in Rio Negro flooded forests.

they are of the detritus they remove from flooded forest vegetation. Watching them feed, however, gives the impression that they are selective because they move from one trunk, limb or leaf surface to another in what appears to be a food search, though detritus can still be seen on the areas they leave. During the high water period, these fishes lie down large fat reserves while they are feeding in flooded forest (Ribeiro, 1983; pers. obser.). This fattening period is well known to fishermen, and the fishes, subsequent to the floods, are referred to locally as *fat fish*, an allusion not only to their body characteristics but also to their enhanced flavor within the Amazonian cuisine.

The detritus matter and communities that are found on submerged trees are derived from: 1) the suspension and deposition of matter transported in the water column; 2) the colonization of flooded forest vegetation by micro-organisms with rising water levels, and 3) perhaps the flaking of bark on the trunks of many flooded forest tree species. As mentioned above, most of the decomposition of flooded forest litter appears to take place during the emersed period (Irmler, 1975). When the forest is inundated with the annual floods, much of the litter that has been degraded into fine detritus is mixed in the water column, thus some of it becomes attached to trunk, limb and leaf surfaces. Based on field observations, we believe that flooded forest detritus communities associated with tree substrates could derive additional nutrients from the living vegetation. It is here suggested that this occurs through relatively nutrient-rich exudates released from the living vegetation. The fact that algal production in Rio Negro waters is often associated with floodplain and riparian vegetation also suggests that live woody vegetation is releasing nutrients into the water.

7. INVERTEBRATES AS FISH FOOD

CRUSTACEANS

Crustaceans are common food in Rio Negro fish communities (Tab. 7.1 and Appendix 5). Most studies of Amazonian crustaceans have concentrated on planktonic organisms in the Rio Solimões-Amazonas floodplain area near Manaus and tributary mouth-lakes of the lower Rio Negro. These investigations have elucidated the seasonal abundance of zooplankton and the identification of many species that live in open water (Hardy, 1980; Robertson & Hardy, 1984). Studies have not yet been made, however, of perizoon communities, that is, of the small animals that live on substrates. Perizoon communities are closely linked to detritus, fungi and algae, and the three elements together are usually called aufwuchs. Perizoon and aufwuchs are especially important in Amazonian inundation forests because of the huge surface area that tree trunks, limbs and leaves offer for the establishment of these communities.

Cladocera

The Rio Negro has all of the cladoceran families that are known in tropical freshwaters: Bosminidae, Daphnidae, Sididae, Moinidae, Holopedidae, Macrothricidae and Chydoridae. The dominant family in the Rio Negro is Bosminidae, which contrasts sharply with the situation in the Rio Solimões-Amazonas where Daphnidae appears to be by far the most abundant (Robertson & Hardy, 1984). The Daphnidae appears less adapted to nutrient-poor waters. Holopedidae was the only Rio Negro cladoceran family not found in fish stomach contents.

1. **Bosminidae**: - The Rio Negro has five known bosminid species. *Bosminopsis deitersi* and *Bosmina* spp. (2 species) were found respectively in 38 and 31 fish species (see Tab. 7.1). Brandorff (1977) reported that *B. deitersi* was the most abundant cladoceran species of the lower Rio Negro. *B. deitersi* appears to be mostly a surface species, though in shallow waters, such as in beach waters where it is most commonly eaten in the Rio Negro, it is also part of the perizoon since it was found in fishes that feed on the substrate. A second, and apparently new, species of *Bosminopsis* was found in the stomach contents of the catfish *Hypophthalmus fimbriatus*, though the crustacean has yet to be collected in zooplankton samples (Carvalho & Goulding, 1985).

2. **Chydoridae**: - For the purposes of this study, we did not quantitatively separate each of the chydorid species in the stomach contents of individual specimens, as this would have been too time consuming within the context of our goals. Chydorid taxa, however, were subsequently identified from subsamples taken from the fish species that had eaten them. All together 20 chydorid species were identified from the 62 fish

Tab. 7.1. The numbers of fish species in various habitats that fed on crustaceans.

	Beaches	Confluence Swamp	Floating Meadows	Flooded Forest	Island Lakes	Rocky Pool	Woody Shores	Total Species That Fed on Item
Bosmina spp.	13	7	6	7	5	2	7	31
Bosminopsis deitersi	24	3	2	6	10	2	3	38
Calanoida	3	2	2	3	14	2	2	27
Chydoridae	29	13	12	7	6	10	13	62
Cladocera	16	6	5	15	13	1	6	45
Conchostraca	4	2	–	5	–	–	2	7
Copepoda	9	2	–	6	1	–	2	14
Crabs	3	5	–	14	–	1	5	22
Cyclopoida	30	8	12	8	14	11	8	64
Harpacticoida	2	1	–	2	1	2	1	9
Isopoda	1	2	1	4	–	–	2	7
Macrothricidae	9	3	7	–	2	3	3	28
Ostracoda	20	10	4	13	5	7	10	46
Shrimp	21	14	2	19	8	5	14	53

species that had eaten them. The genera included *Alona, Alonella, Camptocercus, Chydorus, Dadaya, Disparalona, Dunhevedia, Euryalona, Graptoleberis, Leydigia* and *Pleuroxus*. These cladocerans were only dominant food items in bottom feeding fishes. Although chydorids showed a high frequency of occurrence in stomach contents, they are generally not as important as other cladocerans.

3. **Daphnidae**: - The only two known species of Rio Negro Daphnidae are *Ceriodaphnia cornuta* and *Daphnia gessneri*. *Daphnia* species are probably the most important zooplankton taxa eaten by freshwater fishes the world over (Brooks, 1968; Galbraith, 1967; Green, 1967). They have also been shown to be important in zooplanktivorous fish diets in the floodplain waterbodies of Amazonian turbid rivers (Carvalho, 1981; 1984; Goulding & Carvalho, 1982). No *Daphnia* species were found, however, in the stomach contents of Rio Negro fishes, though *D. gessneri* is known from at least the lower Rio Negro (Robertson & Hardy, 1984; pers. obser.). The evidence suggests that *Daphnia* species are unable to maintain large populations in the blackwaters of the Rio Negro.

Cerodaphnia cornuta has been reported to be a relatively common species in the lateral lakes of the lower Rio Negro, though it appears to become rarer upstream of the large mouth-bay (Robertson & Hardy, 1984). The species was only found in stomach contents of fishes captured in the flooded forests of the lower Rio Negro, and even there the cladoceran was rare. The absence of *C. cornuta* in fish diets of the middle and upper Rio Negro suggests that the species is missing or rare in these stretches of the river.

4. **Macrothricidae**: - Among the cladocerans associated with substrates, the family Macrothricidae is less diverse in species than Chydoridae, the dominant taxon in the

Rio Negro. At least five macrothricid species were found in fish stomach contents. *Ilyocryptus* sp. was more abundant than all of the other taxa together.

5. **Moinidae**: - The Rio Negro has three known species of the family Moinidae: *Moina minuta, rostrata* and *reticulata*. Only *M. minuta* was found in fish stomach contents. As far as is known, *M. minuta* lives mostly near the surface. The types of fishes that had eaten the species are also surface dwellers.

6. **Sididae**: - *Diaphanosoma sarsi* and *fluviatilis* are the only two known sidid species in the Rio Negro. Because of identification problems with Sididae, they were relegated to the unidentified Cladocera category, thus we can only report that Rio Negro fishes eat them, but to what extent is still unclear.

Conchostraca

All that is known about Conchostraca in the Rio Negro is that the group is there and that some of the species are occasionally eaten by fishes. Little work has been done on Amazonian species, and to date there are few clues as to the diversity of the group in this region (Loffler, 1981). As far as is known, Amazonian conchostracans are mostly substrate dwellers of quiet waters (Junk, 1973).

Copepoda

Copepods are generally reported to be of much less importance in fish diets than are cladocerans (Brooks, 1968; Confer & Blades, 1975; Frost, 1977; Jansen, 1976). This was also true for the Rio Negro. Zaret (1975, 1980) hypothesized that copepods escape potential predators through vertical migrations. In the shallow waters of many Amazonian habitats, however, migration would be greatly limited by water depth. O'Brien (1979) has observed that copepods display intermittent in contrast to continuous movements for cladocerans, thus it is suggested that the former are more easily able to escape prey.

For the purposes of this study, copepods were divided into three groups (usually considered suborders): Calanoida, Cyclopoida and Harpacticoida.

1. **Calanoida**: - Robertson and Hardy (1984) reported 14 species of Calanoida from the lower Rio Negro. Calanoida taxa were consumed mostly by zooplanktivorous fishes, though bottom feeders suggest that they can also be removed from substrates.

2. **Cyclopoida**: - Three species are known from the lower Rio Negro. The predators that had consumed relatively large quantities of Cyclopoida species shared the characteristics of small size and numerous, well developed gillrakers.

3. **Harpacticoida**: - The Amazonian species are poorly known, but general anatomical characteristics (short antennules and elongate bodies) of Harpactiocoida suggest that they live on or in soft substrates (Kiefer, 1967). Furthermore, most of the 10 fish species that had eaten these crustaceans are bottom or substrate feeders.

Decapoda

1. **Shrimp**: - Shrimp were collected along with fishes during our Rio Negro investigations, and this collection was incorporated into the latest revision of the Palaemonidae, the principal shrimp family in the Amazon Basin (Kensley & Walker, 1982). The

principal palaemonid genera in the Rio Negro are *Macrobrachium*, *Pseudopalaemon* and *Euryrhynchus*, of which there are at least 10 species. The family Sergestidae is represented by one species of *Acetes*. All of the above genera were found in stomach contents. No shrimp-eating specialists were found in the Rio Negro, though a total of 53 fish species, especially in flooded forest and beach waters, had eaten these decapods. There is some evidence that shrimp-eating is more common in the turbid river floodplain areas. For example, certain species of the croaker genus *Plagioscion* feed heavily on shrimp in turbid river areas, but switch mostly to fish in nutrient-poor waters where the production of this food item is greatly reduced (Goulding & Ferreira, 1984).

2. **Crabs**: - The Rio Negro has two described crab families, the Trichodactylidae and Pseudothelphusidae. Each of the families is reported to have at least four species in the Rio Negro, though the taxonomy is still in a precarious state (Bott, 1967, 1969; Pretzmann, 1972; Rodriguez, 1981). Fish stomach contents revealed four Rio Negro crab species — *Sylviocarcinus pictus*, *Dilocarcinus page*, *Trichodactylus ehrhardti* and *Poppiana laevifrons* — all of the family Trichodactylidae. The evidence did not reveal any fish species that specialize on crabs, but rather the large crustaceans are eaten as part of broader diets.

Isopoda

The order Isopoda is very poorly known in South American waters, though apparently it is better represented in aquatic than terrestrial habitats of the continent (Penny & Arias, 1982). Soil isopods have been observed migrating up tree trunks in flooded forest at the onset of the annual floods in the lower Rio Negro (Adis, 1984). Less than one percent of the arthropod fauna found on the flooded forest floor during the emersed phase of a site in the lower Rio Negro consisted of isopods, and the group appears to represent only a small part of the invertebrate biomass in this habitat (Adis, 1981). In no habitat were more than four fish species found that had eaten isopods.

Ostracoda

Amazonian ostracod studies are still in their infancy, and few of the species can be identified. Ostracods are known to be common on substrates in Amazonian waterbodies, and especially abundant in the soil of flooded forests during the inundation period (Junk, 1973; Reiss, 1977; Irmler, 1975). All together 46 Rio Negro fish species had eaten ostracods, and from all habitats studied.

MOLLUSKS

Mollusks are relatively common in Amazonian turbid and clearwater rivers (Haas, 1949a,1949b,1950, and pers. obser.). They are not commonly seen in the Rio Negro, however, and the very poor calcium and phosphorous levels of the river are probably the main limiting factors. Large snails (*Eupera* spp.) are the mollusks most often encountered in the Rio Negro region. During the low water period when the floodplains are drained, these snails remain attached to trees and pass the

Tab. 7.2. The numbers of fish species in various habitats that fed on miscellaneous invertebrate groups.

	Beaches	Confluence Swamp	Floating Meadows	Flooded Forest	Island Lakes	Rocky Pool	Woody Shores	Total Species That Fed on Item
Annelida	5	1	–	7	2	–	1	15
Bryozoa	2	5	–	–	13	–	5	23
Diplopoda	1	–	–	10	–	–	–	12
Mollusca	3	3	–	9	2	1	3	13
Nematoda	13	4	–	1	6	3	4	31
Porifera	29	19	–	9	12	8	19	67
Rotifera	7	5	2	5	12	2	5	27

dry season in a diapause state (Irmler, 1975,1976a). Bivalves are present, but rare, in the Rio Negro. Most of the mollusks eaten by Rio Negro fishes appeared to be land forms that had failed to escape rising river levels (Tab. 7.2 and Appendix 5).

BRYOZOANS

South American bryozoans are poorly known. The Neotropical region has at least nine genera and 17 species/subspecies of bryozoans. The Rio Negro is reported to have three bryozoan genera – *Fredericella*, *Plumatella* and *Hislopia* – and perhaps five species, most of which are not well defined (Wiebach, 1967).

Most of the moss animacules found in Rio Negro fish stomach contents belonged to the genus *Plumatella* (see Tab. 7.2 and Appendix 5). Rio Negro fishes apparently do not feed on the sessile bryozoan colonies, but rather eat their statoblasts, or free-floating buds that detach themselves for asexual reproduction and dissemination. The predatory fishes that eat bryozoan statoblasts in the Rio Negro are, for the most part, small and surface dwelling species. *Leporinus klausewitzi*, an anostomid fish with greatly enlarged teeth, had also eaten relatively large quantities of part of a colony of what appeared to be a species of the genus *Hislopia*.

PORIFERA

The great majority of sponge species are marine. In terms of freshwater, however, tropical American sponges constitute a relatively rich and varied fauna. Most of the information available on Amazonian sponges, however, is sporadic and deals with taxonomic descriptions. There appear to be several sponge genera in the Rio Negro, but further details are meager (Volkmer-Ribeiro, 1981). Sponge growths attached to trees in Rio Negro flooded forests are common and easily seen, and the animals can also be observed on rocks and other substrates. Sponges are able to survive in habitats that dry out, such as flooded forests, by the production of resistant gemmules that germinate with the next inundation.

Most of the fish species that eat Rio Negro sponges are bottom or substrate feeders (see Tab. 7.2 and Appendix 5). Megascleres, or smooth spicules that make up the fibers or skeletal network of sponges, were the main poriferan item found in stomach contents, and these were usually associated with sand. The evidence suggests that sponge spicules, which consist mostly of silica, are ingested along with other food items, and the poriferan material is probably of little importance in fish diets.

ROTIFERS OR ROTATORIA

The Amazon Basin has over 250 known rotifer species (Koste, 1972; Robertson & Hardy, 1984). At least 50 rotifer species are known from the Rio Negro, but the total is thought to be much higher as intensive sampling has only just begun. The most speciose genera of the Rio Negro are *Lecane, Trichocerca, Keratella*, and *Brachionus*, and these included the principal rotifer taxa found in stomach contents. Judging from the fish species that had eaten them in the Rio Negro, rotifers are taken in open waters and on substrates. The largest quantities of rotifers, however, were found in small fishes with adaptations for capturing zooplankton. Of the 27 fish species that had eaten rotifers, most were from the confluence swamp sampled and island lakes (see Tab. 7.2 and Appendix 5).

NEMATODA

Almost any substrate sample in Amazonian waters will contain nematodes. The phylum is still poorly known, in terms of its tropical diversity, and numerous species undoubtedly remain to be described (Riemann, 1981). We have found no information on Rio Negro nematodes. Bottom-feeding catfishes that burrow into sand for small invertebrates were the fishes that most consumed nematodes (see Tab. 7.2 and Appendix 5). Sand was usually associated with roundworms in stomach contents.

OLIGOCHAETA

The taxonomy of Amazonian aquatic segmented worms is still poorly known, and more attention has been given to their ecology than classification. The Rio Negro is known to have at least five oligochaete families — Naididae, Aeolosomatidae, Opystocistidae, Enchytraeidae and Octochaetidae (Irmler, 1976a; Adis, 1981; Nessimian, 1985; Walker, 1985). Oligochaete sampling in the Rio Negro indicates that the group is common in flooded forest litter, on lake bottoms and in the substrates of beaches. In terms of relative biomass, however, aquatic segmented worms appear to be most abundant, per unit area, in beach substrates (Nessimian, 1985); however, they often account for the largest biomass of any single invertebrate group in flooded forest litter (Irmler,1975). Most of the 15 fish species that had eaten oligochaetes were from flooded forest and beaches (see Tab. 7.2 and Appendix 5)

INSECTS

Insects are extremely important trophic links in the foodchains that sustain Rio

Tab. 7.3. The numbers of fish species in various habitats that fed on insects and spiders (and relatives).

	Beaches	Confluence Swamp	Floating Meadows	Flooded Forest	Island Lakes	Rocky Pool	Woody Shores	Total Species That Fed on Item
Chaoboridae Larvae	8	3	–	6	1	–	3	14
Chironomidae Larvae	43	20	16	20	13	12	20	88
Coleoptera	25	18	4	27	11	4	18	66
Coleoptera Larvae	6	3	2	12	1	–	3	25
Collembola	2	3	–	6	4	2	3	14
Corixidae	15	7	2	5	–	3	7	27
Culicidae Larvae	–	–	5	5	–	–	–	10
Dermaptera	–	–	–	1	–	–	–	1
Diptera	12	4	5	6	2	1	4	29
Diptera Larvae	29	19	2	13	9	9	19	69
Diptera Pupae	31	17	12	8	4	4	17	64
Ephemeroptera	1	1	–	–	–	–	1	1
Ephemeroptera Nymphs	27	19	6	12	6	9	19	66
Formicidae	17	9	5	25	7	2	9	51
Hemiptera	10	11	5	13	3	1	11	37
Homoptera	1	4	4	4	–	–	4	12
Hymenoptera	7	3	–	8	1	–	3	17
Isoptera	1	–	–	8	–	–	–	10
Lepidoptera Larvae	1	1	–	10	–	–	1	11
Microlepidoptera	2	–	–	–	–	–	–	2
Neuroptera	–	–	–	–	–	1	–	1
Odonata	1	6	–	–	–	–	6	7
Odonata Nymphs	12	2	5	14	2	4	2	33
Orthoptera	1	4	1	11	1	–	4	14
Orthoptera Nymphs	–	–	–	–	–	–	–	1
Plecoptera	–	–	–	1	–	–	–	1
Psocoptera	–	–	–	2	–	–	–	2
Trichoptera	38	8	4	16	3	9	8	61
SPIDERS & RELATIVES								
Hydracarina	27	17	5	15	6	7	17	67
Pseudoscorpionida				7				7
Spiders	4	2	4	13	1	1	2	22

Negro fishes (Tab. 7.3 and Appendices 5 and 6). These arthropods trophically bridge a structural or biochemical chasm that exists between indigestible or inaccessible forms of primary production and Rio Negro fish communities (Irmler, 1973, 1975,1978a,1979a,1979b,1981,1982). At the present time, identification of most Amazonian insects below about the order or family level is not possible, at least within practical time and effort limits, because of the tremendous diversity involved and the generally poor taxonomic knowledge of most groups. Initial investigations have concentrated on determining the relative biomass, abundance and seasonal movements of mostly orders or families (Adis, 1981; Penny & Arias, 1982). Our study complements these first efforts from the point of view of Rio Negro fish life and its dependence on insects as food.

Coleoptera

Most flooded forest beetles probably escape the annual inundation by migrating up the trees or to dry land (Irmler, 1975,1976b,1979b,1981). The exact reasons why so many beetles fall into the water are unclear, though storms and faulty movements would appear to be the principal factors. Imagines were eaten by 66 and larvae by 25 fish species. Most of the beetles eaten were arboreal or terrestrial taxa, of which Curculionidae, Cerambycidae and Scarabaeidae were identified. Aquatic representatives included Hydrophilidae, Elmidae and Dytiscidae. No beetle-feeding specialists were found, though the *Osteoglossum* species, the largest insectivorous fishes [reaching about 90 cm in total length] of the Rio Negro, take relatively large quantities of them along the shores of woody areas.

Collembola

In the Amazonian flooded forests springtails are found in trees, in soils (during emersed period) and probably on water surfaces. Some (or all?) of the flooded forest species are thought to survive the annual inundation, either as adults or eggs, in the soil or under loose bark. It has been hypothesized that the submerged adults may undergo a dormant period (Adis, 1984). The majority of collembolans found in stomach contents of Rio Negro fishes belonged to the family Entomobriidae.

Dermaptera

Earwigs are rarely seen in Rio Negro habitats, and sampling has also shown them to be scarce in flooded forest areas (Adis, 1984). Only one fish specimen had eaten an earwig.

Diptera

Dipterans are very important as fish food in Rio Negro waters. Fishes eat dipteran larvae, pupae and winged adults. We divided dipterans from stomach contents into five groups, based only on the criterion that they could be identified as such: Chaoboridae larvae, Chironomidae larvae, Culicidae larvae, unidentified Diptera larvae, unidentified Diptera pupae and Diptera adults.

Chaoborus species are usually reported to undergo vertical movements, that is, confining themselves to the bottom during the day and rising to surface waters at night. The biology of the Chaoboridae is very poorly known in South American waters (Cook, 1981). Chaoborids are attacked by small and medium sized fishes, though the prey was never found in large quantities in stomach contents [the possi-

71

bility exists that they might be digested very rapidly].

About 90 chironomid species have been described from the Amazon Basin, though entomologists now have at least another 400 undescribed taxa (Reiss, 1977). A few species are only known from the Rio Negro (Fittkau, 1971). Chironomid larvae were eaten by a diverse array of fish species, of small to medium size, but the predators did not share any outstanding morphological characteristics.

The Culicidae represents a very large group of mosquitoes in Amazonian waters, but very little work has been done on the ecology of riverine and floodplain taxa. Culicid studies away from urban centers still largely concentrate on systematic problems (Ward, 1981). Most research has focused on malaria and yellow fever transmitting culicids found near human population centers. One of the striking entomological characteristics of the Rio Negro is the general absence of haemotophagous mosquitoes, at least in the middle and upper stretches of the river that are away from urban centers. The poor appearance of mosquito larvae in Rio Negro fish diets further confirms the observation, as noted by many naturalists, that the group has a much reduced biomass in this river (e.g., Spix & Martius, 1823; Wallace, 1853; Spruce, 1908). Mosquito larvae, and hence adults, are most abundant in turbid water regions, such as the Rio Solimões-Amazonas and Rio Madeira. Experimental evidence will be needed to determine if their poor showing in the Rio Negro is due to nutrient poverty and/or, as Janzen (1974) suggested, to toxicity factors.

Because of identification problems, no attempt was made to separate dipteran pupae into families, as was done with larvae. The pupal stages of dipterans usually last less than two weeks, at least according to text books, though there are no reports we are aware of for Amazonian riverine species. Many of the dipteran pupae identified undoubtedly belong to the larval groups discussed above.

Ephemeroptera

Nymphs are the mayfly stage most eaten by Rio Negro fishes. All together 66 fish species had eaten mayfly nymphs. The first author witnessed mating swarms of imagines on two different occasions in the area of the upper Rio Negro. In one case, the mayfly imagines were so abundant that we were forced to abandon our evening meal, which became plastered with them, and turn off the boat lights, to which the ephemeropterans were attracted. Small auchenipterid catfishes (*Tatia*) were observed with the aid of a flashlight rising to the surface to eat the winged mayflies when they fell back into the water. Adult mayflies, however, were only found in fish stomach contents on two other occasions, and then in small quantities.

Hemiptera

At least five hemipteran families — Corixidae, Gerridae, Belostomatidae, Naucoridae and Veliidae — could be recognized in fish stomach contents. There are, however, several more bug families in Rio Negro waters. Most of the hemipterans eaten by Rio Negro fishes were aquatic forms. Waterstriders (Gerridae) are the bugs most easily observed in, or on, Rio Negro waters, and they are among the fastest surface hemipterans known (Nieser, 1981). It is possible that they are too fast and perceptive for most fishes to capture them. Belostomatids have also been reported to feed on larval fishes (Bachmann, 1977).

Homoptera

Unlike the hemipterans, as separated in our study, most of the homopterans consumed by fishes appeared to be arboreal forms. The only family that could be identified was Cicadellidae, though others were undoubtedly involved.

Hymenoptera

For the purposes of this study, we divided hymenopterans into ants and bees/wasps. Bees and wasps were relatively unimportant as fish food, though they are common insects seen along the Rio Negro. Ants seem to be everywhere in rainforests and they are abundant in inundation and riparian forests as well. All together 51 fish species had eaten ants (Formicidae). In flooded forest they are forced to make seasonal migrations to avoid inundation. These movements are either up the trunks or to higher *terra firme* with the coming of the floods. Most of the ant biomass, however, appears to migrate upwards rather than to flee to higher ground (Adis, 1981,1984). Some dispersal by swimming may also take place. Other than falling out of the vegetation and into the water in apparently large quantities, ants also enter the aquatic milieu when they crash during nuptial flights across waterbodies. Among the ants identified as fish food were *Solenopsis geminata*, *Pseudomyrmex* sp., *Odontomachus chelifer* and *Componotus*. Saul (1975) has also emphasized the importance of ants in many Amazonian fish diets.

Isoptera

The flooded forests of the lower Rio Negro have at least 21 termite species, and these belong to the families Kalotermitidae, Rhinotermitidae and Termitidae (Mill, 1982). Termite nests are easily observed in Rio Negro flooded forests, and parts of termitaria are often seen floating in the water, evidently having been knocked loose by storms or arboreal predators. A few winged forms had been eaten, but most termite remains were apterous workers and soldiers.

Lepidoptera

Butterflies are commonly seen flitting though flooded forests or flying over open waterbodies of the Rio Negro. Naturalists have noted butterfly migrations across Amazonian waterbodies, though few of the winged lepidopterans seem to fall into the water (Bates, 1863; Spruce, 1908). On very few occasions did we see adult butterflies or moths on the water's surface. Most of the lepidopterans that are eaten by fishes belong to larval or pupal stages, and these instars fall out of the trees and into the water.

Neuroptera

The Amazon Basin contains two aquatic neuropteran families, Corydalidae and Sialidae, both of which are in the Rio Negro system. Neuropterans do not appear to be common in the Rio Negro or in its floodplain, but they have been captured in rainforest streams draining into the river (Penny & Arias, 1982). Only one fish species had eaten neuropterans (a corydalid) and the predator was taken in a rocky pool. Penny (1981) notes that neuropterans can be predators of larval fishes.

Odonata

The odonates, owing to the abundance of colorful winged forms that hover and fly about over waterbodies, are among the most conspicuous insects of the Rio Negro. Imagines, however, are relatively rare in Rio Negro fish diets and this may be because few of them fall into the water. Larvae were found in the diets of 33 fish species. The highest occurrence was in the flooded forest habitat where 14 fish species were found feeding on them. Odonate larvae have also been reported to be predators of small neotropical fishes (Santos, 1981).

Orthoptera

In the Rio Negro region, crickets appear to be the most abundant orthopterans. Grasshoppers, and especially *Paulinia acuminata*, are abundant in the floating herbaceous vegetation of turbid rivers (Carbonell, 1981; Junk, 1973). The limited development of herbaceous aquatic plants in the Rio Negro would appear to be the principal reason that grasshoppers are not more common in the blackwater system. None, in fact, were found in stomach contents of fishes. Most of the orthopterans eaten by fishes were crickets of the family Gryllidae. Crickets betray their presence, to humans but probably not to fishes, by the sounds they make by rubbing one wing over another. Their acoustical renderings are often heard coming from the flooded forests of the Rio Negro.

Plecoptera

Both stomach contents from fishes and insect sampling of flooded forests suggest that stoneflies are not abundant in the Rio Negro [the latter observation based on Adis, 1981]. Only one plecopteran was found in fish stomach contents.

Psocoptera

Wood lice larvae are non-aquatic and, as Adis (1981) has shown, all forms living in flooded forest must migrate upwards or elsewhere to avoid the annual inundations. Though present in flooded forests, they are not among the most common insects of this habitat in the Rio Negro (Adis, 1984). Only two fish species were found that had eaten wood lice, and these were captured in flooded forest.

Trichoptera

Caddisfly imagines are seldom seen in the Rio Negro area. This is not because the group is not present, as their larvae attest they are, but because they seldom move about and are well camouflaged in the vegetation. We found no trichopteran imagines in fish stomach contents, though larvae were among the most important insects eaten in piscine communities. All together 61 fish species had fed on caddisfly larvae. They appear to be especially abundant in beach habitats where 38 fish species were found preying on them. They are also known to be relatively abundant in flooded forests (Sattler, 1963,1968). Trichopteran larvae are obligatorily aquatic. They form silken nets, to which they retreat, or cases of plant or mineral matter in which they are encapsulated, and which they take with them when they seek out their food (Flint, 1981). The majority of trichopterans eaten by Rio Negro fishes were ingested along with their sand cases.

Thysanoptera

Thrips are entirely terrestrial or arboreal. They do not appear to be common in Rio Negro flooded forests, but they may also escape detection because of their small size. Only one fish species was found that had eaten a thrip.

SPIDERS AND RELATIVES AND DIPLOPODA

Acari, Mainly Hydracarina

Most of the acarines eaten by Rio Negro fishes appeared to belong to the Hydracarina, a mostly aquatic group. Hydracarine larvae are usually parasitic on other insects, whereas adults are predaceous (Cook, 1981). All together 67 Rio Negro fish species had eaten acarines, most of the latter of which were apparently adult forms (see Tab. 7.3 and Appendix 5). They appear to be relatively common fish food in all the Rio Negro habitats sampled.

Araneida or Spiders

Spiders are abundant in Amazonian flooded forests, and they are easily seen scurrying about on tree trunks in search of prey. In flooded forests, spiders ambush, or net, other insects and arthropods that flee up the tree trunks to avoid the annual inundation. Other than in flooded forests, many spiders that land in the water are probably wafted there by strong winds that precede torrential downpours. Various spider groups also use the forest floor during the emersed period, and it is possible that some of these become inundated before escaping upwards (Friebe & Adis, 1983). They are most important as fish food in flooded forest (see Tab. 7.3 and Appendix 6).

Pseudoscorpionida or Pseudoscorpions

The pseudoscorpions are common inhabitants of Amazonian flooded forests, and they have evolved life cycles that allow them to escape annual inundations. Neither larval nor adult pseudoscorpions have adaptions for living in water. At the beginning of the floods, adults migrate up the trees where they spend the inundation period on the trunks or in the canopy. When the flooded forests are drained, adults and larvae move downward and colonize the soil substrate (Adis, 1981). About 40 pseudoscorpion species are now recognized for the Amazon Basin, of which at least 15 species have been captured in flooded forest associated with the Rio Negro (Mahnert, 1979; Adis, 1981). Pseudoscorpions were only found in fish diets in the flooded forest habitat (see Tab. 7.3 and Appendix 6).

DIPLOPODA OR MILLIPEDES

Millipedes are relatively common on the forest floor of the Amazonian rainforest. Millipedes are strictly terrestrial or arboreal, and the flooded forest taxa apparently migrate up the trees at the onset of the annual inundation. Only occasionally do they fall into the water, thus they are not very important as fish food.

8. PISCIVORY

The Rio Negro has representatives of all of the major piscivorous groups of the Amazon. Fishes are by far the most diverse group of Amazonian piscivores, but the Rio Negro also has two dolphin species, two turtle species, two caiman species and various snakes and birds that have yet to be studied, but which are known to feed on fishes to at least some extent.

Of the non-piscine piscivores, the large river turtle, *Peltocephalus tracaxa* (Pemelodusidae), appears to be the most common. It has a large mouth and extremely strong jaws, and is able to bite-out pieces of prey in a manner reminiscent of piranha feeding behavior. The dolphin, *Inia geoffrensis*, has been shown to feed on a wide variety of fish species and sizes (Silva, 1983). Dolphins are probably the only predators other than man in the Rio Negro that regularly attack prey larger than about 80 cm or 5 kg. Both the black caiman (*Melanosuchus niger*) and the spectacled caiman (*Caiman crocodilus*) have been largely decimated in the Rio Negro for the illegal skin trade, though there are a few places, such as in the Anavilhanas Ecological Reserve in the lower course of the river, where they can still be seen fairly easily. They are also taken for food. Neither caiman species is entirely piscivorous, but include fish in their diets along with a wide variety of vertebrate and invertebrate prey (Staton & Dixon, 1975; Medem, 1981; Vanzolini & Gomes, 1979; Best, 1984). Except for kingfishers (*Cloroceryle*), piscivorous birds are relatively rare in the Rio Negro, though flocks of egrets and cormorants are occasionally encountered.

There are five principal forms of piscivory practiced by Rio Negro fishes: flesh-eating, scale-eating, fin-eating, mucus-eating and blood-eating. Only the first is unquestionably a form of predation. The other four habits appear to represent varying degrees of parasitism.

FLESH-EATING OR PREDATION

Most of the piscivorous fishes of the Rio Negro are predators, that is, they kill the fishes whose flesh they eat. There are three ways that Rio Negro fishes eat piscine prey. The most common habit is to swallow it whole, usually head first. A few species appear to masticate small fishes. Finally, piranhas bite-out pieces of flesh. Flesh-eating fishes were present in all of the habitats that we sampled. They accounted for about 11-18 percent of all species present in the various habitat types, with the exception of floating meadows where little piscivory was detected [probably because of sampling error]. All together 87 species, or about 35 percent of the 250 fish species examined for food, had eaten piscine flesh to some extent (Tab. 8.1 and Appendix 12). Of the 87 piscivorous species, however, only about 20 species appear to restrict their diets mostly to fish flesh. For the other taxa, fish is eaten as part of broader-based diets and appears to be relatively unimportant in terms of the total volume

Tab. 8.1. The numbers of fish species in various habitats that practiced piscivory.

	Beaches	Confluence Swamp	Floating Meadows	Flooded Forest	Island Lakes	Rocky Pool	Woody Shores	Total Species That Fed on Item
Fish (as prey)	42	30	2	34	24	12	30	87
Fin Rays	4	4	–	4	–	–	4	5
Scales	51	32	2	33	22	6	32	100

total volume of food consumed [see Chapter 10 for discussion of piscivory at the community level].

There do not appear to be any specialized piscivores in the Rio Negro in the sense of a predator feeding mostly on only one or a few prey species [see Appendix 11 for piscivore/prey ratios]. In general, Rio Negro piscivorous fishes eat prey less than about one-third their own lengths. The relatively unspecialized piscivorous habits of Rio Negro fishes and the predator/prey ratios are largely in agreement with observations from other tropical freshwater systems (Lowe-McConnell, 1975,1987).

SCALE-EATING OR LEPIDOPHAGY

Scales may appear in fish stomachs for any of the following reasons: as part of an entire fish that was swallowed whole or in part; removal from a live fish or from carrion; or because the item was scavenged from the detritus layer. It is not always easy to determine which was the case when examining stomach contents. For the purposes of this study, if fish bones or flesh were found along with scales, then it was assumed that the last item was from the prey that had been eaten. In other words, the fish was eaten for the flesh, bones and scales. When only scales were found, lepidophagy was assumed to be the case.

There is now substantial evidence that the removal of scales from live fishes represents a specialized feeding habit among fishes from South America and elsewhere (Roberts, 1970; Sazima, 1977,1984; Sazima & Machado, 1982; Goulding, 1980; Vari, 1986). The principal fish groups in the Rio Negro that remove scales from live fishes are characins and trichomycterid catfishes. Several adult piranha species regularly remove scales from other fishes. It is also suspected that the young of nearly all piranha species of the Rio Negro may practice lepidophagy to some extent. Piranha juvenile specimens, however, were not studied in detail because of the need to preserve them intact for systematic investigations in progress. Two characin groups (*Roeboides* spp. and *Serrabrycon magoi*) of the Rio Negro have teeth on the outside of the mouth which they apparently use to remove scales from other fishes. Too few scale-eating trichomycterid catfish specimens were captured in the Rio Negro for a meaningful analysis, but the evidence from here, and elsewhere collected by the first author, indicates that the habit is common with certain species of this group in the Amazon Basin.

About 40 percent, or 100 of the 250 fish species examined, had eaten scales, though this was usually in very small quantities. Most scales are probably found when scavenging the bottom, but why so many fish species eat them is unclear. The physiology of scale digestion has not been investigated in any detail. Fish scales that have been studied chemically contain about 40-85 percent protein, though few other values have been elucidated (Van Oosten, 1957). Mucus is also associated with scales, and it is known to be rich in proteins and lipids (Wessler & Werner, 1957; Lewis, 1970). It is possible that in calcium and phosphorous-poor waters, such as the Rio Negro, many fish species occasionally take scales as a sort of dietary supplement.

FIN-EATING

Fin-eating appears to be a form of parasitism, and the habit has been reported for several piranha species in South America (Roberts, 1970; Goulding, 1980; Vieira & Gery, 1979). The fin-eaters of the Rio Negro are also piranhas, of which there are at least five species [piranha ecology will be discussed in a subsequent work awaiting taxonomic and systematic investigations now in progress by others who are studying our specimens].

BLOOD-EATING OR HAEMOTOPHAGY

Some trichomycterid catfishes of the Rio Negro specialize, at least in part, on the blood of larger fishes. Their hosts are usually other catfishes and stingrays. The haemotophagous trichomycterids have needle-like teeth which they can use to puncture the skin in order to reach blood vessels.

MUCUS-EATING

Mucus-eating is widely reported in Amazonian fish folklore. In aquaria the juveniles of discus cichlids (*Symphysodon*) are easily observed feeding on parents. The principal adult mucus-feeders of the Amazon Basin are various, to date poorly known, species of the catfish family Trichomycteridae. We did not study the habit in the Rio Negro, and can only report here that some of the trichomycterid catfishes removed from other fishes appeared to have mucus in their stomachs.

9. TROPHIC PATTERNS IN RIO NEGRO FISH COMMUNITIES

HABITATS, FOOD CATEGORIES AND TROPHIC STRUCTURE SUSTAINING HIGH FISH DIVERSITY

To summarize the nature of the foodchain sustaining Rio Negro fishes in different habitats, only sites were chosen in which at least 30 species were examined for food contents. The 10 sites analyzed included three beaches, one confluence swamp, one flooded forest, two island lakes, one rocky pool and two woody shores (Fig. 9.1). All together 64 food items were recognized from fish stomach contents (Tab. 9.1). These items were divided into six categories based on general likeness and their aquatic or arboreal/terrestrial derivation: 1) terrestrial/arboreal plant material; 2) aquatic plant material; 3) terrestrial/arboreal invertebrates; 4) aquatic invertebrates; 5) detritus/litter, and; 6) fish. The respective volumetric contributions of like food items, within the categories defined above, were then summed for each population of each species for each of the 10 sites considered. All volumetric values within the six categories defined that were at least 25% were then considered to represent *significant* food categories for the respective population samples. For example, a population whose diet consisted of 10% ants, 15% non-aquatic beetles, 5% fruits and 70% detritus would be assigned two *significant* food categories, that is, invertebrates from terrestrial/arboreal sources and detritus. The 25% baseline is not meant to imply that food groups occurring in small quantities, such as the 5% occurrence for fruits in the above example, would never be important in diets, or that all values 25-100% would mean the same thing nutritionally. Such detail, however, is more a consideration in the experimental nutritional ecology of individual species than in an overall analysis of trophic patterns in communities.* Detailed analyses of individual species are presented in Goulding, Carvalho & Ferreira (no date).

Beaches

Of the six principal habitats studied, beaches are the most homogeneous morphologi-

---

* Volumetric measurements do not in themselves indicate how various food items are proportioned among the total fish biomass, as the trophic patterns detected reflect the feeding ecology of individual species regardless of their relative biomasses. These measurements, then, indicate the types of foods that sustain the high diversity of fishes, though we suspect in the case of the Rio Negro that the patterns would probably be more or less the same for the total biomass as well. Furthermore, volumetric measurements do not say anything directly about the nutritional and energetic values of the various food items eaten. For example, a food item, such as ants, might only represent 25% of the volume in the given diet of a sampled population of a species, whereas detritus might account for the other 75%. Volumetric measurements lack comparative nutritional information, thus they cannot be interpreted to mean that detritus is three times more important in the diet than ants. Only controlled experiments can determine the relative nutritional importance of the various food types in the diet of any particular species.

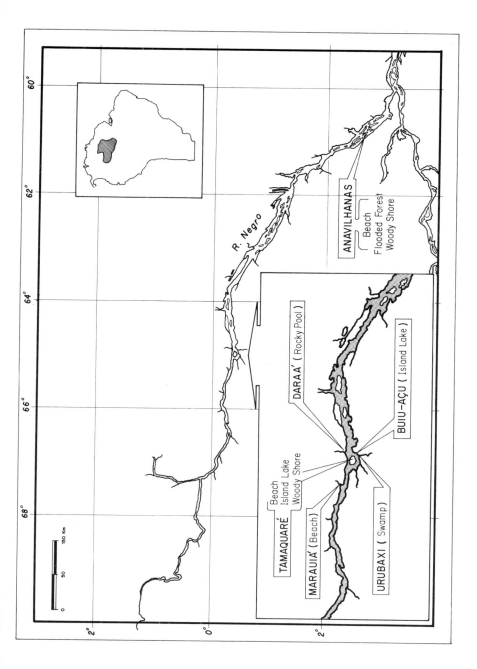

Fig. 9.1. Sites and habitats studied for analysis of foodchain patterns in Rio Negro fish communities.

Tab. 9.1. Principal food items recognized in Rio Negro fish diets.

AQUATIC INVERTEBRATES	ARBOREAL/TERRESTRIAL INVERTEBRATES
1. Annelida	34. Coleoptera
2. *Bosmina* spp.	35. Collembola
3. *Bosminopsis deitersi*	36. Dermaptera
4. Bryozoa	37. Diplopoda
5. Calanoida	38. Diptera
6. Chaoboridae Larvae	39. Formicidae
7. Chironomidae Larvae	40. Homoptera
8. Chydoridae	41. Hymenoptera
9. Cladocera	42. Insect Remains
10. Coleoptera Larvae	43. Isopoda
11. Conchostraca	44. Isoptera
12. Copepoda	45. Lepidoptera Larvae
13. Corixidae	46. Lepidoptera Pupae
14. Crabs	47. Microlepidoptera
15. Crustacean Remains	48. Neuroptera
16. Culicidae Larvae	49. Odonata
17. Cyclopoida	50. Orthoptera
18. Diptera Larvae	51. Plecoptera
19. Diptera Pupae	52. Pseudoscorpionidae
20. Ephemeroptera	53. Psocoptera
21. Ephemeroptera Nymphs	54. Spiders
22. Harpacticoida	55. Tysanoptera
23. Hemiptera	
24. Hydracarina	
25. Macrothricidae	
26. Mollusca	
27. Nematoda	
28. Odonata Nymphs	
29. Ostracoda	
30. Porifera	
31. Rotifera	
32. Shrimp	
33. Trichoptera	

AQUATIC PLANT MATTER	TERRESTRIAL PLANT MATTER
56. Filamentous Algae	60. Fruits/Seeds
57. Microalgae	61. Leaves/Flowers
58. Herbaceous Plant Roots	
59. Herbaceous Stems/Leaves	

DETRITUS	FISH
62. Coarse Litter	65. Fish (prey)
63. Detritus	66. Fin Rays
64. Plant Remains	67. Scales

cally because of the relatively uniform nature of their substrates and shallow waters. One would expect trophic structure to be grossly similar in beach sites, and our data suggest that this is probably true, though the input of plant material from forests may vary considerably (Tab. 9.2).

In at least two of the three beach sites considered, four of the six food categories – aquatic invertebrates, terrestrial/arboreal invertebrates, fish and detritus – were important to the fish communities. Aquatic invertebrate consumption was uniformly high in the beach trio. One beach site demonstrated that forest plant matter can be important in this habitat type. This was probably due to local current conditions

Tab. 9.2. The percentages of species from selected sites and habitats that fed *significantly* in each of the trophic categories. *Significantly* means that at least 25% of the volume of food consumed by any population consisted of the respective trophic category. The row values do not sum to 100% because some species feed significantly on more than on food category, thus placing them in more than one trophic category. At least 30 fish species from each site were studied for stomach contents.

	Terrestrial/Arboreal Plant Matter	Aquatic Plant Matter	Terrestrial/Arboreal Invertebrates	Aquatic Invertebrates	Detritus	Fish
Beach: Anavilhanas	2	4	12	35	31	31
Beach: Marauiá	9	–	30	27	33	33
Beach: Tamaquaré	17	9	32	34	12	11
Swamp: Urubaxi	5	28	11	37	33	5
Flooded Forest: Anavilhanas	20	10	30	30	29	18
Island Lake: Buiu-açu	–	8	18	28	41	20
Island Lake: Tamaquaré	16	16	10	3	53	10
Rocky Pool: Below Daraá	4	15	17	43	39	17
Woody Shore: Anavilhanas	25	21	8	21	21	32
Woody Shore: Tamaquaré	3	36	9	6	53	18

and the drift of fruits, seeds and leaves from nearby upstream riparian and inundation forest. The fact that terrestrial/arboreal invertebrates were more common than forest plant material in the diets of beach communities appears related to arthropod movements from the forests and across the sandy areas or open waterbodies. Involuntary wind transport might also be an important factor that causes relatively large numbers of forest invertebrates to be wafted across emerged beaches and into the water.

Detritus entering beach communities is introduced from upstream drift of organic matter and, due to current activity, there is probably a relatively constant supply for most beaches. Beach algae is found mostly on the substrate but, overall, it is the least important food category for sandy shore fish communities. Piscivores are abundant in Rio Negro beach waters and, as mentioned earlier, they are probably responsible for the schooling behavior of most of the species. The data suggest that there is a relatively diversified food supply drifting or falling into Rio Negro beach waters.

Confluence Swamp

As mentioned in the Introduction, the swamps found at the confluences of many tributaries with the middle and upper Rio Negro are very complex ecologically. They contain a network of diverse biotopes, including small beaches usually covered with leaves, palm-covered hummock-like islands with extensive root mats and shrub and tree vegetation that is flooded during most of the year. These biotopes are usually within a few meters of one another and repeated in various combinations over a large area. Because of the complexity of this habitat, our effort allocation only allowed us to study one site. The foodchain sustaining the fishes was dominated by aquatic invertebrates, detritus and algae during the low water period when collections were made (see Tab. 9.2). Forest food sources were relatively poorly represented in the confluence swamp despite the heavily vegetated area. This is perhaps explained by the dominant vegetation being palms, suggesting that these more homogeneous plant communities supply less fish food, at least during the low water period, than do the more diverse and typical inundation forests of the Rio Negro.

Flooded Forest

The trophic structure of Rio Negro flooded forest, as revealed by the Anavilhanas sample, is characterized by relatively high percentages of fish species feeding on all of the major food groups except aquatic plants (Fig. 9.2 and see Tab. 9.2). Though not considered here because of the small sample involved, even the contiguous herbaceous plant communities found along the edge of Anavilhanas flooded forests appear to have few species that eat macrophytes, and algae production is limited because of poor light penetration and nutrient levels. Forest plant matter is important because of frugivorous species that have access to fruits and seeds that fall into the water during the floods. The numbers of fish species feeding heavily on aquatic and terrestrial/arboreal invertebrates was 32% and 34% respectively. The high level of detritivory demonstrates that even in flooded forests, where foods are undoubtedly in greater supply than in the other habitats, Rio Negro fish communities are still closely linked trophically to the detritus cycle.

Island Lakes

The outstanding trophic characteristic of the two island lakes considered was the dominance of detritivory, where 41% and 51% of the species fed significantly on detritus (see Tab. 9.2). Island lakes collect a large quantity of organic debris from surrounding inundation forests when waters recede, and their bottoms are covered with organic mud and leafy and woody material in various stages of decomposition. Aquatic invertebrate consumption was high in one lake, but very low in the other. Furthermore, the lake that was fished latest in the low water period was the one where aquatic invertebrates were most important. This suggests that the aquatic invertebrate biomass of island lakes is not necessarily decreased by predation as the dry seasons progresses. The reasons for this are unclear.

Rocky Pool

Per area, the rocky pool was by far the most taxonomically diverse fish community that was found in the Rio Negro. In a surface area approximately 4-8m x 30m, 108 species were identified living in very close proximity. Most of the species were hidden in rock crevices, though the entire habitat was occupied by various taxa. The rocky pool was the Rio Negro habitat where the highest percentage (43%) of fish species fed significantly on aquatic invertebrates (see Tab. 9.2). A nearly comparable number (39%) of fish species fed on detritus. The percentage of species (17%) that fed on terrestrial/arboreal invertebrates illustrates that even in a small area there can be a significant input of this food source into the water. Though most of the species appeared to be hidden in rock crevices by day, there were still a relatively large number of piscivores present, with 17% of the species sampled for food having consumed significant quantities of fish.

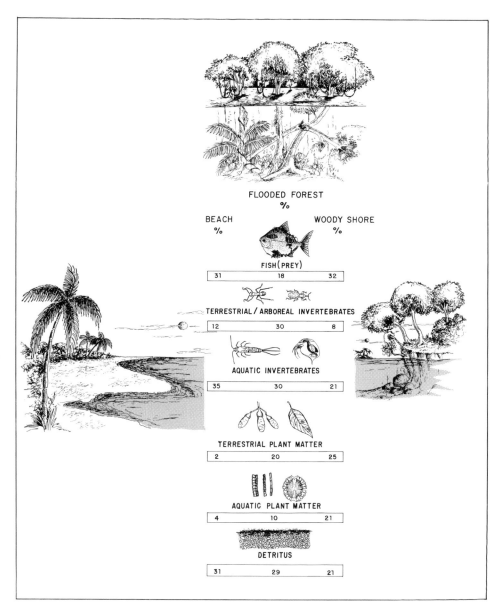

FLOODED FOREST
%

BEACH   WOODY SHORE
%   %

FISH (PREY)

| 31 | 18 | 32 |

TERRESTRIAL / ARBOREAL INVERTEBRATES

| 12 | 30 | 8 |

AQUATIC INVERTEBRATES

| 35 | 30 | 21 |

TERRESTRIAL PLANT MATTER

| 2 | 20 | 25 |

AQUATIC PLANT MATTER

| 4 | 10 | 21 |

DETRITUS

| 31 | 29 | 21 |

Fig. 9.2. Schematic illustration of the nature of the foodchain sustaining fish diversity in the three most common habitat types of the Anavilhanas Archipelago of the lower Rio Negro. The numbers represent the percentages of species that fed significantly on each food category.

Woody Shores

The fish communities in the two woody shores considered fed heavily on detritus, aquatic plants and fish (see Tab. 9.2). Forest plant matter and aquatic invertebrates were also important at the Anavilhanas site. This might be a reflection of the fact that this area was sampled for a much longer period during the low water period than was the case at the upper Rio Negro site. Both sites, surprisingly, showed relatively few species feeding heavily on terrestrial/arboreal invertebrates, despite the presence of overhanging vegetation and large areas of contiguous inundation rainforest [drained at the time woody shore samples were taken].

Invertebrate input into the water could be related to spatial and/or seasonal variation in arthropod densities. Pearson and Derr (1986) report that forest arthropod biomass is greatest during the wet season in a floodplain area of the Peruvian Amazon. The data collected by Adis (1984) in an inundation forest area of the lower Rio Negro, however, suggests that a large part of the trunk and canopy arthropod biomass migrates downwards to the forest floor during the dry season, and this factor, more than relative changes in biomass, might explain why fewer arboreal/terrestrial insects and other invertebrates are available to woody shore fish communities during the low water period. Air turbulence (fewer storms) also appears to be less during the low than the high water period, and perhaps woody shore invertebrates are less susceptible to fall into the water during the dry season. However, this does not explain why the beach, island lake and rocky pool habitats showed, at least in one case each, relatively large numbers of fish species that fed on terrestrial/arboreal invertebrates. Air turbulence along the forests of these relatively open habitats might be sufficient to cause a greater abundance of canopy invertebrates to fall into the water. Furthermore, as mentioned above in reference to beaches, many invertebrate groups appear to use the open habitats along rivers for migration and dispersal purposes, thus explaining why they are more common in fish diets in these areas than along woody shores. Data collected by Angermeier and Karr (1983) along a rainforest stream in Panamá suggest similar patterns of invertebrate input into open waterbodies.

ALLOCHTHONOUS AND AUTOCHTHONOUS FOOD SOURCES

HYPOTHESIS: The foodchain sustaining Rio Negro fishes is largely based on primary production taking place in the floodplain or riparian rainforests. Arboreal/terrestrial invertebrates, detritus and fruits/seeds are the main trophic conduits through which rainforest energy and nutrients are transferred to the majority of fishes in Rio Negro fish communities.

Allochthonous riverine food sources are ones that originate outside of the aquatic medium; autochthonous sources are linked to primary production taking place in water. For management and conservation considerations of fish communities, the distinction is important because it indicates where the foodchains are linked.

Of the six trophic categories we defined, terrestrial/arboreal plants and invertebrates are undoubtedly allochthonous in origin. All studies to date of Rio Negro detritus also indicate that this source is mostly allochthonous, as the major part of it is composed of leaves and dead wood (Irmler, 1975). Though very little is yet known about the feeding habits of Rio Negro aquatic invertebrates, initial studies of protozoan and a few insect and shrimp communities have shown that their foodchains are linked, often via fungi and bacteria living on detritus or forest plant debris, to allochthonous food sources (Irmler, 1975,1976a; Irmler & Furch,1976; Walker, 1985; Walker & Ferreira, 1985; Kensley & Walker, 1982). The very poor *in situ* primary production of the Rio Negro, in contrast to extensive riparian and floodplain forests, further suggests the importance of allochthonous food sources in aquatic foodchains. The importance of exogenous foods for fish communities has also been emphasized for most other tropical lowland rivers, in the Amazon and elsewhere (Roberts, 1972; Lowe-McConnell, 1975, 1987; Goulding, 1980,1981; Ferreira, 1984; Saul, 1975; Welcomme, 1979,1985).

DIET OVERLAP

The study of tropical fish diets has generated special interest because of controversial hypotheses concerning the competitive exclusion principle as applied to diverse communities (Lowe-McConnell, 1987). As Welcomme (1985) has pointed out, however, tropical studies have tended to classify fishes into static niches based on dietary patterns detected in limited time and space and without ontogenetic and size class considerations. This appears to have been the case because of textbook-derived notions that species have to exist in well defined niches as a result of the competitive exclusion principle.

The evidence from the Rio Negro suggests that the competitive exclusion principle, as applied to fish diets in large Amazonian rivers, will probably shed little light on the evolutionary processes influencing speciation. Most food items are fed on in the same habitat by many species. For example, in flooded forest 25 fish species fed on ants, 27 species on arboreal/terrestrial beetles, 19 species on shrimp and there are many more examples [the numbers of species feeding on various food items are summarized in the tables presented in Chapters 5,6,7 and 8]. Even in a more confined habitat, such as the rocky pool we studied, 12 fish species were feeding on chironomid larvae, 12 species on dipteran pupae, 9 species on Ephemeropteran nymphs and 9 species on trichopterans.

It could conceivably be argued that competitive exclusion is much more specific, that is, 'fine-tuned', than our data would reveal because most of the food items could not be identified to the species level. Observations in Rio Negro flooded forests and previous studies of frugivorous fishes, however, confirm that many species in the same area, and often under the same tree, feed on the same fruit or seed species (Goulding, 1980). For invertebrate food, we can site the example of the cladoceran crustacean, *Bosminopsis deitersi*, which we identified to the species level whenever it was found in stomach contents. In the flooded forest habitat, 6 fish species were captured that fed on the cladoceran, and 11 species doing so were found in the confluence swamp sample.

Tab. 9.3. The percentages of species from 10 selected sites and six habitats whose food habits embraced no more than one of the six food categories defined.

1. Beach: Anavilhanas	87 percent
2. Beach: Tamaquaré	86
3. Beach: Marauiá	72
4. Confluence Swamp	73
5. Flooded Forest: Anavilhanas	65
6. Island Lake: Buiu – açu	79
7. Island Lake: Tamaquaré	86
8. Rocky Pool: Below Daraá	69
9. Woody Shore: Anavilhanas	90
10. Woody Shore: Tamaquaré	69

FOOD PARTITIONING AND OMNIVORY

HYPOTHESIS: Most Rio Negro fish species appear to be omnivorous on a seasonal basis, but most taxa tend to feed on only one general category of plant or animal food in a particular habitat. This suggests that most of the species are sufficiently adapted for some degree of facultative feeding behavior, but that omnivory within any particular habitat or community is limited. At this time it is not obvious what factors discourage greater omnivory on a community or habitat basis.

Logic suggests that omnivory would be the ideal trophic behavior, as the species would not have to depend on only one type of food, especially in highly seasonal environments such as the Rio Negro. Most dictionaries define an omnivore as an animal that feeds on both plants and animals. Foodweb modelers, however, have emphasized the number of trophic levels that are involved rather than the plant/animal dichotomy (Pimm & Lawton, 1978; Pimm, 1982). Both definitions are useful, the latter requiring much more foodweb data than is now generally available, and certainly more than we can present for the Rio Negro. For the present discussion, omnivory is defined as the consumption of significant quantities of both plant and animal matter [*significant*, to reiterate the definition presented earlier, means that at least 25% of the volume of the diet of a population consisted of any given plant or animal food category].

The data reveal that Rio Negro fish communities in specific habitats are represented by relatively few omnivorous feeders. In no community were more than 15% of the species studied found to be omnivorous according to the above definition. Furthermore, most of the species tend to concentrate their feeding in only one of the six trophic categories defined (Tab. 9.3). In terms of the six trophic categories we defined, in flooded forest there was an increase in the number of species that ate invertebrates from both aquatic and forest sources, and in low water habitats there was a considerable increase in the percentage of species that combined relatively large quantities of algae and detritus in their diets (Appendix 4). Neither of these cases, however, increased omnivory because of the plant or animal integrity of the food categories involved.

To test the possibility of omnivory on a seasonal basis, that is, of species switching food types during the course of the year, we used only those taxa that were captured in flooded forest and in at least one of the six low water habitats studied. In addition, only those species for which at least 10 specimens from each habitat were examined for food were considered, as smaller samples might not indicate omnivorous tendencies. A total of 21 species was selected for the above test (Tab. 9.4). The results show that 18 species, that is, approximately 85 percent of the taxa considered, switched their diets seasonally within the six food categories defined.

Many of the smaller characin species (*e.g.*, *Hemigrammus*, *Nannostomus*) showed a distinct switch from aquatic and/or terrestrial/arboreal invertebrates consumed in the flooded forest to aquatic plants (mostly algae) or detritus eaten during the low water period. For these species, the data suggest that the flooded forest represents a habitat for relatively high protein intake because of the abundance of aquatic and forest invertebrates. The larger, mainly vegetarian fishes (*e.g.*, *Myleus*, *Metynnis*) switch from fruits and seeds taken in flooded forest to other types of plant material, especially leaves, flowers and aquatic herbaceous stems and leaves.

88

Tab. 9.4. Seasonality in the major food categories eaten by selected Rio Negro fishes during the high = H and low = L water periods.

Aquatic Plant Matter Terrestrial Plant Matter Detritus Aquatic	Aquatic Plant Matter	Terrestrial Plant Matter	Detritus	Aquatic Invertebrates	Terrestrial Invertebrates	Fish
Hemigrammus analis?	L	–	L	L	H	–
Hemigrammus analis B	L	–	L	–	H	–
Hemigrammus levis	L	–	L	H	H	–
Hyphessobrycon diancistrus	L	–	L	HL	HL	–
Metynnis sp. BS	–	H	L	–	–	–
Moenkhausia collettii	–	–	–	–	HL	L
Myleus schomburgkii	L	H	–	–	–	–
Myleus sp. BR	L	H	–	–	–	–
Myleus sp. IR	L	HL	–	–	–	
Serrasalminae sp. (piranha)	–	H	–	–	–	HL
Tetragonopterus chalceus	–	L	–	HL	–	–
Hypselecara coryphaenoides	–	–	–	–	H	L
Geophagus altifrons	–	L	HL	H	–	–
Heros severus	– –	HL	–	–	L	
Hoplarchus psittacus	–	–	–	H	–	HL
Uaru amphiacanthoides	HL	L	HL	–	–	–
Hassar lipophthalmus –	–	–	HL	–	–	
Copella nattereri	–	–	–	H	HL	–
Nannostomus eques	–	–	L	HL	H	–
Nannostomus marilynae	L	–	L	H	H	–
Osteoglossum ferreirai	–	–	–	–	HL	–

HIGH DIVERSITY OF DENTITION

One of the principal characteristics of the Amazon fish fauna is the great diversity of dentition types, especially within the characin groups [see Eigenmann (1917-1929) and Gery (1977) for a large number of drawings of characin dentition types]. Diversity in dentition is undoubtedly one of the factors that allows Rio Negro fish communities to utilize many types of foods. For example, if there were no species with strong jaws and heavy molariform-like teeth, many of the larger seeds with hard nut walls could not be broken, which is necessary for their digestion. It also appears that labial teeth allow detritivores (*e.g.*, *Semaprochilodus*) to graze selectively on certain kinds of detritus found on submerged tree parts. Large canine-like teeth (*e.g.*, *Hydrolycus*, *Acestrorhynchus*) are most often associated with piscivory, though in smaller species (*e.g.*, *Agoniates*, *Asiphonichthys*) this dentition type can also be used for capturing invertebrates. Piranhas have sharp teeth that, for most Rio Negro species, are used for masticating seeds and for various degrees of piscivory, including lepidophagy (scale-eating). Most of the anostomids have tusk-like teeth which, viewed on anatomical terms alone, appear highly specialized. Anostomid diets, however, usually include many different kinds of plant and animal foods. Pharyngeal teeth, most developed in cichlids, are used for trituration of items that might otherwise be difficult to digest (Ferreira, 1981).

The tetras and cheirodontine characins present the greatest diversity of dentition-types, and teeth are often used as subordinal, generic and specific characters to classify these fishes. The dental ontogeny of very few species is known. Some species are known to go through a dental developmental process from conical to cuspidate teeth, and vice versa for other taxa (S. H. Weitzman, pers. comm.). This suggests that a dental classification, in reference to dietary patterns of these fishes, will have to await ontogenetic studies of both the dentition and diets of young and juvenile size classes. Diet specializations might be most pronounced during early life history stages.

Rio Negro fishes show many different patterns of manipulation, mastication and swallowing of the diverse array of foods they eat. For example, some of the tetras swallow whole the insects they eat while other species masticate them first. It is possible that dental structure in most species is more correlated with gastrointestinal organization than with food capture. This must be true for the frugivores with molariform-like teeth. Their teeth are not that important for food capture, but rather for the crushing of hard nuts. Fruit-eating fishes, such as the catfishes, that do not have molariform-like teeth can just as easily ingest large quantities of fruit, but they cannot masticate it. Anatomical and physiological comparisons of the gastrointestinal systems of diverse tetra and cheirodontine groups might reveal why some species masticate their foods and others do not. This is turn might throw more light on the reasons for high dental diversity than does the study of food habits alone.

COMPARISON OF RIO NEGRO TROPHIC PATTERNS WITH OTHER AMAZONIAN RIVERINE SYSTEMS

Nearly all of the fish trophic studies in the Central Amazon have been carried out in Rio Solimões-Amazonas floodplain/island lakes near Manaus. Only about 50 percent of the floodplain forest in this area remains (Bayley & Petrere, 1986). Marlier (1967,1968) presented data on about 47 fish species captured in a Rio Solimões floodplain lake. His classification of fishes as stenophages or euryphages is unjustified and should not be cited in this sense as he only studied 2-3 specimens of most species, thus his small samples do not really indicate much about the trophic ecology of individual taxa. His paper, nevertheless, is useful for suggesting the complexity of foodweb patterns in a Rio Solimões floodplain lake where the inundation forest has largely been removed due to agricultural activities. Marlier's survey indicates that macrophytes are probably at the base of the foodchain in the small floodplain lake area he studied. He suggested, however, that forest material was probably important before deforestation took place.

Bayley (1979,1980,1981,1982) and Bayley and Petrere (1986) have also suggested that a large part of fish production in this area must be linked to macrophytes, either directly or through the detritus cycle. There is still no evidence of large-scale feeding on macrophytes, though a few species are known to eat roots and stems (Santos, 1981). For the lower Rio Solimões floodplain area, Bayley and Petrere (1986) estimated that macrophytes, forest litter and phytoplankton contributed carbon in the ratio of 58:36:6, respectively, remembering that only about half of the floodplain forest remains. Carbon input ratios alone do not indicate where fish foodchains are linked, as only foodweb studies can do that. It should also be mentioned that production is not the only question. Of importance is the nature of the foodchain that sustains the high diversity of fishes. The major part of the fish biomass in this area might be linked to macrophyte production, but this does not mean that most of the species are. Furthermore, because the area is so heavily deforested, it is not representative of natural conditions. The only conclusion that can be drawn at this time is that in heavily deforested areas of the lower Rio Solimões, herbaceous plant production is more important to the trophic ecology of fishes than is this type of primary production source in the Rio Negro. Even in Rio Solimões deforested areas, however, allochthonous foods often make up a large, or the largest, part of the fish diets that have been investigated (*e.g.*, Santos, 1981; Paixão, 1980; Almeida, 1984; Carvalho, 1981).

The Rio Machado is a nutrient-poor clearwater tributary of the upper Rio Madeira. The trophic patterns found in the Rio Machado, where only large species were studied, generally agree with the conclusions of the Rio Negro investigation, especially in the dependence of many fishes on allochthonous food sources and great overlap in diets (Goulding, 1980). The Rio Negro data suggest that detritus is more important in nutrient-poor systems than was emphasized in the earlier study where mainly frugivorous fishes were investigated. Clearwater and blackwater rivers appear to have very similar trophic structures because of poor *in situ* primary production. There are probably clearwater exceptions (*e.g.*, lower Rio Tapajós and lower Rio Xingu) where intensive phytoplankton blooms are present and foodchains in some areas may largely be based on this primary production.

COMPARISONS OF RIO NEGRO TROPHIC PATTERNS WITH RAINFOREST STREAMS

Streams, like floodplains, beaches or rocky pools are habitats or biotopes of rivers. Most rainforest stream studies, however, leave one with the impression that these waterbodies are self-contained units in terms of fish community development. Many fish species move in and out of streams seasonally, just as they do in floodplains, thus none of these waterbodies is a self-contained unit. Furthermore, recent surveys over a larger part of the Amazon Basin have revealed that usually 50% or more of the fish species found in streams are also in the nearby riverine habitats (Goulding, in prep.).

Knoppel (1970) has made the only trophic study of rainforest stream fish communities in the Rio Negro area, including a clearwater stream draining into a floodplain lake of the Rio Solimões. He concluded that the food resource was virtually unpartitioned by fishes and that there were no highly specialized feeders, at least in the sense of diets being restricted to narrow taxonomic limits. The data from Rio Negro riverine habitats are in concordance with Knoppel's conclusion. However, we prefer to divide the trophic resource into general categories by lumping morphologically similar taxonomic groups, and, as noted earlier in this chapter, when this is done in terms of the relative volumes of food consumed, the food resource is partitioned. This would also appear to be the case for the rainforest streams Knoppel investigated, though he did not define general food categories.

Saul (1975), Soares (1979) and Lowe-McConnell (1987) have also noted that Amazonian rainforest stream fishes do not appear to specialize on narrow taxonomic food types. Zaret and Rand (1971) thought that Panamanian stream fishes become more specialized in their diets during the low water period, but their samples were too small to justify this conclusion [which they related to the untestable hypothesis of competitive exclusion]. All of the rainforest stream studies cited above stress the importance of allochthonous foods, which is also our conclusion for Rio Negro riverine habitats.

Angermeier and Karr (1983), based on the study of several Panamanian rainforest streams during the dry season, concluded that the distribution of feeding guilds among habitats is not generally correlated with food availability (which they measured), but perhaps more to the presence of predatory birds and mammals. Power (1984b,1984c) also felt that terrestrial birds and mammals, in addition to food availability, might influence the distribution and/or densities of loricariid catfishes in a Panamanian stream she investigated. Piscivorous birds, with the exception of kingfishers, are relatively rare in the Rio Negro area. Kingfishers do not appear to be abundant enough to have much influence on fish distributions, and certainly no non-aquatic mammals have. Aquatic piscivores (fishes, caimans, some turtles and dolphins) are sometimes very abundant locally in Rio Negro waters, and they could possibly influence the distribution of fish feeding guilds more than does food supply. In general, however, the Rio Negro fish fauna appears to be sufficiently diverse taxonomically and trophically that there is a high chance statistically that the same general feeding guilds will be repeated in similar habitats, with different combinations and abundances of species, regardless of the possible reduction of some populations due to heavy predation.

PART III

DIVERSITY, COMMUNITY DEVELOPMENT & CONCLUSIONS

10. TAXONOMIC DIVERSITY, ENDEMICITY AND MISSING SPECIES

FAMILIAL, GENERIC AND SPECIFIC DIVERSITY OF RIO NEGRO FISHES

HYPOTHESIS: Extreme nutrient-poverty, low pH and high levels of humic compounds, which taken together are expressed in the aquatic environment as blackwaters, are not limiting factors to the diversity of fish families, genera and species in Amazonian rivers.

For the purposes of this chapter, diversity is defined as the numbers of fish families, genera and species. It is clear that tropical fish communities are generally far more diverse than their temperate latitude counterparts (Lowe-McConnell, 1969,1975,1987). The reasons for high fish diversity in tropical lowland riverine systems, of which the Amazon system is the most complex ichthyologically, are not clear and the hypotheses thus far presented are not testable with any of the data that are presently available. Testable hypotheses attempting to explain high fish diversity will have to await detailed phylogenies, accurate historical geologies of the drainage systems and much more distribution information than is at present available.

The three most common hypotheses that attempt to explain high diversity are time, climatic stability and spatial heterogeneity [reviewed in reference to fishes in Lowe-McConnell, 1975,1987]. According to the time hypothesis, tropical lowland communities are very old, thus many species have accumulated over long periods of time. The climatic stability hypothesis suggests that because low latitudes remained much more stable than temperate regions during the Ice Ages, there was no decimation of the faunas, at least in some areas, such as the Amazon Basin. The spatial heterogeneity hypothesis claims that more niches exist in tropical than temperature systems. Weitzman & Weitzman (1982) have also pointed that the complicated geomorphological and climatological history of the area since the early Cenozoic, especially in relation to the bordering shields, may be responsible for much of the fish diversity witnessed today.

Fish Families

The Amazonian fish fauna is relatively well known at the family level, though no one classification is universally accepted, with most debate centered on various characin groups (Greenwood, Rosen, Weitzman & Myers, 1966; Gery, 1977; Vari, 1983). The Amazonian Lowlands has at least 46 fish families, of which our collections reveal that the Rio Negro has no fewer than 41 of these (Tab. 10.1). The families which are missing from our collections are: Charcharinidae (sharks), Pristidae (sawfishes) Hemirhamphidae (halfbeaks), Batrachoididae (toadfishes), Tetraodontidae (puffers), Lepidosirenidae (lungfishes), Nandidae (leaffishes) and Helogenidae (a group of small catfishes).

Tab. 10.1. An estimation of the minimum numbers of fish families, genera and species now known for the Rio Negro. The taxa are divided into five major groups: characins, catfishes, electric fishes, miscellaneous fishes and marine derivatives. Characins, catfishes and electric fishes each represent related groups. Miscellaneous fishes are here in considered those taxa that do not fit into any of the other defined groups. Marine derivatives are taxa whose relatives are mostly oceanic.

FAMILY	NUMBER OF GENERA	NUMBER OF SPECIES
CHARACINS		
Anostomidae	6	23 +
Characidae	51 +	134 +
Chilodontidae	2	2
Ctenoluciidae	1	3
Curimatidae	4	20 +
Cynodontidae	2	4
Erythrinidae	2	7 +
Gasteropelecidae	2	2
Hemiodontidae	6	11
Lebiasinidae	3	6 +
Prochilodontidae	1	3
Subtotal	80 (40%)	211 + (46%)
CATFISHES		
Ageneiosidae	1	3-4
Aspredinidae	1	2 +
Auchenipteridae	8 +	12 +
Callichthyidae	2	4 +
Cetopsidae	2	2
Doradidae	9	15 +
Hypophthalmidae	1	2
Loricariidae	17	42 +
Pimelodidae	17	35 +
Scoloplacidae	1	1
Trichomycteridae	6	13 +
Subtotal	65 (32%)	132 (29%)
ELECTRIC FISHES		
Apteronotidae	5	8 +
Electrophoridae	1	1
Gymnotidae	1	2
Hypopomidae	2	4
Rhamphichthyidae	2	5
Sternopygidae	4	15 +
Subtotal	15 (07%)	35 (08%)
MISCELLANEOUS FISHES		
Arapaimidae	1	1
Cichlidae	22	50 +
Rivulidae	2	3 +
Osteoglossidae	1	2
Poeciliidae	1	1
Synbranchidae	1	1
Subtotal	28 (13%)	58 (12%)
MARINE DERIVATIVES		
Belonidae	3	3
Clupeidae	2	2-3
Eleotridae	1	2 +
Engraulidae	3	5 +
Potamotrygonidae	2	3 +
Sciaenidae	3	5
Soleidae	2	2
Subtotal	14 (07%)	23 (05%)
TOTAL	202 +	450 +

The bullshark (*Charcharhinus leucus*) and sawfish (*Pristis perotteti*) are their respective families only representatives in the interior waters of Amazonia. The bull-shark has been captured as far upstream as Iquitos, Peru, but there is only one report of a specimen from any tributary of the Amazon, and that was from the lower Rio Madeira (Thorson, 1974; Roberts, 1972). The sawfish is occasionally captured in turbid affluents (*e.g.*, Rio Madeira and Rio Purus) of the Central Amazon, but we heard of no reports of it being in the Rio Negro. If the above species are in the Rio Negro, it appears safe to assume that they are only occasional wanderers from the Rio Solimões-Amazonas.

In addition to sharks, toadfishes and puffers were the only other two families whose species are mostly marine and that have representatives in the Central Amazon, but that appear to be missing from the Rio Negro. Only one toadfish (*Thalassophryne amazonica*) species is known from the Central Amazon, and its type locality is listed as the mouth of the Rio Negro (reviewed by Collette, 1966). Very few specimens of Amazonian toadfishes have been captured, and the family appears to be rare in this region. The first author has captured *T. amazonica* in another blackwater river, the Rio Tefé, and thus this evidence, along with its type locality, suggests that it might be in the Rio Negro as well. Puffers (*Colomesus asellus*) are relatively abundant in the turbid and clearwater rivers of the Central Amazon, but we did not capture any in the Rio Negro. The species is, however, in the clearwater Rio Branco, the Rio Negro's largest tributary [see below for more comments on blackwater avoidance].

Fishermen report that lungfishes (*Lepidosiren paradoxa*, Lepidosirenidae) and leaffishes are in the Rio Negro, but we were unable to confirm this, and we have found no literature citations of the families in the blackwater river. Halfbeaks (*Hyporhamphus brederi*, Hemirhamphidae) are rare in Amazonian fish collections, and the fact that we did not capture them in the Rio Negro could be more a reflection of their rarity rather than their absence. No livebearers of the family Poeciliidae have been captured in or reported for the Rio Negro. The only poeciliid known for the river is the common *Fluviphylax pygmaeus*, which is an aberrant member of its family because it is oviparous (Roberts, 1970a; Parenti, 1981). The one catfish family, Helogenidae, missing from our collections has been reported for streams of the lower Rio Negro (Knoppel, 1970). The genus *Helogenes* appears to be restricted mostly to streams (Vari & Ortega, 1986).

Fish Genera of the Rio Negro

In the present state of systematic knowledge, the Rio Negro has at least 200 genera of fishes (see Tab. 10.1 and Appendix 3). Many if not most of these genera are not yet well defined and relationships are based mostly on superficial analyses and subjective opinions (Weitzman & Fink, 1983). It appears safe to assume, however, that future revisions will split, redefine or conserve available generic names more than lump them into larger groups. This trend is illustrated by recent revisions of genera in the families Cichlidae (Kullander, 1983, 1986), Curimatidae (Vari, 1982,1984) and Loricariidae (Isbrucker, 1980).

Our data demonstrate that the Rio Negro does not have reduced generic diversity. The high generic diversity of the Rio Negro is further attested to by the fact that, of the taxa we examined, there are 200 genera out of a total of about 450 species. There are few speciose genera in the Rio Negro, and no genus appears to have more than seven species [future revisions might reveal more speciose genera].

There appears to be little endemism of Rio Negro fish genera, at least as they are now defined, though rainforest streams need to be studied in more detail, as they could reveal quite different patterns than those found in the main river. It has become apparent that the blackwater regions of the western Orinoco Basin and the upper Rio Negro share many genera in common, thus even those genera that appear endemic to the latter drainage at this time, are suspected to be in the former system as well [this observation is based on conversations with Richard Vari, a Smithsonian ichthyologist who has collected the western Orinoco region and who has studied parts of our own collections; also for Orinoco fauna see Mago-Leccia (1970,1972,1978) and Cala (1977)]. The first evidence, then, suggests that the Rio Negro shares nearly all of its fish genera with other Amazonian or Orinoco rivers.

Rio Negro Fish Species

Fowler (1954), using original descriptions and the few revisions available at the time, was the first ichthyologist to census piscine diversity of the Rio Negro. He listed 218 known fish species for the Rio Negro as of the early 1950's. The present study more than doubles the first estimate, and there are undoubtedly many more species to be found. Fishing with electrode detectors for gymnotoids [see Heiligenberg & Bastian (1980,1981)], and collections geared to capture small, arenicolous (sand dwelling), lithophilous (living in stony or rocky habitats) and leaf-inhabiting taxa will probably increase the Rio Negro (without tributaries) fish list by at least another 250 species, that is, to a total of more than 700 species.

For comparison of species diversity, it may be noted that the Rio Negro alone has at least twice as many fish species as all the European rivers taken together [European data from Ladiges & Vogt (1979)]. Its diversity probably exceeds that of all of North America, the ichthyofauna of which is relatively well known and contains about 600 freshwater and brackish species (Patterson, 1981). Comparisons with tropical rivers are probably more relevant. The Zaire system, including its tributaries, has at least 669 species and, though much taxonomic work still needs to be done there, it is relatively better known ichthyologically than the Amazon drainage (Lowe-McConnell, 1987). First impressions indicate that the Rio Negro alone − even without its tributaries − may rival the entire Zaire Basin in total fish species diversity. The Rio Negro does not appear to be significantly more diverse ichthyologically than other large Amazonian rivers, based on the first author's collections over a large part of the Amazon Basin and a recent study of the Rio Tocantins that lists 300 fish species alone for the lower course of this clearwater river (Santos, Jegu & Merona, 1984).

ENDEMICITY

HYPOTHESIS: The region centering on the middle and upper Rio Negro drainage appears to be an area of potentially important fish species endemicity.

A total evaluation of the degree of species endemicity in the Rio Negro would be premature at this time, as most of the taxa have not been studied in taxonomic detail and many new species remain to be described. It is much easier to separate the species of one river system than it is to determine if these species are the same as very similar taxa in an adjacent or farther removed system. It should also be kept in mind that there is still no generally accepted method of recognizing fish species, and splitting and lumping are done rather subjectively according to each ichthyologist's preferences. At present there are probably more typological taxonomists than phylogenetic systematists working on the Amazon fish fauna, thus a stable nomenclature is unlikely in the near future. An evaluation of possible endemicity in the Rio Negro region is best approached at this time by considering only taxa that are relatively well known systematically and that do not appear to present identification controversies. The first species that comes to mind is the cardinal tetra (*Paracheirodon axelrodi*), the most important aquarium fish captured in the river, and a member of one of the best revised Amazonian fish genera (Weitzman & Fink, 1983). The cardinal tetra, as far as is known, is confined to the Rio Negro drainage and parts of the southwestern Orinoco system. The species has been heavily procured by commercial fishermen, and it now appears fairly safe to assume that it is restricted to the region outlined above, as there are no reliable reports of it being elsewhere, unless introduced there by the aquarium trade.

Our perception of species endemicity will greatly improve when speciose genera are revised in detail. For the purposes of this discussion, a speciose genus is considered one that has at least 10 known species, and for which little taxonomical controversy exists. Though few speciose South American fish genera have been revised in detail, those that have reveal that the Rio Negro region (with adjacent drainages) has endemic species. Three genera that support this observation are *Acestrorhynchus* (Characidae), *Nannostomus* (Lebiasinidae) and *Apistogramma* (Cichlidae) [see, respectively, Menezes (1969) and Menezes & Gery (1983); Weitzman & Cobb, 1975 and Weitzman (1978); Kullander (1980)]. In concluding this discussion, we proffer a tentative list of fish species that appear in the present state of knowledge to be endemic to the region that centers on the Rio Negro (Tab. 10.2).

MISSING SPECIES

HYPOTHESIS: Although Rio Negro hydrochemistry has not resulted in any apparent reduction in familial, generic of specific fish diversity in the river, it nevertheless appears to preclude the entrance of some species that would otherwise be expected to be present.

A species may be missing from a river either because of biogeographical or ecological reasons. In the first case, a species might be absent because it evolved elsewhere, such as in western Amazonia, and has not dispersed, historically, as far as the Rio Negro or any other river under consideration. This must be the case for the majority of Amazonian species that could tolerate Rio Negro hydrochemistry but that are missing from the river. A good example of this type of species appears to be the neon tetra (*Paracheirodon innesi*), a fish that is restricted to blackwater and clearwater areas west of the Rio Negro drainage (Weitzman & Fink, 1983). In other words, it and other species like it, are not in the Rio Negro because time, chance and space did not coincide for them to be there. The absence of these kinds of species, then,

Tab. 10.2. Species that appear to be endemic to an area that centers on the Rio Negro drainage. See Collette (1974) for distribution information on *Pseudotylosurus microps* and Weitzman (1960) for *Thoracorharax stellatus*. Distribution patterns for all of the species are also based on the first author's collections and observations.

Asterophysus batrachus	Auchenipteridae
Ammocryptocharax elegans	Characidae
Acestrorhynchus grandoculis	Characidae
Astyanax scologaster	Characidae
Asiphonichthys condei	Characidae
Atopomesus pachyodus	Characidae
Brittanichthys axelrodi	Characidae
Hemigrammus cf. rhodostomus	Characidae
Hoplocharax goethei	Characidae
Hyphessobrycon socolofi	Characidae
Lonchogenys ilisha	Characidae
Microschemobrycon callops	Characidae
Paracheirodon axelrodi	Characidae
Rhinobrycon negrensis	Characidae
Serrabrycon magoi	Characidae
Thrissobrycon pectinifer	Characidae
Apistogramma doppelbinden	Cichlidae
Apistogramma sp.	Cichlidae
Apistrogramma hippolytae	Cichlidae
Hoplarchus psittacus	Cichlidae
Curimatopsis evelynae	Curimatidae
Hydrolycus sp.	Cynodontidae
Amazonsprattus scintilla	Engraulidae
Anchoviella spp.	Engraulidae
Copella compta	Lebiasinidae
Nannostomus marilynae	Lebiasinidae
Micromischodus sugillatus	Hemiodontidae
Acestridium discus	Loricariidae
Hassar praelongus	Loricariidae
Osteoglossum ferreirai	Osteoglossidae
Myoglanis marmoratus	Pimelodidae
Gymnorhamphichthys sp.	Rhamphichthyidae
Pygidianops eigenmanni	Trichomycteridae
Sarcoglanis simplex	Trichomycteridae
Typholbelus ternetzi	Trichomycteridae

cannot logically be used as evidence that Rio Negro hydrochemistry acts as an ecological barrier.

It has also become clear that many Amazonian fish species are restricted to turbid water rivers or, that is, to waters that are about neutral in pH [see below]. The fact that species from the Rio Solimões-Amazonas do not enter the Rio Negro is not evidence that the latter river's high content of organic compounds or low pH are toxic to them. It should also be remembered that the organic acids of the Rio Negro become part of the Rio Amazonas, though admittedly in diluted form, but to what degree has not yet been elucidated.

Hypotheses suggesting that Rio Negro waters might be inimical to animal life appear to be based on assumptions that low pH, a high content of organic compounds or nutrient poverty – or some combination of these factors – might limit diversity

(Geisler, Knoppel & Sioli, 1971,1976; Janzen, 1974). The Rio Negro data suggest that these assumptions are incorrect as generalizations, but that there is some truth in them relative to specific groups of fishes. To test hypotheses of Rio Negro hydrochemistry acting as an ecological barrier, only fish species should be used that meet the following conditions:

1) they must be missing from the Rio Negro, or at least very rare in it;
2) they must be abundant in the Rio Solimões-Amazonas near its confluence with the Rio Negro, and;
3) they must be present in clearwater rivers, in addition to being present in the Rio Solimões-Amazonas.

The reason for eliminating rare species from the above hypothetical test is that their absence in collections, from any particular river, might only be a reflection of sampling error. The third condition is necessary because some Amazonian fish species are restricted to turbid water rivers, that is, they are neither found in blackwater nor clearwater rivers. If they are missing from both the latter river types, then blackwater toxicity alone cannot logically be hypothesized to be an ecological barrier [since clearwater rivers are not hypothesized to be toxic].

There are at least seven genera and 10 species that satisfy the above conditions with reference to the Rio Negro (Tab 10.3). Some of these taxa are occasionally captured in the lower Rio Negro but, as indicated by our collections, they are never found very far from the mouth area. The lower 50 km of the Rio Negro should be eliminated from any discussion of the blackwater river's fish diversity, as the area receives *wanderers* from the nearby Rio Solimões-Amazonas channel and floodplain. For example, species whose collection site in the literature is cited as Manaus (12 km up the Rio Negro) should not be listed, biogeographically, as Rio Negro fishes until captures farther upstream confirm their presence in this river. Furthermore, many of the fish species that were described in the last century, and whose type localities are listed as Manaus, were probably collected in the Rio Solimões-Amazonas.

Five of the missing genera (*Rhytiodus, Schizodon, Mylossoma, Prochilodus* and *Psectrogaster*) of the Rio Negro that are identified herein as strong candidates to test Rio Negro ecological barrier hypotheses are known to be abundant and important food taxa of the Rio Solimões-Amazonas area and in the turbid Rio Madeira and the lower reaches of its clearwater tributaries (Smith, 1979,1981; Petrere, 1978; Goulding, 1979,1980,1981). The fact that fishes of these genera do not enter the Rio Negro, or only occasionally, and then just in the lower reaches or near the upstream clearwater confluence areas, suggests that Rio Negro hydrochemistry is inimical to some species.

There is at least one alternative hypothesis to the hydrochemical barrier argument presented above: *competitive exclusion*. The first step in this line of reasoning would be to establish that there are very similar fishes, *vis-à-vis* the missing taxa of the Rio Negro, and that these species competitively exclude potential competitors. All of the missing species cited do, in fact, have ecological analogues in the Rio Negro. Competitive exclusion, however, can be dismissed because the missing taxa are sympatric with these analogues, or with what appear to be very closely related species, in Amazonian clearwater rivers [this observation is based on collections of the first author from many Amazonian rivers]. Since they can live sympatrically in other Amazonian rivers, there is no reason to believe that they could not in the Rio Negro, if hydrochemical barriers did not prevent their entrance into this river.

Tab. 10.3. Species for which the Rio Negro appears to represent an ecological and biogeographical barrier. See Collette (1974) for distribution information on *Pseudotylosurus microps* and Weitzman (1960) for *Thoracorharax stellatus*. Distribution patterns for all of the species are also based on the first author's collections and observations.

Rhytiodus argenteofuscus	Anostomidae
Rhytiodus microlepis	Anostomidae
Schizodon fasciatus	Anostomidae
Pseudotylosurus microps	Belonidae
Mylossoma (3 species)	Characidae
Cichlasoma spp.	Cichlidae
Thoracocharax stellatus	Gasteropelecidae
Psectrogaster spp.	Curimatidae
Colomesus asellus	Tetraodontidae

11. FISH COMMUNITY DEVELOPMENT IN THE RIO NEGRO

For the purposes of this study, fish communities are defined as the species associations found in each of the habitat sites we sampled. The general thrust of tropical freshwater fish community studies has been to attempt to glean evolutionary information from ecological interactions [see Lowe-McConnell (1975,1987) for review]. Large tropical river systems, however, present great methodological problems for testing evolutionary theory extrapolated from ecological interactions alone. In the case of the Amazon Basin, the historical geology is very poorly known and most hypothesized phylogenetic relationships of fish groups below the family level are based on assumptions for which there is still little evidence. At present there is no way of knowing whether the Amazonian species that now live sympatrically in river systems have also evolved together. The following discussions are designed to characterize present-day fish community patterns in the Rio Negro from which testable hypotheses can be gleaned.

SEASONALITY AND PERIODIC EXTREMES IN RIVER LEVELS

HYPOTHESIS: Periodic extremes in river levels could be one of the principal factors that influences the species abundances and associations found in Rio Negro fish communities. This factor would be in addition to the seasonal fluctuation of river level.

The principal factor that influences the nature of Rio Negro habitats, and hence the seasonal development of fish communities, is river level fluctuation. Viewed in the short run, the Rio Negro appears to have a relatively predictable seasonal oscillation. The several years of extreme high or low water levels that have been recorded in this century, however, suggest that the Rio Negro is not as stable, or predictable, as most annual oscillations indicate (Vanzolini, 1977).

The ecological effects on fish communities of extreme water levels, and especially of dry spells that could lead to very high mortality and the local extinction of species, has yet to be reported on in the Amazon Basin. Ecological hypotheses extracted from seasonal events alone would ignore the possible and probable role of periodic extremes. In 1926, for example, the Rio Negro did not rise sufficiently to flood its inundation forest, which it has done in all other years since 1902. This observation is based on a comparison of recorded river levels and field observations of the minimum level at which inundation forest of the lower Rio Negro becomes flooded to any significant degree. Without flooded forest, many of the fishes would be denied breeding and feeding habitats to which their life cycles are adapted. We would expect very high fish mortality in the Rio Negro for an extremely weak flood year, such as 1926, but the hypothesis can only be tested when a comparable hydrological year appears again and fish mortality is recorded.

Tab. 11.1. The percentages of species captured in one to seven habitat types. Note that most species were found in more than one habitat. In reality, the percentages are probably much higher in the two or more habitat categories, and our data only reflect the minimum number of habitats that are used by the various species. This analysis was based on about 450 species.

Captured In:	Percentage
One Habitat Only	34%
More Than One Habitat	66
Two Habitats	19
Three Habitats	12
Four Habitats	14
Five Habitats	8
Six Habitats	8
Seven Habitats	5

Tab. 11.2. The numbers and percentages of Rio Negro fish species captured in each of the principal habitat types sampled. The analysis was based on 450 species. These data should be interpreted as the minimum number of species that are known to use each kind of habitat. The actual number is undoubtedly much higher.

Beaches	248 (51%)	Island Lakes	163 (34%)
Confluence Swamp	123 (26%)	Rocky Pool	108 (22%)
Floating Meadows	56 (12%)	Woody Shores	219 (45%)
Flooded Forest	184 (38%)		

SEASONALITY, HABITAT USE AND SIMILARITY OF FISH COMMUNITIES

HYPOTHESIS: There appear to be few, if any, Rio Negro fish species that are confined to, or confine themselves to, only one habitat. The exigencies of food, reproduction and other aspects of life history encourage a eurytopic existence. The use of many habitats in response to fluctuating river level during the course of the year by Rio Negro fishes also results in relatively random species associations.

The annual floods produce two major effects in Rio Negro ecology. First, they greatly expand the aquatic environment, and this is both vertically with increased depths and horizontally with lateral flooding. Second, the floods inundate floodplain rainforest, thus the waters provide an aquatic highway into a terrestrially rooted source of primary production. All together 184 fish species were captured in flooded forest, out of a total of 450 species from all habitats. It is probable, however, that nearly all species use the flooded forest, but a very large amount of fishing effort would be needed to demonstrate this by actual collections because of the difficulty of sampling this habitat.

With falling river levels and the draining of the flooded forest, the fish species, depending on the exact location, shift to woody shores, floodplain and island lakes, beaches, channels, rocky pools, swamps and other habitats. This is clearly reflected by the numbers of species found in more than one habitat and also the percentage of taxa, of the total species captured, that were present in each of the major habitats (Tabs. 11.1 and 11.2).

To measure the presence and absence of species, Sorensen's coefficient of community (CC) was used, and it is defined as follows:

Tab. 11.3. The lower triangles of the matrices indicate the coefficients of community similarity for various combinations of habitats and/or sites. The calculations are based on Sorensen's Coefficient of Similarity.

1. ANAVILHANAS (LOWER RIO NEGRO)

	Beach	Flooded Forest
Beach	–	–
Flooded Forest	44	–
Woody Shores	48	63

2. UPPER RIO NEGRO

	Rocky Pool	Island Lake 1	Island Lake 2	Beach
Island Lake 1	40	--	--	--
Island Lake 2	36	48	--	--
Beach	28	13	21	--
Confluence Swamp	45	54	42	24

3. ISLAND LAKES (UPPER RIO NEGRO)

	Island Lake 1	Island Lake 2
Island Lake 2	52	--
Island Lake 3	47	47

4. BEACHES

	Anavilhanas	Cumuru	Urumari	Arirará	Arirará Confluence	Tamaquaré
Anavilhanas	--	--	--	--	--	--
Cumuru	42	--	--	--	--	
Urumari	36	31	--	--	--	--
Arirará	32	49	27	--	--	--
Arirará Confluence	35	42	47	34	--	--
Tamaquaré	22	22	38	14	35	--
Marauiá	33	27	44	24	40	41

$$CC = \frac{2c}{s1 + s2}$$

c = number of species common to both sites
s1 and s2 = number of species in community 1 and 2

Community similarity was compared from a fourfold perspective, which includes both geographical and ecological factors that might contribute to the species organization of fishes in Rio Negro communities: 1) lower versus middle and upper Rio Negro; 2) unlike habitats within a 10 km radius of each other; 3) comparable habitats (lakes) of upper Rio Negro, and; 4) comparable habitats (beaches) the length of the Rio Negro (Tab. 11.3).

The division of the lower from the middle and upper Rio Negro, for purposes of testing community similarity, seems reasonable based on the fact that the two areas have different river level fluctuation patterns and geologies. As mentioned in Chapter 2, the lower Rio Negro is centered in the mostly Tertiary lowlands, whereas the middle and upper Rio Negro region embraces a large part of the western extension of the Guiana Shield. The coefficient of community similarity, however, was high ($=79$). This suggests that the two areas do not differ greatly in their overall faunistic composition, though the middle and upper Rio Negro appears to have more endemic species [see Chapter 5].

Two different areas – the Anavilhanas of the lower Rio Negro and the stretch near the Urubaxi confluence, 700 km upstream – were chosen to test the species similarity of communities in habitats within close proximity to each other. The lower Rio Negro comparisons were based on flooded forest, woody shore and beach habitats. The flooded forest represents the high water period and the woody shore and the beach the low water season. As might be expected, the flooded forest and the woody shore habitats showed the highest similarity. In a sense, the woody shore habitat is the low water counterpart of the flooded forest as, physiognomically, it is only the riverward extension of the larger community. With 63% similarity, the evidence strongly suggests that populations of most species in the Anavilhanas area pass the low water period hovering along the edge of the drained inundation forest, though these taxa can be found in other habitats as well. With the new floods, the species recolonize the inundation forest.

A large number of species is also found in beach waters during the low water period. Beaches and woody shores showed 48% similarity. We have no evidence to suggest why preference might be given to beaches versus woody shores, or vice versa, during the low water period. Along woody shores, fishes can gain protection from cover, as is easily observed. There is little if any cover on beaches and piscivores are common in these habitats (but in all other habitats as well). Many if not most of the non-piscivorous species found on beaches appear to form larger schools than are found in the woody shore areas. Schooling is generally reported to be an adaptation that decreases predation pressure. Predators evidently have a more difficult time focusing on a single prey when it is mixed with many of its same kind than when it is alone (Partridge, 1982). That hypothesis, however, seems weak in the case of nocturnally active piscivores, especially the catfishes that rely more on tactile, olfactory and senses other than vision to locate their prey. As discussed in Chapter 9, beaches also provide food for many species, and this might also be a factor that allows so many taxa to use this habitat type during the low water period.

For the upper Rio Negro, five adjacent sites representing a rocky pool, two island lakes, a beach and a confluence swamp were compared (see Tab. 11.3). All of these habitats represented low water fish communities. It was not possible to sample flooded forest in this region. Of the four habitats, the beach site shared the least number of species. In all but one case, community similarity of the five sites was below 50%.

In the above examples comparisons were made by matching only two sites. The three island lakes sampled in the upper Rio Negro were chosen for their similar size and morphology. These waterbodies measured approximately 75-150 m length, 30-50 m width and 50-150 cm depth. All three lakes were surrounded by inundation forests that, at the time collections were made, were not flooded. The fish communities were removed with piscicide. All together the three lakes contained at least 140 fish species. The species from this lacustrine trio were combined to test community similarity (see Tab. 11.3). Island lakes 'collect' species when river level falls, and their fish communities would appear to be a representative sample of a large number of the species that are also found in the contiguous inundation forests during the floods. Thus, island lake collections, if our view is correct, are fairly representative samples of the species associations found in any particular area along the main river. The island lake communities suggest that usually no more than about one-half of the species are shared between different sites.

Beaches were the most uniform habitat sampled and, since they are common during the low water period the length of the Rio Negro, they were selected as the basis to compare community similarity along a 900 km transect from near the mouth of the river to the confluence of the Rio Marauiá. All beaches were sampled with a 30 m seine and in a similar manner. Only beaches with at least 45 species were used for testing community similarities. If spatial proximity were an important factor influencing community similarity of species, then one would expect the beaches closest to each other to also have the most similar fish communities. This was not the case. None of the beaches sampled showed more than 49% similarity with any other beach. The above evidence from beaches and island lakes suggests that the fish species composition, at the level of the community, is largely random in the Rio Negro. Lowe-McConnell (1979, 1987) presents evidence from various tropical studies indicating that highly seasonal rivers tend to have stochastic assemblages of species. The Rio Negro data are in concordance with that hypothesis.

COMMUNITY DIVERSITY AS A FUNCTION OF SPECIES AND ABUNDANCE

HYPOTHESIS: Rio Negro fish communities may be characterized as relatively random associations of species with high taxonomic and high abundance diversities.

Differential abundances and biomasses are the two principal factors, other than species composition, that determine the diversity of a community. We did not attempt to measure biomass and here, as in most ecological studies, we will use abundance, or the number of individuals of each species, as the basis for calculating numerical diversity. The measurement of the diversity of abundance is useful because it quantitatively suggests the evenness or unevenness of species in communities. The Shannon Diversity Index (or Shannon-Weiner Index) was used to calculate the diversity of abundance, and it is defined as follows:

$$H_s = - \sum_{i=1}^{S} (p1)(log2p1)$$

H_s = the amount of diversity in an association of S species
S   = the number of species in the association
p1   = the relative abundance of *i*th species measured from 0 to 1.0
log p1   = the logarithm of p1; for our analyses it is to the base 2

The larger the H, or diversity value, then we would be less certain of our chances

Tab. 11.4. Diversity of abundance indices based on the Shannon Diversity Index and the number of species captured in selected habitats of the Rio Negro. Index values above 3.0 indicate high diversity of abundance.

	Diversity	N Species
BEACHES		
Anavilhanas	4.37	106
Paraná do Jacaré	3.66	57
Cumuru	3.40	66
Massarabí	3.67	31
Urumarí	2.61	60
Arirará Confluence	2.46	62
Tamaquaré	3.70	64
Marauiá	3.78	89
ISLAND LAKES		
Below Barcelos	4.70	78
Below Rio Daraá	4.31	58
Buiu-açu	4.11	91
Tamaquaré	3.45	88
ROCKY POOL		
Below Rio Daraá	4.68	108

of finding an individual species at random in any particular community. For example, if there were only one species in a sample, then the uncertainty about the random organization is zero. For any given number of species, H will be highest if the abundances approach equability, as the uncertainty about catching one particular taxon is highest if all of the possible species to which it can belong are equally abundant.

For the diversity of abundance analyses, only sites were chosen where only one fishing method, which was either a seine or piscicide, was used. These sites included beaches, island lakes and a rocky pool. For the majority of sites in the three habitat types considered, the diversity index was over 3.0 (Tab 11.4). The generally high indices for these habitats suggest that Rio Negro fish communities are not only diverse in total species numbers, as discussed above, but also in the relative abundances of most of the species. There is a fairly close correlation between the number of specimens captured at each of the sites we sampled and the total number of species identified for that location. There is no obvious correlation, however, between the numbers of species captured and the diversity of abundance indices. Communities with 40 or 50 species can be just as diverse, as measured by the Shannon Index, as counterparts containing over 100 species. The high diversity of abundance, in conjunction with the low values for the similarity indices discussed earlier, favor the hypothesis that the seasonal development of Rio Negro fish communities is a relatively random process.

DOMINANT SPECIES

HYPOTHESIS: Rio Negro fish communities contain dominant species, the first two of which usually account for over 40 percent of the total individuals. There is only

Tab. 11.5 The most dominant fish species in selected Rio Negro fish communities. CDI = Community Dominance Index based on two most dominant species (McNaughton, 1968).

	CDI	DOMINANT SPECIES
BEACHES		
Anavilhanas	28	CHARACIDAE: *Astyanax guianensis*
		CHARACIDAE: *Microschemobrycon casiquiare*
Arirará Confluence	80	CHARACIDAE: *Hemigrammus mimus*
		CHARACIDAE: *Hyphessobrycon sp.*
Ilha Cumuru	56	LEBIASINIDAE: *Nannostomus marilynae*
		CHARACIDAE: *Hemigrammus analis ?*
Ilha Tamaquaré	52	CHARACIDAE: *Hemigrammus analis B*
		CHARACIDAE: *Moenkhausia lepidura ?*
Marauià Confluence	52	CHARACIDAE: *Microschemobrycon sp.*
		CHARACIDAE: *Hemigrammus mimus*
Massarabi	45	CHARACIDAE: *Microschemobrycon casiquiare*
		CHARACIDAE: *Astyanax scologaster*
Paraná do Jacaré	54	CHARACIDAE: *Microschemobrycon casiquiare*
		CHARACIDAE: *Hyphessobrycon sp. 2*
Urumari	66	CHARACIDAE: *Moenkhausia lepidura D*
		DORADIDAE: *Hassar lipophthalmus*
FLOATING MEADOWS		
Anavilhanas	62	CHARACIDAE: *Hemigrammus levis*
		POECILIIDAE: *Fluviphylax pygmaeus*
Anavilhanas	56	CHARACIDAE: *Hemigrammus levis*
		CHARACIDAE: *Moenkhausia lepidura D*
ISLAND LAKES		
Barcelos	29	GASTEROPELECIDAE: *Carnegiella marthae*
		CHARACIDAE: *Hyphessobrycon diancistrus*
Below Rio Daraá	27	CHARACIDAE: *Hyphessobrycon cf.serpae*
		CURIMATIDAE: *Curimata sp.*
Ilha Buiu-açu	43	CHILODONTIDAE: *Chilodus punctatus*
		CURIMATIDAE: *Curimata plumbea*
Ilha Tamaquaré	53	CURIMATIDAE: *Curimata sp.*
		CURIMATIDAE: Curimatidae sp.
ROCKY POOL		
Below Rio Daraá	42	CHARACIDAE: *Astyanax sp.*
		CHARACIDAE: *Hyphessobrycon sp.*

a slight tendency for decreased dominance with increased taxonomic diversity. In other words, abundance dominance and taxonomic diversity, contrary to logic, are not highly correlated.

HYPOTHESIS: The dominant species in the Rio Negro, in terms of numbers of individuals, are taxa that, as adults, are under about 40 mm length. Conversely, it may also be said that the young of medium to large sized species represent only a small proportion of the total individuals found in the communities. This pattern is in striking contrast to that found in the floodplain waterbodies of turbid water rivers such as the Rio Solimões-Amazonas and Rio Madeira, wherein relatively large numbers and biomasses of the young of the medium sized fishes (many of which are commercial taxa) tend to dominate. The contrasting patterns suggest that community dominance by fishes that mature at a small size is inversely proportional to the nutrient quality of the water.

Community dominance was measured with the following index (McNaughton, 1968):

$$\text{Community Dominance Index} = \frac{y_1 + y_2}{y}$$

y_1 = abundance of the first most abundant species
y_2 = abundance of the second most abundant species
y = total abundances of all species

The advantage of using the two most abundant species, instead of just one, is that it more clearly indicates dominance. The evidence suggests that dominance varies greatly in Rio Negro fish communities, both in terms of comparisons of like and unlike habitats (Tab 11.5). With increased taxonomic diversity, there is a slight tendency towards decreased dominance, and this suggests that there may be a point where the addition of more species would theoretically result in a reduction in the abundance of dominants rather than the exclusion of less dominant forms. This theoretical point, however, is probably not generally reached because community structure is destroyed seasonally by fluctuating river level.

The dominant species in Rio Negro fish communities are, for the most part, under about 40 mm standard length. In no case were the young of the medium or large size species found to be dominants. Their very poor showing or absence in habitats where a small-meshed seine or piscicide was used could not be due to sampling error, as both of these methods are efficient at capturing all size classes except for very tiny larvae. Furthermore, visual surveys of collecting sites did not reveal significant numbers of fish larvae that might have been missed by our fishing techniques. It is possible that the young of many of the medium and large species live mostly in biotopes or habitats that we did not sample, though at this time it is unclear what or where these might be.

In the lower Rio Negro, the most common food fishes exploited for the Manaus market are medium-sized taxa of the genera *Semaprochilodus* (Prochilodontidae) and *Brycon* (Characidae). Young of these taxa less than about 15 cm length are rarely found in the Rio Negro, and they were never in any of the communities that we studied. They are very common, however, in the floodplain waterbodies of the Rio

Solimões-Amazonas (Bayley, 1982; Ribeiro, 1983; Araujo-Lima, 1984; pers. obser.). It is from the latter waterbodies that they are recruited into the blackwater river (Ribeiro, 1983; Borges, 1986) [also see discussion below on migration patterns in the Rio Negro].

Goulding (1980) speculated that such a pattern might have arisen due to competitive exclusion, that is, species that attain maturity at a small size, as do the majority of Rio Negro dominants, would be able to exclude comparably sized fry and alevins of the medium sized species in nutrient-poor river systems where food supply might be a limiting factor. It seems more logical, however, to first determine whether the types of foods on which the larval and young size classes of the medium sized fishes feed in the turbid river areas are also present in significant quantities in the Rio Negro. Poor zooplankton production might be a limiting factor to larval community development in the Rio Negro, thus explaining why some species migrate downstream to spawn in the Rio Solimões-Amazonas, and in whose floodplain waterbodies their larvae are among the dominant species [see migration discussion below].

The maximum number of sites for which any single species was found to be dominant was four, and this included three different habitats (see Tab. 11.3). Eight species were dominant in at least two sites, and three in three sites. The evidence suggests that dominance is highly variable in Rio Negro fish communities and, supportingly, this is also the opinion of the aquarium trade fishermen who report that the abundances of the species that they exploit are highly patchy, at least in terms of dense concentrations of individual species.

Lowe-McConnell's (1964,1967,1975) observations of fish communities in the Rupununi area and elsewhere and syntheses of comments presented in the literature suggest that there can be a marked changeover in activity at dawn and dusk between the diurnal fishes (mostly cichlids and characins) and the nocturnal catfishes and gymnotoid electric fishes. Dominance, then, could be greatly influenced by whether samples were taken diurnally or nocturnally. Diurnal catches might underestimate catfishes and gymnotoid electric fishes. This is probably the case with our day captures, though in general it appears that the numbers of characins are far more numerous than catfishes and electric fishes and that biases are slight. Furthermore, characins were still by far the dominant fishes in our nocturnal samples (see Tab. 11.3).

NOTES ON MINIATURE FISHES IN RIO NEGRO FISH COMMUNITIES

Louis Agassiz was the first to suggest that the Amazon Basin probably has a large number of fishes that mature at small size (Agassiz & Agassiz, 1867). Over a century later Roberts (1972,1984) emphasized that small Amazonian fishes were still relatively rare in collections because of inadequate sampling techniques. His own field experience in the Amazon Basin led him to suspect that most Amazonian fishes that mature at small size would belong to fish groups ordinarily of, or tolerating, marine or euryhaline waters. He referred to these groups as 'marginal' fishes, by which he apparently means less competitive in an evolutionary sense vis-à-vis the more dominant characins and catfishes.

Weitzman and Vari (1988) list 85 described fish species from the forested regions of South America that appear to mature sexually at less than 20 mm standard length. They refer to these taxa as miniature fishes, and this appears to be a more appropriate term than pygmy fishes, as some of these groups have also been called in the literature. They state that the fish fauna of South America has proportionally more miniatures than have been reported for Old World tropical freshwaters. In contrast to Robert's (1984) suggestion that most miniature fishes would probably belong to groups whose relatives are mostly marine or euryhaline taxa, Weitzman and Vari (1988) showed that in fact most of very small species that have been described to date from forested South American areas belong to the primary freshwater groups, the characins and catfishes. Primary freshwater fishes, for the most part, can only tolerate freshwater.

Based on either the superficial examination of gonad states or the presence of external characteristics usually associated with mature fish, our data suggest that the Rio Negro alone appears to have at least 40 fish species that are suspected to be able to mature sexually under 20 mm standard length (SL), and perhaps as many as 100 species under 30 mm SL [mean standard length ranges are given in Appendix 3]. The majority of miniature fishes in the Rio Negro are characins, followed by catfishes, cichlids, engraulids and eleotrids. At present there is no evidence to suggest why there are so many miniature fishes in the Amazon Basin, and much of South America for that matter, and we cannot think of any testable ecological hypotheses to explain advantages of size reduction. It would also appear premature to assume that miniature fishes are a phenomenon of recent evolutionary history. Until proven the contrary, if that is at all possible, it must also be assumed that miniature fishes could have had a long evolutionary history in the Amazon Basin and elsewhere.

SEASONAL MIGRATIONS AND COMMUNITIES WITH LOW SPECIES DIVERSITY

HYPOTHESIS: Most of the medium sized fish species of the Central Amazon that have large biomasses, at least as indicated by fisheries catch data, are migratory and have life histories that include both relatively nutrient-rich waters of the turbid rivers and the nutrient-poor blackwater and/or clearwater tributaries. The nutrient-rich waters are used as nursery habitats, whereas the nutrient-poor tributaries provide extensive feeding environments in flooded forests for pre-adult and adult fishes of the same migratory species. This pattern in the lower Rio Negro is dominated by the genera Semaprochilodus and Brycon.

The seasonal migration of fish schools results in large-scale dispersal within the Rio Negro and, for some species, to other systems. When not migrating during the low water period, many if not most of the migratory species observed in the Rio Negro tend to form large schools or communities in which 2-3 species of the same genus are involved. The principal migratory species that are observed in large schools belong to the genera *Semaprochilodus* (Prochilodontidae); *Brycon, Triportheus, Chalceus, Myleus*, and *Metynnis* (Characidae); *Hemiodus* and *Argonectes* (Hemiodontidae); *Psectrogaster* and *Curimata* (Curimatidae), and; *Pimelodus* (Pimelodidae). For the most part, the migratory taxa appear to avoid dispersing themselves, at least on a large scale, in the diverse communities outlined in the discussions above. This is the principal reason why the migratory species were usually not among the dominant species of the diverse communities we sampled. Instead, they appear to form their own low diversity communities and these usually inhabit slightly deeper waters (*e.g.*,

111

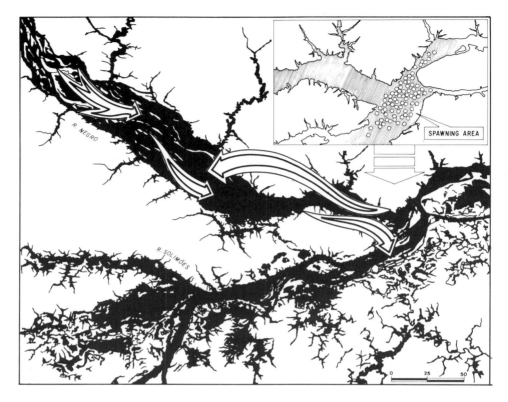

Fig. 11.1. The arrows indicate the downstream migration of *Semaprochilodus* schools at the beginning of the floods to spawn in the turbid waters of the Rio Solimões-Amazonas. Based on Ribeiro (1983).

farther offshore in beach habitats). During the floods the pattern is reversed and the migratory fishes disperse themselves among the diverse communities found in the inundation forests.

The Central Amazon Basin contains about 20 genera and perhaps 30 characin species that present a migration pattern that is highly aberrant when compared with movements detected in other South American rivers (Goulding, 1980,1981; Ribeiro, 1983; Petrere, 1985). Most South American fish species that undergo long seasonal migrations move upstream just prior to or at the beginning of the floods. These movements are correlated with spawning activity in the upper reaches of the rivers (*e.g.*, Godoi, 1962,1967,1972; Bayley, 1973). Most of the migratory characins of the Central Amazon inhabit both turbid water rivers (*e.g.*, the Rio Solimões-Amazonas and Rio Madeira) and their blackwater and clearwater tributaries. Those populations of these species inhabiting the blackwater and clearwater tributaries migrate *downstream* to spawn, and this usually occurs, depending on the species, from the beginning of the floods to about the peak of the annual inundation. Spawning takes place in turbid water and is probably confined mostly to channels (pers. obser. and Araujo-Lima, 1984). From the channels the newborn fry find their way to adjacent floodplain waterbodies that serve as their nursery habitats (Bayley, 1982; Araujo-Lima,

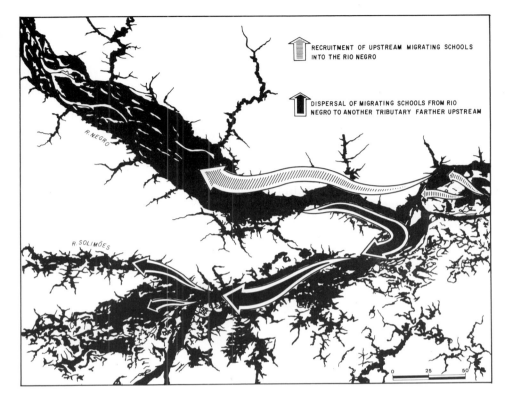

RECRUITMENT OF UPSTREAM MIGRATING SCHOOLS INTO THE RIO NEGRO

DISPERSAL OF MIGRATING SCHOOLS FROM RIO NEGRO TO ANOTHER TRIBUTARY FARTHER UPSTREAM

R. NEGRO

R. SOLIMÕES

0   25   50

Fig. 11.2 Migration patterns of *Semaprochilodus* species into and out of the Rio Negro during dispersal movements. These migrations take place subsequent to the peak of the annual floods. Based on Ribeiro (1983)

1984,1985; Araujo-Lima & Hardy, 1987). Subsequent to spawning, the spent adults return to the tributaries, or nearby affluents, that they migrated down to realize their reproductive act. The adults then enter flooded forests where they feed heavily (Fig 11.1). After the peak of the floods or during the low water period, dispersal migrations are also observed. These involve recruitment of new schools into the Rio Negro and the dispersal of other schools out of it and to another tributary system farther upstream (Fig. 11.2).

The Rio Negro appears to have fewer migratory characin species than do clear-water rivers. This is probably due to both ecological factors and the overexploitation of some migratory species (*e.g.*, of the genera *Colossoma*, *Piaractus* and perhaps *Triportheus*) in the Central Amazon. Only three species (*Semaprochilodus* spp. and *Brycon* sp.) are captured in any quantity by commercial fishermen and, as mentioned earlier, our collections reveal that the other migratory species are absent or very rare in the Rio Negro. The possible reasons for their rarity or absence in the Rio Negro are discussed in Chapter 5.

The migration pattern outlined above is not the only one that is encountered in the Rio Negro. There are also migrations that are confined to the Rio Negro or between it and its clearwater or blackwater tributaries. Fishermen of the middle and upper Rio Negro report two annual migrations, the exact timing depending on the location. In the upper Rio Negro, and especially at the São Gabriel rapids where fishes can easily be observed, large-scale upstream migrations are witnessed in late May, June and July with rapidly rising water levels and the onset of the main floods. The local residents report that these migrations are related to spawning activity, and the large number of ripe fish found near the rapids at his time of year support that opinion. These upstream migrations are reminiscent of patterns reported for extra-Amazonian rivers of South America.

Large schools of upstream migrating fishes are also encountered in the middle and upper Rio Negro in October, November and December at the time of the small floods when river might rise rapidly only to fall again shortly thereafter. As far as we could tell, these movements do not appear to be related to spawning activity. They are probably dispersal movements.

12. CONCLUSIONS*

A total of at least 450 fish species was collected in the blackwaters of the Rio Negro, making it the single most ichthyologically diverse tributary river in the world yet reported on. Considering the fact that many more types of biotopes and habitats need to be collected on a large scale, the actual diversity of the river could be as high as 700 species. If the Rio Negro is representative of other Amazonian blackwater rivers, and it probably is, then high levels of humic compounds, low pH and nutrient poverty have no limiting effect on fish species diversity.

Evidence is presented to suggest that high levels of humic compounds or low pH, or a combination of these factors, might limit the entrance of some fish species into the Rio Negro. Many of the species for which the Rio Negro appears to represent an ecological barrier belong to genera that are among the most common fishes of turbid and clearwater rivers in the Amazon Basin. For example, fishes of the genus *Prochilodus* (Prochilodontidae) are the single most common food fishes in the large rivers of South America as a whole (Lowe-McConnell, 1984), but they are unable to establish themselves in the Rio Negro.

The high diversity of the Amazon fish fauna has been known since Agassiz's reports to Brazilian Emperor Dom Pedro II in the last century (Agassiz & Agassiz, 1867). As with most large tropical river systems, however, it has remained unclear whether *alpha* or *beta* diversity, or both types, were responsible for the large numbers of species that have been reported (Lowe-McConnell, 1987). *Alpha* diversity is the absolute number of species in a community, whereas *beta* diversity is the number of habitat-oriented species added along an environmental gradient.

The evidence presented in this work suggests that the Rio Negro is best characterized as an *alpha*-diversity system with relatively random fish species associations. *Beta*-diversity is not pronounced, at least in the 1200 km stretch from the mouth of the river to the São Gabriel rapids. This appears due to similar habitat structure along most of the river and the absence of cataracts or other barriers that might have otherwise led to greater geographical isolation. The rocky areas of the upper Rio Negro need to be sampled on a much larger scale than was the case for this study, as these habitats might reveal greater *beta*-diversity than can be gleaned from our data. For example, Myers (1944) and Myers & Weitzman (1966) described small and very peculiar trichomycterid catfish species from the upper Rio Negro that were collected in the early part of this century, but these taxa were not revealed in our collection efforts. Also, if tributaries, including small rainforest streams, were added to the diversity equation, *beta* diversity would probably increase significantly.

*The management and conservation implications derived from this investigation will be presented in another volume that incorporates Rio Negro ecological patterns into the broader framework of the Amazon Basin (Goulding, in prep.)

In terms of species diversity, some Rio Negro fish communities, at least during the low water period in several habitat types, are comparable to coral reefs and surpass other freshwater systems that have thus far been reported on in the literature. Individual coral reef communities are generally reported to have 50-100 fish species, or about the same as the rocky pool and island lake communities in the Rio Negro [for coral reef reviews see Ehrlich (1975); Emery (1978); Lowe-McConnell (1975,1987)]. Sale (*e.g.*, 1980a,1980b) has suggested that relatively random recruitment explains the high fish diversity found in coral reefs with many species that apparently have identical or similar ecological requirements. Largely stochastic species assemblages, with many taxa having similar food habits, also appears to be the pattern for Rio Negro fish communities.

Rio Negro fish communities appear to be more diverse than any that have thus far been reported for freshwater lakes, rivers or streams anywhere in the world. Much attention has been given to the great diversity of cichlid species found together in small areas in African lakes. For example, Hori, Yamaoka and Takamura (1983) reported 38 fish species from a 20 X 20 m quadrat in a rocky shore of Lake Tanganyika. The 4-8 X 30 m rocky pool from the upper Rio Negro that we sampled contained over 100 species. Nearly all of the beaches we sampled each had over 40 fish species. Small island lakes contained 58-91 species. Whereas the cichlids have radiated in the Great Lakes of Africa, in the Rio Negro, and in the Amazon in general, characins and catfishes account for most of the diversity, though cichlids are also well represented.

Lowe-McConnell (1987) characterizes the fish diversity in tropical seasonal environments as usually less but with a higher degree of dominant species than non-seasonal waterbodies. As discussed above, Rio Negro fish community diversity appears to rival or, in some cases, even surpass the most diverse associations that have thus far been reported for tropical freshwaters. Pronounced seasonality, therefore, does not necessarily reduce species diversity, at least in the case of the Rio Negro, and probably in most other large Amazonian rivers as well. Underestimated diversity in Amazon rivers has largely been due to inadequate sampling techniques and identification problems. The presence of dominant species in Rio Negro fish communities, however, agrees with the general pattern that has been detected in other highly seasonal tropical river systems.

Lowe-McConnell's (1987) synthesis of the literature suggested that tropical seasonal and non-seasonal environments often show different ecological attributes in the trophic development of fish communities. In seasonal environments, for example, she characterizes fish feeding habits as facultative or specialized mostly for the lower trophic levels. Most Rio Negro fish species appear to be facultative feeders on a seasonal basis, which agrees with the above generalization, but there is no concentration of taxa in the lower trophic levels. The diversity of feeding habits found in Rio Negro fish communities agrees more with reports from non-seasonal than seasonal environments, such as for the former the East African Lakes, where many specializations have been noted (Fryer & Iles, 1972).

Though many Rio Negro fish species are able to practice specialized feeding patterns, few taxa appear to be behaviorally, morphologically or physiologically limited to these habits. For example, frugivores are also able to take arthropods that fall into the water and some seed-eating piranhas have specializations for removing fins and scales. Even the most specialized scale-eaters (*e.g.*, *Serrabrycon magoi*) also feed on other foods, such as insects, at least during part of the year. Many piscivores, at least as adults, restrict their diets to fish, but a wide range of prey types is eaten. In some cases specialized feeding habits are easily correlated with seasonal food availability (*e.g.*, frugivores feeding on fruits and seeds when these foods are abundant in flooded forests). It appears that community structure somehow limits omnivory within individual habitats. Limited omnivory, however, has not resulted in highly specialized feeding associations, but rather in many species sharing the same general categories of food types.

APPENDICES

APPENDIX 1

SUMMARY OF TOTAL SAMPLE STUDIED

Fishing Gear
D = dipnet
G = gillnet
L = line-and-pole
S = seine
P = piscicide

Time of Day Fished
D = diurnal
N = nocturnal

	Date	Time	Gear	N Specimens	N Species
BEACHES					
Anavilhanas	Oct 1980	D/N	S	6886	106
Anavilhanas	21 Nov 1979	D	S	40	10
Arirará Confluence	6 Oct 1979	D	S	5068	62
Below Barcelos	29 Jan 1080	D	S	135	18
Ilha Cumuru	1 Feb 1980	D	S	4759	66
Ilha Tamaquaré	10 Oct 1979	D	S	1601	64
Marauiá Confluence	13 Oct 1979	D	S	7354	89
Massarabi	18 Oct 1979	D	S	485	31
Paraná do Jacaré	7 Oct 1979	D	S	3538	57
Rosa Maria	24 Oct 1979	D	S	100	25
São Gabriel	20 May 1979	D	S	262	23
São Gabriel	1 May 1979	D/N	S,G	389	47
São João	4 Oct 1979	D	S	194	6
Urumari	6 Oct 1979	D	S	3730	60
			Subtotal	37084	248
CONFLUENCE SWAMP					
Urubaxi Confluence	Feb 1980	D	S	35138	153
FLOATING MEADOWS					
Anavilhanas	Feb 1982	D	S	510	25
Anavilhanas	Jan 1980	D	S	1183	46
			Subtotal	1693	56

	Date	Time	Gear	N Specimens	N Species
FLOODED FORESTS					
Anavilhanas	Ja-Ju 1980	D/N	G,D,S,L	5780	140
Arirará Confluence	28 May 1979	D/N	G	15	9
Cuiuni	3 Jun 1979	D/N	G	184	31
Ilha Mari-mari	31 May 1979	D/N	G	28	13
Mandiquié Confluence	8 Oct 1979	D/N	G	161	30
Marauiá Confluence	27 May 1979	D/N	G	195	36
São Gabriel	18 May 1979	D/N	G	186	40
São Pedro	23 May 1979	D/N	G	227	37
			Subtotal	6903	184
ISLAND LAKES					
Barcelos	29 Feb 1980	D	P	1248	78
Below Rio Daraá	17 Feb 1980	D	P	2966	58
Ilha Buiu-açu	6 Feb 1980	D	P	6579	91
Ilha Tamaquar	11 Oct 1979	D	P	4396	88
			Subtotal	15189	163
ROCKY POOL					
Below Rio Daraá	16 Feb 1980	D	P	1386	108
WOODY SHORES					
Above Barcelos	2 Feb 1980	D	G,S	315	35
Anavilhanas	Sep 1980	D	G,S	1816	104
Anavilhanas	Oct 1979	D	G,S	510	53
Arirará Confluence	8 Oct 1979	D	G,S	107	28
Below Rio Daraá	12 Feb 1980	D	G,S	1269	41
Ilha Taiu-assu	23 Oct 1979	D	D	9	6
Ilha Tamaquaré	7 Feb 1980	D	S,G	6799	67
Ilha Tamaquaré	10 Oct 1979	D	S,G	147	14
Marauiá Confluence	14 Oct 1979	D	G,S	434	53
São Pedro	23 Oct 1979	D	S,G	223	1
			Subtotal	11629	219
			TOTAL	111482	

APPENDIX 2

GENERAL HABITAT CHARACTERISTICS OF THE SITES STUDIED

	Date	River Level	pH	Substrate	Depth	Current
BEACHES						
Anavilhanas	Oct 1980	Low	<4.8	Silt	<2m	None
Anavilhanas	21 Nov 1979	Low	<4.8	Sand	<2m	Slow
Arirará Confluence	6 Oct 1979	Falling	5.0	Sand	<2m	Moderate
Below Barcelos	29 Jan 1080	Low	<4.8	Silt	<2m	None
Ilha Cumuru	1 Feb 1980	Low	<4.8	Sand	<1m	None
Ilha Tamaquaré	10 Oct 1979	Falling	<4.8	Sand	<1m	None
Marauiá Confluence	13 Oct 1979	Falling	5.2	Sand	<2m	Moderate
Massarabi	18 Oct 1979	Falling	<4.8	Sand	<2m	Slow
Paran do Jacaré	7 Oct 1979	Falling	<4.8	Sand	<2m	Slow
Rosa Maria	24 Oct 1979	Falling	<4.8	Sand	<2m	Slow
São Gabriel	20 May 1979	Rising	<4.8	Sand	<3m	Moderate
São Joaò	4 Oct 1979	Falling	<4.8	Sand	<2m	Moderate
Urumari	6 Oct 1979	Falling	<4.8	Sand	<2m	Slow
São Gabriel	1 May 1979	Rising	<4.8	Rocky	<2m	Moderate
CONFLUENCE SWAMP						
Urubaxi Confluence	Feb 1980	Low	–	Leafy	<1m	None
FLOATING MEADOWS						
Anavilhanas	Feb 1982	Rising	<4.8	Plant	<2m	None
Anavilhanas	Jan 1980	Rising	<4.8	Plant	<2m	None
FLOODED FORESTS						
Anavilhanas	Ja – Ju 1980	High	<4.8	Forest	<10m	Slow
Arirará Confluence	28 May 1979	High	–	Forest	<10m	Slow
Cuiuni	3 Jun 1979	High	–	Forest	<10m	Slow
Ilha Mari – mari	31 May 1979	High	<4.8	Forest	<10m	Slow
Mandiquié Confluence	8 Oct 1979	High	<4.8	Forest	<10m	Slow
Marauiá Confluence	27 May 1979	High	–	Forest	<10m	Slow
São Gabriel	18 May 1979	High	<4.8	Forest	<5m	Slow
São Pedro	23 May 1979	High	<4.8	Forest	<10m	Slow
ISLAND LAKES						
Barcelos	29 Feb 1980	Low	4.5	Leafy	<2m	None
Below Rio Daraá	17 Feb 1980	Low	<4.5	Leafy	<1m	None
Ilha Buiu – açu	6 Feb 1980	Low	4.5	Leafy	<2m	None
Ilha Tamaquaré	11 Oct 1979	Falling	–	Leafy	<2m	None
ROCKY POOL						
Below Rio Daraá	16 Feb 1980	High	<4.8	Rocky	<2m	None
WOODY SHORES						
Marauiá Confluence	14 Oct 1979	Falling	–	Leafy	<2m	Moderate
Above Barcelos	2 Feb 1980	Low	<4.8	Leafy	<3m	Moderate
Anavilhanas	Sep 1980	Low	<4.8	Leafy	<3m	Moderate
Anavilhanas	Oct 1979	Low	<4.8	Leafy	<3m	Moderate
Arirará Confluence	8 Oct 1979	Falling	–	Leafy	<3m	Moderate
Below Rio Daraá	12 Feb 1980	Low	<4.8	Leafy	<3m	Moderate
Ilha Taiu – assu	23 Oct 1979	Falling	<4.8	Leafy	<3m	Moderate
Ilha Tamaquaré	7 Feb 1980	Low	<4.8	Leafy	<3m	Moderate
Ilha Tamaquaré	10 Oct 1979	Falling	<4.8	Leafy	<3m	Moderate
São Pedro	23 Oct 1979	Falling	<4.8	Leafy	<3m	Moderate

APPENDIX 3

RIO NEGRO FISH SPECIES CAPTURED

The species summary presented here for the Rio Negro should be considered only a *first approximation* of a large part of the fish diversity now known for the river. Many binomial name changes will undoubtedly be made as systematic studies progress and many more species will be added to the list.

Although approximately 450 fish species were identifed from the Rio Negro, this summary only includes about 410 species. Herein are only included, with a few exceptions, those species that could be identified to at least the generic level.

Many of the taxa have code names for unidentified species or following specific names when it is suspected that the group needs to be split taxonomically.

The species are listed alphabetically by their families.

	N Sites	N Habitats	N Specimens	Mean Length Range
AGENEIOSIDAE				
Ageneiosus sp. 1	10	4	52	125 - 340
Ageneiosus sp. 2	8	3	21	130 - 170
Ageneiosus sp. A	6	3	18	100 - 195
Ageneiosus sp. FP	1	1	1	175
ANOSTOMIDAE				
Anostomus anostomus	1	1	1	42
Anostomus ternetzi	1	1	1	65 - 65
Laemolyta cf. *taeniatus*	12	6	100	76 - 237
Laemolyta sp. ?	11	5	24	124 - 243
Laemolyta sp. A	1	1	45	232
Laemolyta sp. GR	1	1	1	24
Laemolyta sp. n.	1	1	1	208
Leporinus brunneus	6	3	22	47 - 300
Leporinus cf. *agassizi*	13	5	85	45 - 305
Leporinus cf. *friderici*	7	4	48	35 - 322
Leporinus desmotes	1	1	1	200
Leporinus fasciatus	18	6	588	40 - 318
Leporinus klausewitzi	5	3	34	60 - 242
Leporinus nattereri	2	2	3	190 - 295
Leporinus sp. n.	10	6	154	62 - 310
Pseudanos gracilis	5	4	49	64 - 117
Pseudanos trimaculatus	1	1	1	71
Rhytiodus argenteofuscus	1	1	1	257
Schizodon fasciatus	1	1	1	292
APTERONOTIDAE				
Adontosternarchus sp. C	1	1	4	83
Adontosternarchus sp. D	1	1	6	46
Apteronotidae sp. A	1	1	1	172
Apteronotidae sp. B	1	1	1	195
Apteronotidae sp. C	1	1	2	139
Apteronotus albifrons	1	1	1	75
Sternachogiton sp.	1	1	1	113
Sternarchorhynchus mormyrus	2	2	6	343 - 543
Sternarchorhynchus oxyrhynchus	1	1	3	270

	N Sites	N Habitats	N Specimens	Mean Length Range
ARAPAIMIDAE				
Arapaima gigas	1	1	4	395
ASPREDINIDAE				
Bunocephalus sp.	2	2	4	38 - 77
AUCHENIPTERIDAE				
Asterophysus batrachus	4	2	10	126 - 185
Auchenipterichthys sp. 1	7	2	88	128 - 140
Auchenipterichthys sp. 2	6	3	12	105 - 155
Auchenipterichthys sp. ?	1	1	8	119
Auchenipterus nuchalis	3	2	5	41 - 97
Centromochlus cf. *heckeli*	2	2	174	66 - 75
Centromochlus sp.	2	2	35	53 - 73
Centromochlus sp. ?	2	2	46	44 - 56
Parauchenipterus sp. 1	2	1	5	127 - 160
Parauchenipterus sp. 6	1	1	1	79
Parauchenipterus sp. 9	1	1	3	178
Tatia sp. 6	1	1	2	31
Tatia sp. ?	1	1	23	40 - 43
Tetranematichthys quadrifilis	1	1	1	111
Trachelyichthys sp.	1	1	27	28 - 28
Trachelyichthys sp. ?	2	2	8	27 - 31
Trachycorystes sp. 1	5	3	27	163 - 250
Trachycorystes sp. 2	5	2	17	160 - 277
BELONIDAE				
Belonion apodion	6	4	206	29 - 40
Potamorrhaphis guianensis	5	4	15	81 - 225
Potamorrhaphis petersi	5	3	52	110 - 187
CALLICHTHYIDAE				
Corydoras sp.	1	1	18	15
Hoplosternum thoracatum	2	2	8	104 - 147
CETOPSIDAE				
Cetopsis sp.	5	3	6	78 - 235
CHARACIDAE				
Acestrocephalus sardina	7	1	123	50 - 82
Acestrorhynchus falcirostris	15	5	183	109 - 357
Acestrorhynchus grandoculis	10	4	187	72 - 94
Acestrorhynchus microlepis	13	5	72	81 - 143
Acestrorhynchus minimus	9	6	611	48 - 87
Acestrorhynchus nasutus	4	1	357	56 - 68
Agoniates sp.	5	4	23	120 - 152
Ammocryptocharax elegans	1	1	1	17
Aphyodite sp.	6	5	219	22 - 27
Asiphonichthys condei	8	5	347	29 - 36
Astyanax cf. *guianensis*	1	1	454	32 - 36
Astyanax cf. *zonatus*	10	5	377	30 - 37
Astyanax guianensis	12	5	1660	27 - 40
Astyanax scologaster	8	1	260	23 - 37
Astyanax sp. A	3	3	396	27 - 30
Atopomesus pachyodus	9	2	823	22 - 33
Brittanichthys axelrodi	7	4	3579	20 - 22

	N Sites	N Habitats	N Specimens	Mean Length Range	
Brycon cf. *cephalus*	5	5	33	84 -	209
Brycon cf. *falcatus*	6	4	23	97 -	279
Brycon erythropterum	2	2	59	253 -	340
Brycon pesu	23	6	280	20 -	129
Brycon sp.	3	3	8	31 -	83
Bryconamericus sp.?	1	1	40		20
Bryconops alburnoides	3	3	17	70 -	114
Bryconops caudomaculatus	9	4	306	30 -	52
Bryconops gracilis	3	2	4	60 -	120
Bryconops melanurus	6	3	172	33 -	71
Bryconops sp.	2	1	7	38 -	61
Catoprion mento	1	1	1		135
Chalceus sp.	20	6	355	36 -	229
Characidium sp. 1	2	2	2	39 -	39
Characidium sp. 2	5	2	55	25 -	32
Characidium sp. 3	3	1	48	30 -	31
Charax gibbosus	2	2	11	48 -	61
Cheirodon sp.	3	3	12	14 -	18
Creagrutus cf. *caucanus*	5	1	62	26 -	41
Creagrutus sp. ?	1	1	2		38
Creagrutus sp. DM	2	1	3	29 -	51
Crenuchus spilurus	3	2	6	27 -	37
Deuterodon cf. *acanthogaster*	5	3	29	20 -	50
Deuterodon sp. n.	3	3	35	17 -	22
Elachocharax pulcher	2	2	3	15 -	17
Gnathocharax steindachneri	6	4	25	20 -	30
Hemigrammus analis ?	15	5	5761	17 -	30
Hemigrammus analis B	15	6	4983	16 -	29
Hemigrammus sp.	1	1	172		16
Hemigrammus bellottii	9	4	2042	18 -	22
Hemigrammus cf. *gracilis*	1	1	125		17
Hemigrammus cf. *guyanensis*	4	3	308	21 -	29
Hemigrammus levis	12	6	2486	22 -	41
Hemigrammus mimus	9	3	3739	21 -	24
Hemigrammus rhodostomus	3	3	6705	26 -	28
Hemigrammus sp. A	5	3	119	26 -	33
Hemigrammus vorderwinkleri	9	4	1559	14 -	20
Heterocharax macrolepis	11	4	623	23 -	34
Hoplocharax goethei	6	4	739	18 -	21
Hyphessobrycon cylindricus	1	1	13		32
Hyphessobrycon diancistrus	14	6	4543	17 -	30
Hyphessobrycon erythrostigma	1	1	15	28 -	28
Hyphessobrycon cf. *serpae*	13	6	1620	18 -	28
Hyphessobrycon socolofi	2	2	5	20 -	26
Hyphessobrycon sp. 1	1	1	65		19
Hyphessobrycon sp. 2	14	6	6991	17 -	27
Hyphessobrycon stictus	6	4	55	24 -	28
Iguanodectes adujai	2	2	198	41 -	52
Iguanodectes cf. *purusi*	1	1	7		40
Iguanodectes geisleri	5	4	609	30 -	39
Iguanodectes spilurus	9	5	163	37 -	55
Jobertina sp.	1	1	1		11
Knodus cf. *heterestes*	1	1	52		22
Knodus sp. 1	8	2	332	28 -	39
Knodus sp. 2	1	1	1		25
Knodus sp. ?	1	1	4		23
Leptobrycon jatuaranae	4	3	214	22 -	25

	N Sites	N Habitats	N Specimens	Mean Length Range
Lonchogenys ilisha	14	5	1034	21 - 59
Metynnis sp. B	2	2	53	102 - 116
Metynnis sp. BR	6	3	1003	47 - 126
Metynnis sp. BS	9	4	83	100 - 134
Metynnis sp. CO	5	4	56	142 - 160
Metynnis sp. GR	2	1	35	121 - 131
Metynnis sp. HS	1	1	68	113
Metynnis sp. PS	1	1	1	156
Metynnis sp. UX	1	1	8	150 - 150
Microschemobrycon callops	2	1	323	23 - 28
Microschemobrycon casiquiare	11	4	2799	21 - 29
Microschemobrycon melanotus	2	1	16	21 - 22
Microschemobrycon sp. E	3	2	166	15 - 18
Microschemobrycon sp. MA	1	1	2218	16
Moenkhausia ceros	5	3	24	32 - 39
Moenkhausia collettii	18	6	1829	24 - 38
Moenkhausia cotinho	14	6	525	32 - 48
Moenkhausia grandisquamis	1	1	41	48
Moenkhausia intermedia	1	1	430	24
Moenkhausia lepidura A	17	6	1470	25 - 62
Moenkhausia lepidura B	17	6	1470	25 - 62
Moenkhausia lepidura C	17	6	1470	25 - 62
Moenkhausia lepidura D	13	3	2829	25 - 47
Moenkhausia lepidura MA	3	2	166	15 -
Moenkhausia oligolepis	5	3	31	46 - 53
Myleus cf. *torquatus*	3	3	22	135 - 178
Myleus schomburgkii	8	4	54	184 - 292
Myleus sp. ?	1	1	2	192
Myleus sp. BR	5	3	93	158 - 191
Myleus sp. IR	8	4	165	150 - 206
Myleus sp. TH	6	2	31	253 - 307
Paracheirodon axelrodi	1	1	156	17
Parapristella sp. 2	1	1	103	30
Phenacogaster sp. 1	4	2	154	24 - 30
Phenacogaster sp. 2	1	1	3	33
Phenacogaster sp. 3	4	3	27	28 - 32
Poptella orbicularis	3	2	5	48 - 53
Rhinobrycon negrensis	6	1	126	22 - 31
Serrabrycon magoi	1	1	165	29
Serrasalminae sp. BU (piranha)	2	2	42	167 - 170
Serrasalminae sp. CH (piranha)	12	4	205	99 - 217
Serrasalminae sp. FU (piranha)	16	6	220	116 - 274
Serrasalminae sp. GI (piranha)	2	2	24	112 - 146
Serrasalminae sp. PA (piranha)	5	4	357	112 - 174
Serrasalminae sp. RH (piranha)	8	5	286	118 - 258
Tetragonopterus chalceus	10	6	98	28 - 96
Thayeria obliqua	8	5	239	28 - 43
Thrissobrycon pectinifer	2	2	10	30 - 30
Triportheus angulatus	1	1	6	138
Triportheus sp. 1	11	4	167	- 220
Triportheus sp. 2	2	1	44	155 - 164
Triportheus sp.	5	4	29	75 - 182
Tyttobrycon sp.	2	2	38	16 - 16
CHILODONTIDAE				
Caenotropus labyrinthicus	7	3	279	48 - 162
Chilodus punctatus	11	6	1674	36 - 49

125

APPENDIX 3 CON'T

	N Sites	N Habitats	N Specimens	Mean Length Range
CICHLIDAE				
Acarichthys heckelii	11	6	130	22 - 84
Acaronia nassa	8	4	60	9 - 123
Aequidens pallidus	10	6	141	23 - 148
Aequidens tetramerus	1	1	11	37 - 37
Apistogramma sp. D	7	4	169	15 - 20
Apistogramma sp. G	6	4	307	15 - 28
Apistogramma sp. P	1	1	45	16
Apistogramma gephyra	1	1	4	16
Apistogramma gibbiceps	2	2	9	16 - 29
Apistogramma hippolytae	2	1	4	24 - 26
Apistogramma pertensis	17	6	1527	12 - 28
Apistogramma regani	2	2	9	19 - 22
Astronotus ocellatus	5	4	21	125 - 280
Biotodoma cupido	8	5	198	38 - 105
Biotodoma sp. CE	2	2	2	50 - 60
Biotodoma wavrini	6	3	36	37 - 105
Biotoecus opercularis	7	5	527	16 - 34
Cichla cf. monoculus	3	3	6	31 - 135
Cichla monoculus	3	3	14	38 - 240
Cichla ocellaris	9	3	28	137 - 380
Cichla orinocensis	3	3	9	112 - 260
Cichla sp. SA	1	1	3	346
Cichla temensis	12	5	35	46 - 400
Crenicara filamentosum	5	4	609	18 - 27
Crenicichla cf. saxatilis	1	1	1	113
Crenicichla johanna	4	4	31	160 - 280
Crenicichla lenticulata	7	4	59	150 - 320
Crenicichla lugubris	7	5	123	150 - 275
Crenicichla macrophthalma	16	6	236	27 - 87
Crenicichla notophthalmus	16	6	236	27 - 87
Crenicichla ornata	5	4	20	114 - 225
Crenicichla reticulata	1	1	1	205
Crenicichla strigata	1	1	1	140
Geophagus sp. E	1	1	4	36
Geophagus sp. EL	1	1	4	53
Geophagus altifrons	17	6	483	36 - 246
Heros severus	19	6	278	18 - 209
Hoplarchus psittacus	15	6	1327	8 - 248
Hypselecara coryphaenoides	8	5	192	19 - 137
Mesonauta insignis	15	6	333	22 - 112
Satanoperca acuticeps	1	1	1	121
Satanoperca daemon 2	17	6	121	21 - 230
Satanoperca jurupari	5	5	58	12 - 153
Satanoperca sp. PS	1	1	1	94
Satanoperca sp.	1	1	1	26
Taeniacara candidi	3	2	12	13 - 16
Uaru amphiacanthoides	9	5	251	21 - 215
CLUPEIDAE				
Pellona castelnaeana	2	2	5	360 - 362
CTENOLUCIIDAE				
Boulengerella lateristriga	10	5	156	96 - 210
Boulengerella lucius	13	6	36	97 - 410
Boulengerella maculata	9	4	33	121 - 328

APPENDIX 3 CON'T

	N Sites	N Habitats	N Specimens	Mean Length Range
CURIMATIDAE				
Curimata abramoides	10	5	208	59 - 180
Curimata cf. *spilura*	2	1	3	28 - 42
Curimata inornata	1	1	1	107
Curimata kneri	1	1	3	173
Curimata ocellata	3	2	6	118 - 190
Curimata plumbea	12	5	1481	42 - 77
Curimata sp. n.	4	2	1886	27 - 42
Curimata spilura	3	3	7	35 - 44
Curimata vittata	12	5	152	29 - 187
Curimatella alburna	1	1	107	56
Curimatopsis evelynae	4	3	650	17 - 27
Curimatopsis cf. *macrolepis*	1	1	427	32
Curimatopsis crypticus	13	6	607	20 - 56
Curimatopsis macrolepis	4	2	372	29 - 36
Potamorhina latior	2	2	30	178 - 192
CYNODONTIDAE				
Hydrolycus pectoralis	6	3	15	160 - 203
Hydrolycus scomberoides	9	5	24	157 - 405
Hydrolycus sp. n.	7	4	92	206 - 280
Rhaphiodon vulpinus	3	3	5	280 - 330
RIVULIDAE				
Rivulidae spp.	2	2	11	11 - 29
DORADIDAE				
Acanthodoras cf. *spinosissimus*	2	2	3	48 - 170
Astrodoras cf. *asterifrons*	7	4	31	19 - 70
Centrodoras sp. n.	1	1	1	184
Hassar cf. *praelongus*	4	2	28	52 - 158
Hassar lipophthalmus	11	4	674	7 - 220
Megalodoras irwini	3	1	3	500 - 600
Opsodoras morei	2	2	81	127 - 152
Physopyxis sp. 1	5	3	41	10 - 12
Physopyxis sp. 2	4	2	116	10 - 12
Platydoras cf. *helicophilus*	2	2	2	200 - 220
Platydoras costatus	4	3	7	110 - 220
Scorpiodoras cf. *heckeli*	3	3	9	101 - 157
ELECTROPHORIDAE				
Electrophorus electricus	4	2	112	252 - 1040
ELEOTRIDAE				
Microphilypnus sp. 1	9	5	759	13 - 22
Microphilypnus sp. 2	1	1	7	21
ENGRAULIDAE				
Amazonsprattus scintilla	1	1	11	24
Anchoviella jamesi	4	2	139	22 - 45
Anchoviella sp. B	8	3	74	22 - 38
Anchoviella sp. E	1	1	11	44
Anchoviella sp. G	5	3	84	20 - 31
ERYTHRINIDAE				
Erythrinus erythrinus	1	1	1	69
Hoplias sp. 1	3	3	12	225 - 242

	N Sites	N Habitats	N Specimens	Mean Length Range
Hoplias sp. 2	2	2	15	245 - 265
Hoplias sp. 3	8	6	28	182 - 251
Hoplias sp. 4	7	3	17	240 - 355
Hoplias sp.	11	6	65	27 - 135
GASTEROPELECIDAE				
Carnegiella marthae	8	4	1067	20 - 23
Carnegiella strigata	4	3	60	24 - 30
GYMNOTIDAE				
Gymnotus anguillaris	3	2	15	107 - 310
Gymnotus carapo	2	1	12	138 - 319
HEMIODONTIDAE				
Anodus elongatus	1	1	2	200
Argonectes longiceps	10	4	47	44 - 232
Bivibranchia protractila	3	1	108	66 - 95
Hemiodus cf. *gracilis*	9	4	263	48 - 68
Hemiodus cf. *unimaculatus*	7	2	65	150 - 250
Hemiodus immaculatus	1	1	12	205
Hemiodus sp. ?	1	1	2	205
Hemiodus sp. A	2	2	8	187 - 208
Hemiodus sp. C	2	2	14	180 - 205
Hemiodus thayeri	3	3	11	25 - 31
Micromischodus sugillatus	3	3	8	82 - 114
Pterohemiodus atranalis	2	2	2	74 - 83
HYPOPHTHALMIDAE				
Hypophthalmus edentatus	1	1	3	277
Hypophthalmus fimbriatus	6	4	12	230 - 260
HYPOPOMIDAE				
Hypopomus sp. A	4	3	23	54 - 73
Hypopomus sp. B	2	2	2	67 - 77
Hypopygus lepturus	3	3	7	30 - 45
Steatogenys elegans	4	3	27	96 - 117
LEBIASINIDAE				
Copella nattereri	6	4	462	14 - 29
Nannostomus eques	10	5	213	20 - 33
Nannostomus marilynae	16	6	3013	16 - 22
Nannostomus trifasciatus	7	5	369	25 - 31
Nannostomus unifasciatus	12	6	2351	24 - 34
Pyrrhulina semifasciata	2	2	42	22 - 31
LORICARIIDAE				
Acestridium discus	3	3	10	41 - 51
Ancistrus dolichopterus	1	1	1	135
Ancistrus sp. 1	1	1	48	42
Ancistrus sp. 2	5	3	101	26 - 49
Ancistrus sp. 3	2	2	3	52 - 69
Ancistrus sp. 4	3	3	3	13 - 100
Ancistrus sp. 6	1	1	1	71
Ancistrus sp. PS	1	1	3	38
Cochliodon sp.	5	3	16	140 - 205
Dekeyseria scaphirhyncha	6	4	36	69 - 180
Dekeyseria sp.	1	1	2	104

	N Sites	N Habitats	N Specimens	Mean Length Range
Hemiancistrus pulcher	2	2	22	59 - 61
Hemiancistrus sp.	1	1	14	63
Hemiodontichthys acipenserinus	2	2	7	47 - 59
Hypostomus carinatus	2	2	42	205 - 217
Hypostomus sp.	1	1	3	175
Lasiancistrus sp.	1	1	1	117
Loricaria sp.	1	1	5	111
Loricariichthys acutus	5	4	18	45 - 220
Oxyropsis acutirostris	3	2	11	30 - 35
Pseudohemiodon sp.	4	2	5	36 - 50
Pseudoloricaria cf. laeviuscula	4	3	17	36 - 44
Pseudoloricaria laeviuscula	9	5	25	24 - 285
Pseudoloricaria punctata	1	1	1	87
Pseudoloricaria sp.	2	1	12	18 - 55
Pterygoplichthys gibbiceps	5	3	19	146 - 375
Pterygoplichthys sp. 1	2	2	11	258 - 270
Pterygoplichthys sp. ?	1	1	3	63
Rineloricaria sp. ?	5	4	7	42 - 70
Rineloricaria sp. NE	1	1	1	31
OSTEOGLOSSIDAE				
Osteoglossum bicirrhosum	6	4	35	460 - 665
Osteoglossum ferreirai	11	6	185	242 - 624
PIMELODIDAE				
Brachyplatystoma flavicans	3	2	3	580 - 780
Brachyplatystoma sp.	5	2	8	530 - 700
Calophysus macropterus	1	1	3	245 - 245
Cheiroceros cf. eques	1	1	4	161
Goeldiella eques	6	6	19	119 - 200
Leiarius marmoratus	3	2	5	117 - 415
Myoglanis marmoratus	3	2	5	117 - 415
Myoglanis sp. 1	2	2	24	38 - 62
Phractocephalus hemioliopterus	4	2	6	273 - 1150
Pimelodus cf. blochii	4	2	19	71 - 182
Pimelodella sp. 1	3	1	70	25 - 64
Pimelodella sp. 2	1	1	1	100
Pimelodella sp. 3	1	1	1	102
Pimelodella sp. ?	1	1	1	226
Pimelodella sp. GR	1	1	2	226
Pimelodella sp. NE	1	1	1	163
Pimelodus cf. blochii	8	3	97	71 - 182
Pimelodus ornatus	2	1	24	66 - 168
Pinirampus pirinampu	2	2	8	250 - 365
Platynematichthys notatus	1	1	1	580
Pseudopimelodus sp. 1	3	2	3	142 - 150
Pseudopimelodus sp. 2	1	1	1	65
Pseudoplatystoma fasciatum	3	2	7	430 - 510
Pseudoplatystoma sp.	1	1	1	440
Rhamdia sp.	1	1	1	143
POECILIIDAE				
Fluviphylax pygmaeus	10	6	518	8 - 13
PROCHILODONTIDAE				
Prochilodus cf. nigricans	1	1	3	276
Semaprochilodus sp. ?	1	1	2	225

	N Sites	N Habitats	N Specimens	Mean Length Range
Semaprochilodus sp. GR	1	1	9	363
RHAMPHICHTHYIDAE				
Gymnorhamphichthys hypostomus	2	1	51	78 - 112
Gymnorhamphichthys rondonii	11	2	158	60 - 90
Rhamphichthys sp. ?	3	2	3	270 - 600
Rhamphichthys sp. A	5	4	9	342 - 710
Rhamphichthys sp. B	8	6	15	390 - 890
SCIAENIDAE				
Pachypops sp. ?	1	1	3	41
Pachypops sp. D	1	1	2	135
Pachyurus schomburgki	1	1	1	102
Pachyurus sp. ?	2	1	46	16 - 38
Pachyurus sp. C	2	1	4	70 - 73
Pachyurus sp. NE	1	1	1	140
Plagioscion cf. *montei*	1	1	1	165
Plagioscion sp. ?	3	2	14	17 - 275
Plagioscion sp. CF	1	1	32	54
Plagioscion sp. n.	1	1	1	290
SCOLOPLACIDAE				
Scoloplax dicra	3	2	15	9 - 12
SOLEIDAE				
Soleidae spp.	1	1	4	17
STERNOPYGIDAE				
Distocyclus conirostris	1	1	1	117
Distocyclus goajira	1	1	1	315
Eigenmannia cf. *humboldtii*	9	4	36	98 - 160
Eigenmannia macrops	1	1	58	67
Eigenmannia sp. ?	4	2	13	101 - 126
Eigenmannia sp. A	7	1	286	58 - 79
Eigenmannia sp. B	4	1	454	64 - 76
Eigenmannia sp. D	1	1	13	47
Eigenmannia sp. E	4	2	9	86 - 186
Eigenmannia sp. F	6	4	34	68 - 92
Eigenmannia sp. G	1	1	2	86
Eigenmannia sp. X	1	1	17	100
Rhabdolichops longicaudatus	6	3	8	123 - 420
Rhabdolichops troscheli	2	2	3	118 - 210
Sternopygus macrurus	7	5	26	191 - 735
SYNBRANCHIDAE				
Synbranchus marmoratus	4	4	5	460 - 790
TRICHOMYCTERIDAE				
Ochmacanthus cf. *orinoco*	8	3	27	23 - 45
Ochmacanthus sp. ?	1	1	1	35
Ochmacanthus sp. MG	4	2	19	36 - 43
Ochmacanthus sp. NE	1	1	12	35
Paracanthopoma sp.	1	1	1	23
Pygidium sp.	1	1	36	12
Pygidium sp. ?	2	2	4	15 - 22
Trichomycteridae sp.	2	2	4	15 - 22
Vandellia cirrhosa/plazzai?	1	1	1	74
Vandellinae sp.	1	1	8	15

APPENDIX 4

RIO NEGRO FISH COMMUNITIES AND THEIR PRINCIPAL FOODS

Principal foods are considered those which represented at least 25% of the volume of the diet of the population studied.Mean fullness was calculated using both specimens with food in their stomachs and empty specimens of each individual population. Mean fullness was not calculated for curimatids.

MSL = Mean Standard Length
Exam = Number of Specimens Examined for Food
M Full = Mean Fullness of Stomach

ALL = Allocthonous food source (terrestrial/arboreal origins)
AUT = Autochthonous food source (aquatic origins)

BEACH: ANAVILHANAS

	MSL	Exam	M Full	Principal Food Items
Ageneiosidae				
Ageneiosus sp. 2	140	1	50.0	fish
Anostomidae				
Leporinus sp. n.	108	2	75.0	detritus
Characidae				
Acestrorhynchus falcirostris	249	2	50.0	fish
Astyanax guianensis	31	15	23.3	invertebrates-all/aut
Astyanax scologaster	23	15	49.0	invertebrates-all
Atopomesus pachyodus	23	13	38.5	invertebrates-aut
Bryconops alburnoides	70	3	30.0	invertebrates-all; detritus
Charax gibbosus	48	5	25.7	fish
Hemigrammus analis ?	29	13	25.3	detritus
Hemigrammus cf. *gracilis*	17	15	39.7	invertebrates-aut
Hemigrammus levis	32	19	60.5	plants-aut; detritus
Hemigrammus mimus	22	10	48.5	invertebrates-aut
Hyphessobrycon diancistrus	21	7	46.4	invertebrates-aut
Hyphessobrycon sp. 2	20	10	47.5	invertebrates-aut
Iguanodectes spilurus	43	5	90.0	detritus
Lonchogenys ilisha	39	18	32.3	invertebrates-all
Metynnis sp. BR	47	7	50.0	invertebrates-aut; detritus
Microschemobrycon casiquiare	22	9	47.5	invertebrates-aut
Moenkhausia lepidura B	31	12	47.9	invertebrates-all
Myleus sp. BR	158	1	100.0	invertebrates-all
Phenacogaster sp. 1	28	15	81.7	invertebrates-aut
Serrasalminae sp. CH	171	2	11.7	fish
Serrasalminae sp. FU	241	1	12.5	fish
Serrasalminae sp. PA	174	4	43.3	plants-all; fish
Serrasalminae sp. RH	251	8	65.0	fish
Cichlidae				
Astronotus ocellatus	235	4	87.5	invertebrates-aut
Crenicichla johanna	203	1	3.3	fish
Crenicichla lenticulata	150	1	14.3	fish
Crenicichla lugubris	218	9	29.8	fish

	MSL	Exam	M Full	Principal Food Items
Geophagus altifrons	59	6	55.0	invertebrates-aut
Heros severus	145	18	59.8	fish
Hoplarchus psittacus	188	58	29.2	fish
Hypselecara coryphaenoides	135	20	50.5	fish
Mesonauta insignis	100	3	100.0	detritus
Satanoperca jurupari	153	24	54.6	fish
Uaru amphiacanthoides	147	10	68.8	plants-aut; detritus
Curimatidae				
Curimata abramoides	93	-	----	detritus
Curimata kneri	173	-	----	detritus
Curimata plumbea	46	-	----	detritus
Curimata spilura	35	-	----	detritus
Curimata vittata	155	-	----	detritus
Curimatella alburna	56	-	----	detritus
Potamorhina latior	178	-	----	detritus
Doradidae				
Doradidae sp. 3	31	10	85.0	invertebrates-aut
Eleotridae				
Microphilypnus sp. 1	22	1	2.5	invertebrates-aut
Erythrinidae				
Hoplias sp. 1	241	1	33.3	fish
Hemiodontidae				
Micromischodus sugillatus	82	2	87.5	invertebrates-aut; detritus
Loricariidae				
Loricariichthys acutus	45	3	50.0	invertebrates-aut
Pseudoloricaria cf. *laeviuscula*	36	3	75.0	invertebrates-aut
Pimelodidae				
Pimelodus cf. *blochii*	73	5	60.0	fish
Rhamphichthyidae				
Gymnorhamphichthys rondonii	70	1	100.0	invertebrates-aut
Sternopygidae				
Eigenmannia sp. B	64	10	73.0	invertebrates-aut
BEACH: ILHA TAMAQUARÉ				
Ageneiosidae				
Ageneiosus sp. 1	230	1	100.0	fish
Apteronotidae				
Apteronotidae sp. B	195	1	100.0	invertebrates-aut
Apteronotidae sp. C	139	1	25.0	invertebrates-all; detritus
Sternachogiton sp.	113	1	50.0	invertebrates-aut
Characidae				
Acestrocephalus sardina	55	4	17.7	fish
Acestrorhynchus grandoculis	76	21	29.0	fish
Astyanax scologaster	34	12	41.3	invertebrates-all
Bryconops caudomaculatus	35	7	67.9	invertebrates-all

	MSL	Exam	M Full	Principal Food Items
Hemigrammus analis B	19	19	36.5	detritus
Hemigrammus mimus	23	7	18.5	invertebrates-all
Knodus sp. 1	39	7	85.7	plants-aut
Lonchogenys ilisha	45	8	33.0	invertebrates-all
Microschemobrycon casiquiare	23	9	52.5	invertebrates-aut
Moenkhausia lepidura D	46	26	30.7	invertebrates-all; plants-aut
Myleus cf. *torquatus*	178	1	10.0	plants-all
Myleus schomburgkii	230	6	91.7	plants-all
Myleus sp. IR	192	14	62.3	plants-all
Myleus sp. TH	286	1	75.0	plants-all
Rhinobrycon negrensis	28	11	57.7	plants-aut
Serrasalminae sp. CH	217	1	100.0	plants-all
Curimatidae				
Curimata plumbea	50	-	----	detritus
Doradidae				
Doradidae sp. 2	25	10	70.0	invertebrates-aut
Hypopomidae				
Steatogenys elegans	96	4	40.0	invertebrates-aut
Osteoglossidae				
Osteoglossum bicirrhosum	665	2	100.0	invertebrates-all
Osteoglossum ferreirai	624	23	100.0	invertebrates-all
Pimelodidae				
Brachyplatystoma flavicans	770	1	100.0	fish
Pimelodidae sp. 2	39	11	70.8	plants-all; invertebrates-aut
Pimelodidae sp. 4	29	7	59.4	invertebrates-aut
Pimelodus cf. *blochii*	145	1	20.0	invertebrates-aut; detritus
Rhamphichthyidae				
Gymnorhamphichthys hypostomus	78	8	48.0	invertebrates-aut
Gymnorhamphichthys rondonii	65	7	86.0	invertebrates-aut
Sternopygidae				
Eigenmannia sp. A	73	10	95.0	invertebrates-aut
Eigenmannia sp. E	113	3	83.0	invertebrates-all
Rhabdolichops longicaudatus	123	1	75.0	invertebrates-all
Rhabdolichops troscheli	118	1	75.0	invertebrates-all/aut

BEACH: MARAUIÁ CONFLUENCE

	MSL	Exam	M Full	Principal Food Items
Characidae				
Acestrocephalus sardina	53	15	31.5	fish
Astyanax guianensis	30	20	31.3	invertebrates-all
Astyanax scologaster	24	5	42.0	invertebrates-all
Bryconops caudomaculatus	30	16	56.4	invertebrates-all
Bryconops melanurus	51	5	70.0	invertebrates-all
Hemigrammus vorderwinkleri	14	3	7.5	invertebrates-all
Lonchogenys ilisha	49	8	7.2	invertebrates-all; fish
Microschemobrycon callops	23	23	43.9	invertebrates-all/aut
Microschemobrycon casiquiare	22	8	6.7	invertebrates-all; detritus
Microschemobrycon sp. MA	16	13	59.3	detritus
Moenkhausia grandisquamis	48	20	73.3	plants-all; detritus
Moenkhausia lepidura B	38	5	64.0	invertebrates-all
Moenkhausia oligolepis	48	6	25.5	plants-all; detritus
Tetragonopterus chalceus	54	17	54.2	plants-all

	MSL	Exam	M Full	Principal Food Items
Cichlidae				
Cichla ocellaris	140	1	10.0	fish
Cichla temensis	175	1	50.0	fish
Geophagus altifrons	163	18	34.3	detritus; fish
Ctenoluciidae				
Boulengerella maculata	215	3	37.5	fish
Curimatidae				
Curimata cf. spilura	28	-	----	detritus
Curimata plumbea	42	-	----	detritus
Curimata plumbea	48	-	----	detritus
Curimata vittata	39	-	----	detritus
Doradidae				
Doradidae sp. 2	26	10	100.0	invertebrates-aut
Hassar cf. praelongus	99	1	100.0	invertebrates-aut; detritus
Hassar lipophthalmus	79	27	84.3	invertebrates-aut
Lebiasinidae				
Nannostomus marilynae	17	2	10.0	detritus
Osteoglossidae				
Osteoglossum bicirrhosum	550	4	80.0	invertebrates-all; fish
Pimelodidae				
Pimelodidae sp. 1	26	20	55.7	invertebrates-aut
Pimelodidae sp. 234	87	5	95.0	invertebrates-aut; fish
Pimelodidae sp. 3	47	15	65.0	fish
Pimelodidae sp. 4	23	6	25.0	invertebrates-aut; detritus
Pimelodus cf. blochii	71	7	82.0	fish
Rhamphichthyidae				
Gymnorhamphichthys rondonii	67	7	65.0	invertebrates-aut
Sternopygidae				
Eigenmannia sp. B	70	10	86.0	invertebrates-aut
Trichomycteridae				
Ochmacanthus sp. MG	37	2	75.0	fish

CONFLUENCE SWAMP: URUBAXI

	MSL	Exam	M Full	Principal Food Items
Ageneiosidae				
Ageneiosus sp. A	100	2	10.0	plants-all; detritus
Auchenipteridae				
Trachelyichthys sp.	28	12	40.0	fish
Belonidae				
Belonion apodion	35	65	41.1	invertebrates-aut
Characidae				
Acestrorhynchus microlepis	117	2	12.5	fish
Acestrorhynchus minimus	59	93	26.1	fish
Agoniates sp.	138	9	91.7	fish
Aphyodite sp.	24	6	25.0	invertebrates-aut

APPENDIX 4 CON'T

	MSL	Exam	M Full	Principal Food Items
Asiphonichthys condei	36	5	15.7	fish
Astyanax cf. *zonatus*	34	6	9.0	plants-all; invertebrates-all
Brittanichthys axelrodi	20	116	51.5	invertebrates-aut; detritus
Bryconops caudomaculatus	52	19	49.8	invertebrates-all
Bryconops melanurus	69	5	75.0	invertebrates-all
Gnathocharax steindachneri	25	7	71.4	invertebrates-all/aut
Hemigrammus analis ?	26	42	78.7	plants-aut
Hemigrammus analis B	20	21	61.3	plants-aut
Hemigrammus bellottii	18	19	45.3	invertebrates-all/aut
Hemigrammus levis	30	29	86.9	plants-aut
Hemigrammus mimus	24	11	75.0	invertebrates-aut
Hemigrammus rhodostomus	27	40	67.8	plants-aut; detritus
Hemigrammus vorderwinkleri	17	40	66.4	plants-aut
Heterocharax macrolepis	30	22	43.1	invertebrates-aut
Hoplocharax goethei	21	25	72.0	invertebrates-aut
Hyphessobrycon diancistrus	20	65	64.9	plants-aut
Hyphessobrycon cf. *serpae*	22	12	47.9	invertebrates-aut
Hyphessobrycon sp. 2	21	12	68.8	invertebrates-aut
Iguanodectes adujai	52	16	88.8	plants-aut; detritus
Iguanodectes geisleri	35	20	87.5	plants-aut
Iguanodectes spilurus	48	5	75.0	plants-aut
Leptobrycon jatuaranae	24	12	66.7	invertebrates-aut
Lonchogenys ilisha	48	20	41.3	invertebrates-aut
Metynnis sp. BS	134	2	37.5	detritus
Metynnis sp. CO	142	12	89.8	plants-aut
Microschemobrycon casiquiare	24	20	68.8	invertebrates-all/aut
Moenkhausia lepidura B	61	22	69.3	invertebrates-all; fish
Myleus schomburgkii	233	10	70.0	plants-aut
Paracheirodon axelrodi	17	23	32.7	detritus
Serrabrycon magoi	29	13	51.7	detritus; fish
Serrasalminae sp. BU	167	19	80.0	plants-all; fish
Thayeria obliqua	43	7	28.9	invertebrates-all
Tyttobrycon sp.	16	8	62.5	plants-aut
Cichlidae				
Aequidens pallidus	121	9	21.5	detritus
Apistogramma sp.	15	7	75.0	detritus
Apistogramma pertensis	16	14	80.4	detritus
Biotoecus opercularis	22	8	40.0	invertebrates-aut
Cichla cf. *orinocensis*	16	10	77.5	invertebrates-aut
Crenicara filamentosum	22	14	43.1	detritus
Crenicichla johanna	280	1	25.0	fish
Geophagus altifrons	246	1	100.0	invertebrates-aut; fish
Hoplarchus psittacus	8	14	98.0	invertebrates-aut
Mesonauta insignis	53	11	93.2	plants-aut; detritus
Satanoperca jurupari	148	1	100.0	invertebrates-aut
Uaru amphiacanthoides	34	11	70.5	plants-all; detritus
Uaru amphiacanthoides	180	18	61.1	plants-all; detritus
Ctenoluciidae				
Boulengerella lateristriga	154	6	17.1	fish
Curimatidae				
Curimata abramoides	130	-	----	detritus
Curimata plumbea	59	-	----	detritus
Curimata vittata	141	-	----	detritus
Curimatopsis evelynae	30	-	----	detritus

	MSL	Exam	M Full	Principal Food Items
Cyprinodontidae				
Fluviphylax pygmaeus	11	18	66.0	plants-aut; detritus
Doradidae				
Doradidae sp. 3	35	7	89.0	invertebrates-aut
Hassar lipophthalmus	103	46	92.4	invertebrates-aut
Physopyxis sp. n.	12	1	7.1	invertebrates-aut
Scorpiodoras cf. *heckeli*	101	9	94.4	plants-aut; detritus
Gasteropelecidae				
Carnegiella marthae	22	32	35.0	invertebrates-all
Hemiodontidae				
Hemiodus cf. *gracilis*	57	24	77.1	plants-aut
Micromischodus sugillatus	114	4	56.3	invertebrates-aut
Hypopomidae				
Hypopygus lepturus	30	1	100.0	invertebrates-aut
Lebiasinidae				
Nannostomus eques	25	17	60.7	plants-aut; detritus
Nannostomus marilynae	17	20	71.3	plants-aut; detritus
Nannostomus trifasciatus	25	1	25.0	plants-aut; detritus
Nannostomus unifasciatus	29	20	39.4	plants-aut; detritus
Loricariidae				
Acestridium discus	51	4	93.7	plants-aut
Ancistrus sp. 2	45	8	49.4	detritus
Dekeyseria scaphirhyncha	69	4	87.5	plants-aut; detritus
Loricariichthys acutus	106	2	62.5	invertebrates-aut
Pimelodidae				
Goeldiella eques	119	1	25.0	invertebrates-aut; fish
Pimelodidae sp. 1	18	15	48.0	invertebrates-aut
Prochilodontidae				
Semaprochilodus sp. GR	363	0	75.0	detritus
Rhamphichthyidae				
Gymnorhamphichthys rondonii	76	7	63.0	invertebrates-aut
Sternopygidae				
Eigenmannia cf. *humboldtii*	123	4	81.3	invertebrates-aut
Eigenmannia sp. F	79	3	100.0	invertebrates-aut

FLOODED FOREST: ANAVILHANAS

Ageneiosidae				
Ageneiosus sp. 1	277	7	16.4	fish
Ageneiosus sp. 2	140	1	75.0	invertebrates-all/aut
Anostomidae				
Leporinus cf. *agassizi*	295	11	43.6	plants-all; detritus
Leporinus cf. *friderici*	290	8	96.9	plants-all; detritus
Leporinus fasciatus	233	145	70.0	detritus
Leporinus sp. n.	222	75	61.7	detritus

	MSL	Exam	M Full	Principal Food Items
Auchenipteridae				
Auchenipterichthys sp. 1	128	16	86.1	invertebrates-all
Characidae				
Agoniates sp.	135	2	87.5	fish
Aphyodite sp.	27	3	80.0	invertebrates-aut
Astyanax guianensis	33	1	5.0	invertebrates-all
Bryconops alburnoides	114	5	80.0	invertebrates-all
Hemigrammus analis ?	17	10	40.0	invertebrates-all
Hemigrammus analis B	16	93	68.9	invertebrates-all/aut
Hemigrammus sp.	16	25	86.0	invertebrates-all
Hemigrammus cf. *guyanensis*	21	10	80.0	invertebrates-all
Hemigrammus levis	25	22	30.5	invertebrates-all/aut
Hyphessobrycon diancistrus	20	18	30.2	invertebrates-all/aut
Hyphessobrycon cf. *serpae*	26	4	50.0	invertebrates-all/aut
Metynnis sp. BR	117	8	87.5	plants-all/aut
Metynnis sp. BS	112	15	81.7	plants-all
Metynnis sp. CO	160	2	37.5	plants-aut
Moenkhausia collettii	24	49	62.5	invertebrates-all
Moenkhausia cotinho	32	2	100.0	invertebrates-all
Myleus cf. *torquatus*	142	15	71.9	plants-all/aut
Myleus schomburgkii	206	14	64.0	plants-all
Myleus sp. BR	166	62	83.6	plants-all
Myleus sp. IR	189	29	82.8	plants-all
Serrasalminae sp. CH	183	58	74.1	plants-all
Serrasalminae sp. FU	182	39	49.3	plants-all; fish
Serrasalminae sp. GI	146	9	30.0	fish
Serrasalminae sp. PA	156	124	57.7	plants-all; fish
Serrasalminae sp. RH	218	70	48.8	plants-all; fish
Tetragonopterus chalceus	77	21	50.9	invertebrates-aut
Triportheus sp. 1	194	29	72.6	plants-all; invertebrates-all
Cichlidae				
Aequidens pallidus	23	1	25.0	detritus; fish
Apistogramma regani	19	1	37.5	invertebrates-aut
Astronotus ocellatus	241	7	92.9	plants-all
Crenicichla johanna	160	1	25.0	invertebrates-all
Crenicichla lenticulata	263	5	22.2	invertebrates-aut; fish
Crenicichla lugubris	217	8	34.1	fish
Geophagus altifrons	188	13	70.4	invertebrates-aut; detritus
Heros severus	140	12	63.1	detritus
Hoplarchus psittacus	181	15	43.7	invertebrates-aut; fish
Satanoperca daemon 2	214	6	79.2	invertebrates-aut
Satanoperca jurupari	142	5	72.0	plants-all
Uaru amphiacanthoides	155	11	88.6	plants-aut; detritus
Curimatidae				
Curimata abramoides	135	-	----	detritus
Curimata cf. *kneri*	191	-	----	detritus
Curimata spilura	44	-	----	detritus
Curimata vittata	150	-	----	detritus
Curimatopsis evelynae	56	-	----	detritus
Potamorhina latior	192	-	----	detritus
Erythrinidae				
Hoplias sp. 1	242	1	16.7	fish
Hoplias sp. 2	245	1	1.0	fish

	MSL	Exam	M Full	Principal Food Items
Hoplias sp. 3	242	1	3.3	invertebrates-aut
Hemiodontidae				
Argonectes longiceps	217	1	8.3	invertebrates-all
Hemiodus cf. *unimaculatus*	178	11	24.7	plants-aut
Hemiodus immaculatus	205	5	100.0	plants-aut
Lebiasinidae				
Copella nattereri	17	20	88.8	invertebrates-all/aut
Nannostomus eques	20	48	76.0	invertebrates-all/aut
Nannostomus marilynae	19	32	32.4	invertebrates-all/aut
Nannostomus trifasciatus	29	1	75.0	detritus
Nannostomus unifasciatus	31	8	39.0	plants-aut; detritus
Pyrrhulina semifasciata	22	14	85.7	invertebrates-all/aut
Loricariidae				
Hypostomus carinatus	217	17	60.3	detritus
Hypostomus sp.	175	3	41.7	detritus
Pterygoplichthys gibbiceps	240	3	83.3	detritus
Pterygoplichthys sp. 1	270	4	65.0	invertebrates-aut; detritus
Osteoglossidae				
Osteoglossum bicirrhosum	523	18	94.7	invertebrates-all
Osteoglossum ferreirai	468	7	87.5	invertebrates-all/aut
Prochilodontidae				
Semaprochilodus sp. ?	225	0	75.0	detritus
Rhamphichthyidae				
Rhamphichthys sp. A	710	1	12.5	invertebrates-aut; detritus
Rhamphichthys sp. B	750	1	50.0	invertebrates-aut
Sternopygidae				
Distocyclus goajira	315	1	100.0	invertebrates-aut
Sternopygus macrurus	336	2	30.0	invertebrates-aut; fish
Trichomycteridae				
Ochmacanthus sp. MG	43	3	92.0	fish
ISLAND LAKE: ILHA BUIU-AÇU				
Anostomidae				
Leporinus klausewitzi	64	7	75.0	invertebrates-aut
Pseudanos gracilis	65	3	75.0	detritus
Characidae				
Acestrorhynchus falcirostris	200	11	34.4	fish
Acestrorhynchus microlepis	93	1	33.3	fish
Acestrorhynchus minimus	62	62	29.8	fish
Acestrorhynchus nasutus	61	35	22.2	fish
Aphyodite sp.	24	4	7.0	invertebrates-aut
Astyanax cf. *zonatus*	37	10	4.7	detritus
Brittanichthys axelrodi	22	11	63.3	invertebrates-aut
Bryconops caudomaculatus	52	5	60.0	invertebrates-all
Hemigrammus analis ?	29	3	14.3	invertebrates-all; detritus
Hemigrammus bellottii	21	5	7.5	invertebrates-all
Hemigrammus vorderwinkleri	17	14	76.8	invertebrates-aut

	MSL	Exam	M Full	Principal Food Items
Heterocharax macrolepis	27	18	70.0	invertebrates-all
Hyphessobrycon cf. serpae	22	14	17.3	invertebrates-aut
Hyphessobrycon sp. 2	21	6	44.3	fish
Iguanodectes cf. purusi	40	3	12.0	plants-aut
Iguanodectes geisleri	38	7	23.0	detritus
Moenkhausia collettii	32	7	25.6	invertebrates-aut; detritus
Moenkhausia cotinho	39	16	52.5	detritus
Thayeria obliqua	38	7	46.9	detritus
Tyttobrycon sp.	16	2	20.0 .	invertebrates-all
Chilodontidae				
Chilodus punctatus	43	10	100.0	invertebrates-aut; detritus
Cichlidae				
Apistogramma pertensis	23	10	87.5	invertebrates-aut; detritus
Hoplarchus psittacus	222	5	7.7	fish
Mesonauta insignis	72	11	90.9	detritus; fish
Ctenoluciidae				
Boulengerella lateristriga	174	42	53.8	fish
Curimatidae				
Curimata ocellata	128	-	----	detritus
Curimata plumbea	55	-	----	detritus
Curimata sp. n.	40	-	----	detritus
Curimatopsis evelynae	27	-	----	detritus
Curimatopsis evelynae	37	-	----	detritus
Curimatopsis macrolepis	36	-	----	detritus
Cyprinodontidae				
Fluviphylax pygmaeus	12	14	26.7	invertebrates-all; detritus
Engraulidae				
Anchoviella jamesi	45	1	3.6	invertebrates-aut
Anchoviella sp. G	31	9	24.0	invertebrates-aut
Erythrinidae				
Hoplias sp. 3	225	1	25.0	fish
Gymnotidae				
Gymnotus anguillaris	136	1	25.0	invertebrates-all
Gymnotus carapo	138	1	17.0	invertebrates-all
Hypopomidae				
Hypopomus sp. A	57	6	58.3	invertebrates-aut
Hypopomus sp. B	77	1	100.0	invertebrates-aut
Hypopygus lepturus	45	1	10.0	detritus
Lebiasinidae				
Nannostomus eques	26	4	40.0	plants-aut
Nannostomus trifasciatus	26	5	55.0	plants-aut; detritus
Nannostomus unifasciatus	30	5	45.0	detritus
Loricariidae				
Ancistrus sp. 2	49	2	100.0	detritus
Loricariichthys acutus	220	1	100.0	invertebrates-aut
Oxyropsis acutirostris	30	1	75.0	plants-aut; detritus

	MSL	Exam	M Full	Principal Food Items
Osteoglossidae				
Osteoglossum ferreirai	424	9	100.0	invertebrates-all; fish
Pimelodidae				
Goeldiella eques	132	6	28.8	invertebrates-aut; fish

ISLAND LAKE: ILHA TAMAQUARE

	MSL	Exam	M Full	Principal Food Items
Anostomidae				
Leporinus cf. *agassizi*	254	4	42.0	plants-all; fish
Characidae				
Acestrorhynchus falcirostris	147	2	2.8	fish
Acestrorhynchus nasutus	56	23	13.2	fish
Agoniates sp.	152	3	45.0	fish
Astyanax sp. A	27	2	12.0	plants-aut; detritus
Hemigrammus cf. *guyanensis*	23	4	10.3	invertebrates-all
Hoplocharax goethei	19	9	20.0	plants-aut
Hyphessobrycon sp. 1	19	6	18.8	detritus
Iguanodectes spilurus	37	7	58.6	detritus
Moenkhausia cotinho	39	2	3.5	invertebrates-all
Moenkhausia oligolepis	46	9	46.0	detritus
Myleus sp. IR	206	1	100.0	plants-all
Serrasalminae sp. FU	267	3	14.0	plants-all
Thayeria obliqua	28	5	47.9	detritus
Triportheus sp. 1	211	8	52.5	plants-all; invertebrates-all
Chilodontidae				
Chilodus punctatus	36	4	50.0	detritus
Cichlidae				
Cichla temensis	301	3	100.0	fish
Geophagus altifrons	214	4	37.5	detritus
Heros severus	209	1	75.0	plants-all
Ctenoluciidae				
Boulengerella lateristriga	96	4	55.0	fish
Curimatidae				
Curimata abramoides	59	-	----	detritus
Curimata sp. n.	27	-	----	detritus
Curimata vittata	29	-	----	detritus
Curimatidae sp. inc.	28	-	----	detritus
Curimatopsis evelynae	20	-	----	detritus
Curimatopsis evelynae	25	-	----	detritus
Curimatopsis macrolepis	32	-	----	detritus
Lebiasinidae				
Nannostomus trifasciatus	25	5	50.0	plants-aut; detritus
Nannostomus unifasciatus	28	5	25.0	plants-aut; detritus
Loricariidae				
Hemiancistrus sp.	63	7	82.1	plants-aut; detritus
Rhamphichthyidae				
Rhamphichthys sp. B	630	2	50.0	invertebrates-aut

APPENDIX 4 CON'T

	MSL	Exam	M Full	Principal Food Items
ROCKY POOL: BELOW RIO DARAÁ				
Anostomidae				
Laemolyta cf. *taeniatus*	151	6	72.9	plants-aut; detritus
Leporinus cf. *agassizi*	195	8	20.0	plants-all
Leporinus cf. *friderici*	288	15	27.9	detritus
Pseudanos gracilis	69	3	66.7	detritus
Apteronotidae				
Apteronotidae sp. A	172	1	50.0	detritus
Sternarchorhynchus mormyrus	343	1	25.0	invertebrates-aut
Sternarchorhynchus oxyrhynchus	270	3	100.0	invertebrates-aut
Callichthyidae				
Hoplosternum thoracatum	104	6	62.0	invertebrates-aut; fish
Characidae				
Asiphonichthys condei	32	5	47.9	invertebrates-aut
Astyanax cf. *zonatus*	32	4	13.6	invertebrates-all
Astyanax guianensis	30	6	32.0	invertebrates-all; fish
Astyanax sp. A	28	22	31.8	invertebrates-all
Crenuchus spilurus	27	1	75.0	invertebrates-aut
Deuterodon cf. *acanthogaster*	20	6	60.7	plants-aut; detritus
Hemigrammus analis B	23	8	23.3	plants-aut
Hyphessobrycon cf. *serpae*	21	9	50.0	invertebrates-aut
Hyphessobrycon sp. 2	21	16	50.0	invertebrates-aut; fish
Iguanodectes geisleri	39	2	12.5	invertebrates-all
Moenkhausia collettii	35	3	55.0	invertebrates-all; fish
Moenkhausia cotinho	39	5	62.0	plants-aut; invertebrates-aut
Chilodontidae				
Caenotropus labyrinthicus	75	7	71.4	invertebrates-aut; detritus
Chilodus punctatus	43	3	83.3	detritus
Cichlidae				
Apistogramma sp.	18	1	15.0	invertebrates-aut
Geophagus altifrons	149	2	10.0	invertebrates-aut
Mesonauta insignis	80	3	75.0	detritus
Curimatidae				
Curimata plumbea	44	-	----	detritus
Curimatopsis evelynae	40	-	----	detritus
Hypopomidae				
Hypopomus sp. A	73	1	13.0	invertebrates-aut
Hypopygus lepturus	35	3	92.0	invertebrates-aut
Lebiasinidae				
Nannostomus marilynae	18	3	75.0	plants-aut; detritus
Loricariidae				
Ancistrus sp. 1	42	14	87.5	detritus
Ancistrus sp. PS	38	2	62.5	plants-aut; detritus
Cochliodon sp.	140	4	93.8	detritus
Dekeyseria scaphirhyncha	112	3	91.7	plants-all; detritus
Hemiancistrus pulcher	59	6	47.5	detritus

141

APPENDIX 4 CON'T

	MSL	Exam	M Full	Principal Food Items
Pterygoplichthys gibbiceps	146	1	8.3	detritus
Pimelodidae				
Goeldiella eques	160	1	100.0	fish
Myoglanis sp. 1	38	5	20.0	invertebrates-all
Pimelodus cf. *blochii*	135	28	65.0	plants-aut
Rhamphichthyidae				
Rhamphichthys sp. B	644	2	25.0	invertebrates-aut; fish
Sternopygidae				
Eigenmannia cf. *humboldtii*	160	1	100.0	invertebrates-aut
Eigenmannia sp. F	92	2	100.0	invertebrates-aut
Eigenmannia sp. G	86	2	100.0	invertebrates-aut
Rhabdolichops longicaudatus	239	1	10.0	invertebrates-all/aut
Rhabdolichops troscheli	210	1	25.0	invertebrates-all/aut; fish
Sternopygus macrurus	194	13	69.0	invertebrates-aut

WOODY SHORE: ANAVILHANAS

	MSL	Exam	M Full	Principal Food Items
Ageneiosidae				
Ageneiosus sp. 1	296	1	16.6	fish
Ageneiosus sp. 2	156	1	12.5	plants-all
Anostomidae				
Leporinus cf. *agassizi*	234	15	50.7	plants-aut
Leporinus fasciatus	198	61	79.6	invertebrates-aut
Leporinus sp. n.	170	4	100.0	plants-aut; invertebrates-aut; detritus
Characidae				
Acestrorhynchus falcirostris	186	1	100.0	fish
Brycon pesu	68	10	82.5	invertebrates-all
Hemigrammus analis ?	28	10	85.0	invertebrates-aut
Hemigrammus levis	28	19	72.4	plants-all
Hyphessobrycon diancistrus	30	14	67.9	invertebrates-all/aut
Metynnis sp. BR	118	14	77.5	plants-aut
Metynnis sp. CO	142	1	10.0	plants-all
Moenkhausia collettii	33	9	57.0	plants-all
Moenkhausia lepidura B	43	15	71.7	plants-all
Moenkhausia lepidura D	34	7	78.6	plants-all
Myleus cf. *torquatus*	135	1	100.0	plants-all
Myleus schomburgkii	184	9	43.2	plants-all
Myleus sp. BR	175	14	77.5	plants-all/aut
Myleus sp. IR	181	12	71.7	plants-all
Serrasalminae sp. CH	153	6	24.0	plants-all
Serrasalminae sp. FU	210	7	32.0	fish
Serrasalminae sp. GI	112	1	25.0	invertebrates-all
Serrasalminae sp. PA	165	19	35.0	plants-all; fish
Serrasalminae sp. RH	251	21	34.7	fish
Tetragonopterus chalceus	64	10	37.0	invertebrates-aut
Triportheus sp. 1	136	5	70.8	detritus
Cichlidae				
Acaronia nassa	123	8	81.3	fish
Aequidens pallidus	148	22	77.6	detritus; fish
Astronotus ocellatus	231	4	75.0	invertebrates-all; fish

	MSL	Exam	M Full	Principal Food Items
Biotoecus opercularis	20	7	40.0	invertebrates-aut
Crenicichla johanna	211	6	5.0	fish
Crenicichla lenticulata	241	12	25.0	fish
Crenicichla lugubris	213	26	19.3	fish
Geophagus altifrons	193	33	66.4	plants-all
Heros severus	148	107	78.8	detritus
Hoplarchus psittacus	175	98	54.4	fish
Hypselecara coryphaenoides	137	82	46.1	fish
Mesonauta insignis	112	17	78.5	detritus
Satanoperca daemon 2	209	19	88.2	invertebrates-aut
Uaru amphiacanthoides	149	46	68.2	detritus
Curimatidae				
Curimata plumbea	61	-	----	detritus
Curimatopsis cf. *evelynae*	25	-	----	detritus
Curimatopsis evelynae	40	-	----	detritus
Doradidae				
Astrodoras cf. *asterifrons*	70	3	15.7	invertebrates-aut
Erythrinidae				
Hoplias sp. 2	265	1	10.0	fish
Hoplias sp. 3	251	2	22.2	fish
Hemiodontidae				
Argonectes longiceps	121	3	58.3	invertebrates-aut
Hemiodus cf. *gracilis*	48	15	68.3	plants-aut
Micromischodus sugillatus	105	2	50.0	invertebrates-aut
Loricariidae				
Hemiodontichthys acipenserinus	47	4	21.3	invertebrates-aut
Hypostomus carinatus	205	1	75.0	detritus
Pterygoplichthys sp. 1	258	4	75.0	detritus
Osteoglossidae				
Osteoglossum bicirrhosum	460	3	100.0	fish
Pimelodidae				
Goeldiella eques	200	1	10.0	fish

WOODY SHORE: ILHA TAMAQUARÉ

	MSL	Exam	M Full	Principal Food Items
Anostomidae				
Leporinus klausewitzi	60	1	75.0	plants-aut; detritus
Characidae				
Acestrorhynchus falcirostris	208	1	50.0	fish
Asiphonichthys condei	35	8	28.3	fish
Astyanax cf. *zonatus*	36	2	17.5	invertebrates-all; plants-aut
Brittanichthys axelrodi	21	9	31.5	invertebrates-aut; detritus
Hemigrammus analis B	23	18	80.6	plants-aut; detritus
Hemigrammus bellottii	22	10	13.8	invertebrates-all
Hemigrammus cf. *guyanensis*	26	6	87.5	plants-aut; detritus
Hemigrammus sp. A	30	13	32.0	invertebrates-aut
Hemigrammus vorderwinkleri	16	14	58.9	plants-aut; detritus
Hyphessobrycon stictus	26	15	83.3	detritus
Iguanodectes geisleri	35	10	87.5	detritus

	MSL	Exam	M Full	Principal Food Items
Iguanodectes spilurus	46	5	90.0	plants-aut
Moenkhausia collettii	34	15	85.0	fish
Moenkhausia cotinho	37	24	50.6	detritus
Thayeria obliqua	34	4	55.0	invertebrates-all; detritus
Chilodontidae				
Chilodus punctatus	36	10	87.5	plants-aut; detritus
Cichlidae				
Apistogramma pertensis	19	10	92.5	detritus
Crenicara filamentosum	27	5	39.0	plants-all; detritus; fish
Crenicichla notophthalmus	38	22	43.8	fish
Ctenoluciidae				
Boulengerella lateristriga	153	9	70.0	fish
Curimatidae				
Curimata sp.	39	-	----	detritus
Curimata sp. n.	36	-	----	detritus
Curimatopsis cf. *evelynae*	27	-	----	detritus
Curimatopsis cf. *macrolepis*	32	-	----	detritus
Curimatopsis evelynae	30	-	----	detritus
Curimatopsis evelynae	33	-	----	detritus
Curimatopsis macrolepis	33	-	----	detritus
Lebiasinidae				
Nannostomus eques	27	5	80.0	plants-aut; detritus
Nannostomus marilynae	20	5	90.0	plants-aut
Nannostomus trifasciatus	25	6	79.0	plants-aut
Nannostomus unifasciatus	31	6	83.0	plants-aut
Loricariidae				
Ancistrus sp. 2	47	3	100.0	detritus
Oxyropsis acutirostris	31	3	66.7	plants-aut

APPENDIX 5

AQUATIC INVERTEBRATES IN FISH DIETS

Only those fish species whose diet consisted per volume of at least 25% of the indicated food item are listed.

For easier reference the food items are listed in alphabetical rather than taxonomical order, as follows:

ANNELIDA
Bosmina spp.
Bosminopsis deitersi
BRYOZOA
CALANOIDA
CHIRONOMIDAE LARVAE
CHYDORIDAE
CLADOCERA
CORIXIDAE
CRABS
CYCLOPOIDA
DIPTERA LARVAE
DIPTERA PUPAE
EPHEMEROPTERA NYMPHS
HEMIPTERA
HYDRACARINA
MACROTHRICIDAE
MOLLUSCA
NEMATODA
ODONATA NYMPHS
OSTRACODA
PORIFERA
ROTIFERA
SHRIMP
TRICHOPTERA

MSL = Mean Standard Length (mm) of fish population feeding on indicated food item.
MZUSP = Registration number of fish population in the Museu de Zoologia da Universidade de São Paulo.

ANNELIDA

		MSL	MZUSP
Beach			
Gymnorhamphichthys hypostomus	Rhamphichthyidae	112	30203
Flooded Forest			
Hoplarchus psittacus	Cichlidae	181	32968
Copella nattereri	Lebiasinidae	17	29344
Pyrrhulina semifasciata	Lebiasinidae	22	29319
Rhamphichthys sp. B	Rhamphichthyidae	700	32233
Rhamphichthys sp. B	Rhamphichthyidae	750	32228
Island Lake			
Rhamphichthys sp. B	Rhamphichthyidae	630	32226

		MSL	MZUSP
BOSMINA spp.			
Beach			
Metynnis sp. BR	Characidae	52	35201
Anchoviella sp. B	Engraulidae	22	29100
Anchoviella sp. E	Engraulidae	44	29112
Woody Shore			
Astrodoras cf. *asterifrons*	Doradidae	70	29068
BOSMINOPSIS DEITERSI			
Beach			
Bryconops caudomaculatus	Characidae	33	29487
Hemigrammus vorderwinkleri	Characidae	15	29450
Anchoviella sp. E	Engraulidae	44	29112
Nannostomus marilynae	Lebiasinidae		17
Confluence Swamp			
Aphyodite sp.	Characidae	24	29876
Cichla cf. *orinocensis*	Cichlidae	16	32752
Hoplarchus psittacus	Cichlidae	8	33358
Island Lake			
Aphyodite sp.	Characidae	24	29874
Aphyodite sp.	Characidae	26	29875
Anchoviella jamesi	Engraulidae	45	29091
Anchoviella sp. G	Engraulidae	20	29114
BRYOZOA			
Island Lake			
Leporinus klausewitzi	Anostomidae	64	29194
Leporinus klausewitzi	Anostomidae	67	29193
CALANOIDA			
Beach			
Hemigrammus vorderwinkleri	Characidae	15	29450
Flooded Forest			
Pterygoplichthys sp. 1	Loricariidae	270	34789
Island Lake			
Moenkhausia ceros	Characidae	32	30273
Rocky Pool			
Hoplosternum thoracatum	Callichthyidae	104	33397
CHIRONOMIDAE LARVAE			
Beach			
Characidium sp. 3	Characidae	30	
Biotoecus opercularis	Cichlidae	34	29728
Doradidae sp. 2	Doradidae	25	29041
Doradidae sp. 2	Doradidae	26	29042
Hassar cf. *praelongus*	Doradidae	158	32525

		MSL	MZUSP
Hassar cf. *praelongus*	Doradidae	99	29034
Hassar lipophthalmus	Doradidae	137	32522
Hassar lipophthalmus	Doradidae	60	29028
Hassar lipophthalmus	Doradidae	79	32517
Steatogenys elegans	Hypopomidae	96	30087
Pimelodidae sp. 1	Pimelodidae	26	
Pimelodidae sp. 4	Pimelodidae	23	
Pimelodidae sp. 4	Pimelodidae	29	30618
Pimelodidae sp. 4	Pimelodidae	33	30617
Gymnorhamphichthys hypostomus	Rhamphichthyidae	78	30202
Gymnorhamphichthys rondonii	Rhamphichthyidae	60	30192
Gymnorhamphichthys rondonii	Rhamphichthyidae	62	34923
Gymnorhamphichthys rondonii	Rhamphichthyidae	65	
Gymnorhamphichthys rondonii	Rhamphichthyidae	66	30187
Gymnorhamphichthys rondonii	Rhamphichthyidae	67	30195
Gymnorhamphichthys rondonii	Rhamphichthyidae	70	
Gymnorhamphichthys rondonii	Rhamphichthyidae	70	30190
Gymnorhamphichthys rondonii	Rhamphichthyidae	71	30191
Eigenmannia cf. *humboldtii*	Sternopygidae	120	29975
Eigenmannia sp. A	Sternopygidae	70	29989
Eigenmannia sp. A	Sternopygidae	72	29990
Eigenmannia sp. A	Sternopygidae	73	29988
Eigenmannia sp. A	Sternopygidae	79	29987
Eigenmannia sp. B	Sternopygidae	64	29995
Eigenmannia sp. B	Sternopygidae	68	29991
Eigenmannia sp. B	Sternopygidae	70	29996
Eigenmannia sp. F	Sternopygidae	68	29966
Confluence Swamp			
Doradidae sp. 3	Doradidae	35	
Hassar lipophthalmus	Doradidae	103	29021
Hypopygus lepturus	Hypopomidae	30	30170
Loricariichthys acutus	Loricariidae	106	35075
Pimelodidae sp. 1	Pimelodidae	18	30638
Gymnorhamphichthys rondonii	Rhamphichthyidae	76	30188
Eigenmannia cf. *humboldtii*	Sternopygidae	123	29972
Eigenmannia sp. F	Sternopygidae	79	29967
Floating Meadow			
Adontosternarchus sp. C	Apteronotidae	83	30077
Adontosternarchus sp. D	Apteronotidae	46	30079
Hyphessobrycon cf. *serpae*	Characidae	25	29854
Apistogramma regani	Cichlidae	22	29733
Mesonauta insignis	Cichlidae	22	29754
Steatogenys elegans	Hypopomidae	110	30086
Nannostomus marilynae	Lebiasinidae	16	
Nannostomus unifasciatus	Lebiasinidae	34	
Eigenmannia cf. *humboldtii*	Sternopygidae	104	
Eigenmannia sp. D	Sternopygidae	47	
Flooded Forest			
Hassar cf. *praelongus*	Doradidae	132	32524
Hassar lipophthalmus	Doradidae	116	32520

		MSL	MZUSP
Opsodoras morei	Doradidae	152	32527
Island Lake			
Hyphessobrycon cf. *serpae*	Characidae	22	29862
Hypopomus sp. A	Hypopomidae	54	30032
Hypopomus sp. A	Hypopomidae	57	30031
Hypopomus sp. B	Hypopomidae	77	30035
Rocky Pool			
Apistogramma sp.	Cichlidae	18	29714
Hypopygus lepturus	Hypopomidae	35	30169
Eigenmannia sp. F	Sternopygidae	92	
Woody Shore			
Hemigrammus vorderwinkleri	Characidae	15	29447
Biotodoma wavrini	Cichlidae	105	29735

CHYDORIDAE

		MSL	MZUSP
Beach			
Doradidae sp. 2	Doradidae	28	29072
Doradidae sp. 2	Doradidae	40	29043
Doradidae sp. 3	Doradidae	31	29073
Bivibranchia protractila	Hemiodontidae	66	29631
Hemiodontichthys acipenserinus	Loricariidae	59	34527
Pseudoloricaria cf. *laeviuscula*	Loricariidae	36	35082
Pseudoloricaria sp.	Loricariidae	55	
Rocky Pool			
Eigenmannia cf. *humboldtii*	Sternopygidae	160	29981
Woody Shore			
Microphylipnus sp. 1	Eleotridae	18	
Micromischodus sugillatus	Hemiodontidae	105	34589

CLADOCERA

		MSL	MZUSP
Flooded Forest			
Aphyodite sp.	Characidae	27	29873
Island Lake			
Apistogramma pertensis	Cichlidae	20	29691
Gymnotus anguillaris	Gymnotidae	107	30068

CORIXIDAE

		MSL	MZUSP
Beach			
Eigenmannia sp. A	Sternopygidae	79	29987

CRABS

		MSL	MZUSP
Beach			
Astronotus ocellatus	Cichlidae	235	
Scorpiodoras cf. *heckeli*	Doradidae	157	

		MSL	MZUSP
Flooded Forest			
Hoplias sp. 3	Erythrinidae	242	34013
Hoplias sp. 4	Erythrinidae	340	34001
Hoplias sp. 4	Erythrinidae	355	33497
Osteoglossum ferreirai	Osteoglossidae	468	
Rhamphichthys sp. A	Rhamphichthyidae	710	34921
Sternopygus macrurus	Sternopygidae	450	32211
Rocky Pool			
Sternarchorhynchus mormyrus	Apteronotidae	343	32202
Woody Shore			
Sternopygus macrurus	Sternopygidae	460	32210

CYCLOPOIDA

		MSL	MZUSP
Beach			
Microschemobrycon casiquiare	Characidae	22	
Anchoviella jamesi	Engraulidae	23	29090
Confluence Swamp			
Pimelodidae sp. 1	Pimelodidae	18	30638
Island Lake			
Brittanichthys axelrodi	Characidae	22	29430
Hemigrammus vorderwinkleri	Characidae	17	29451
Anchoviella jamesi	Engraulidae	45	29091
Anchoviella sp. G	Engraulidae	20	29114
Anchoviella sp. G	Engraulidae	31	29115
Rocky Pool			
Hyphessobrycon cf. *serpae*	Characidae	21	29857
Hypopygus lepturus	Hypopomidae	35	30169

DIPTERA LARVAE

		MSL	MZUSP
Beach			
Sternachogiton sp.	Apteronotidae	113	
Atopomesus pachyodus	Characidae	23	29607
Microschemobrycon casiquiare	Characidae	22	
Microschemobrycon casiquiare	Characidae	23	
Astrodoras cf. *asterifrons*	Doradidae	19	
Rhabdolichops troscheli	Sternopygidae	118	
Confluence Swamp			
Hemigrammus mimus	Characidae	24	
Heterocharax macrolepis	Characidae	30	29226
Lonchogenys ilisha	Characidae	48	29253
Microschemobrycon casiquiare	Characidae	24	
Rocky Pool			
Hypopomus sp. A	Hypopomidae	73	30030
Eigenmannia sp. G	Sternopygidae	86	
Rhabdolichops longicaudatus	Sternopygidae	239	29948

149

		MSL	MZUSP
Woody Shore			
Hyphessobrycon cf. *serpae*	Characidae	18	29855
Argonectes longiceps	Hemiodontidae	121	32450
DIPTERA PUPAE			
Beach			
Bryconops caudomaculatus	Characidae	34	29485
Microphylipnus sp. 1	Eleotridae	22	
Confluence Swamp			
Belonion apodion	Belonidae	35	29383
Gnathocharax steindachneri	Characidae	25	29248
Hemigrammus bellottii	Characidae	18	29463
Heterocharax macrolepis	Characidae	30	29226
Hoplocharax goethei	Characidae	21	29235
Hyphessobrycon cf. *serpae*	Characidae	22	29861
Physopyxis sp.	Doradidae	12	29006
Floating Meadow			
Hemigrammus levis	Characidae	24	29438
Woody Shore			
Hemigrammus analis ?	Characidae	28	
Hemigrammus bellottii	Characidae	21	29457
EPHEMEROPTERA NYMPHS			
Beach			
Apteronotidae sp. B	Apteronotidae	195	
Heterocharax macrolepis	Characidae	28	29228
Lonchogenys ilisha	Characidae	59	29255
Argonectes longiceps	Hemiodontidae	185	32449
Eigenmannia cf. *humboldtii*	Sternopygidae	105	29978
Flooded Forest			
Ageneiosus sp. 2	Ageneiosidae	140	34414
Tetragonopterus chalceus	Characidae	77	29814
Distocyclus goajira	Sternopygidae	315	
Island Lake			
Apteronotus albifrons	Apteronotidae	75	
Rocky Pool			
Sternarchorhynchus oxyrhynchus	Apteronotidae	270	
Crenuchus spilurus	Characidae	27	34763
Sternopygus macrurus	Sternopygidae	194	30167
Woody Shore			
Centromochlus sp.	Auchenipteridae	53	
Tetragonopterus chalceus	Characidae	64	34933

		MSL	MZUSP

HEMIPTERA

Flooded Forest
Trachycorystes sp. 1 — Auchenipteridae — 250 — 34676

Island Lake
Gnathocharax steindachneri — Characidae — 29

HYDRACARINA

Confluence Swamp
Leptobrycon jatuaranae — Characidae — 24 — 29885

Flooded Forest
Apistogramma regani — Cichlidae — 19 — 29734

Woody Shore
Micromischodus sugillatus — Hemiodontidae — 105 — 34589

MACROTHRICIDAE

Beach
Gymnorhamphichthys rondonii — Rhamphichthyidae — 60 — 30192

Floating Meadow
Nannostomus unifasciatus — Lebiasinidae — 31

Island Lake
Loricariichthys acutus — Loricariidae — 220 — 35071

MOLLUSCA

Flooded Forest
Satanoperca daemon 2 — Cichlidae — 230 — 33011
Megalodoras irwini — Doradidae — 600

NEMATODA

Beach
Doradidae sp. 2 — Doradidae — 23 — 29040
Doradidae sp. 2 — Doradidae — 28 — 29072

Woody Shore
Argonectes longiceps — Hemiodontidae — 121 — 32450

ODONATA NYMPHS

Confluence Swamp
Goeldiella eques — Pimelodidae — 119 — 34488

Island Lake
Goeldiella eques — Pimelodidae — 132 — 33190

		MSL	MZUSP

OSTRACODA

Confluence Swamp
Biotoecus opercularis — Cichlidae — 22 — 29727

Floating Meadow
Apistogramma regani — Cichlidae — 22 — 29733

Flooded Forest
Apistogramma regani — Cichlidae — 19 — 29734

PORIFERA

Beach
Metynnis sp. BR — Characidae — 47 — 35200

Flooded Forest
Leporinus sp. n. — Anostomidae — 264

Island Lake
Uaru amphiacanthoides — Cichlidae — 177

ROTIFERA

Beach
Anchoviella sp. B — Engraulidae — 22 — 29100

Confluence Swamp
Brittanichthys axelrodi — Characidae — 20 — 29425

Island Lake
Aphyodite sp. — Characidae — 24 — 29874

Woody Shore
Astrodoras cf. *asterifrons* — Doradidae — 70 — 29068

SHRIMP

Beach
Acaronia nassa — Cichlidae — 70
Pimelodidae sp. 2 — Pimelodidae — 39
Pimelodus cf. *blochii* — Pimelodidae — 145
Pimelodus ornatus — Pimelodidae — 87 — 34481
Eigenmannia sp. E — Sternopygidae — 186 — 29999

Flooded Forest
Ageneiosus sp. A — Ageneiosidae — 125 — 34360

Island Lake
Crenuchus spilurus — Characidae — 37 — 34761
Electrophorus electricus — Electrophoridae — 252 — 32234

Rocky Pool
Asiphonichthys condei — Characidae — 32 — 29245

		MSL	MZUSP
Woody Shore			
Trachycorystes sp. 1	Auchenipteridae	163	34679
TRICHOPTERA			
Beach			
Characidium sp. 3	Characidae	31	
Phenacogaster sp. 1	Characidae	28	29398
Loricaria sp.	Loricariidae	111	35060
Eigenmannia cf. *humboldtii*	Sternopygidae	98	29980
Confluence Swamp			
Micromischodus sugillatus	Hemiodontidae	114	32472
Island Lake			
Pyrrhulina semifasciata	Lebiasinidae	31	29320

APPENDIX 6

TERRESTRIAL AND ARBOREAL ARTHROPODS IN FISH DIETS

Only those fish species whose diet consisted per volume of at least 25% of the indicated food item are listed.

For easier reference the food items are listed in alphabetical rather than taxonomical order, and as follows:

COLEOPTERA
COLLEMBOLA
DIPLOPODA
DIPTERA
FORMICIDAE
HYMENOPTERA
INSECT REMAINS (UNIDENTIFIED)
ISOPTERA
ORTHOPTERA
SPIDERS

MSL = Mean Standard Length (mm) of fish population feeding on indicated food item.
MZUSP = Registration number of fish population in the Museu de Zoologia da Universidade de São Paulo.

COLEOPTERA

		MSL	MZUSP
Beach			
Lonchogenys ilisha	Characidae	45	29264
Lonchogenys ilisha	Characidae	47	29263
Osteoglossum bicirrhosum	Osteoglossidae	665	
Osteoglossum ferreirai	Osteoglossidae	624	
Flooded Forest			
Hemigrammus sp.	Characidae	16	30359
Moenkhausia cotinho	Characidae	32	29825
Osteoglossum bicirrhosum	Osteoglossidae	523	29080
Osteoglossum ferreirai	Osteoglossidae	468	
Osteoglossum ferreirai	Osteoglossidae	585	
Island Lake			
Carnegiella marthae	Gasteropelecidae	23	29330
Carnegiella strigata	Gasteropelecidae	28	29335
Woody Shore			
Osteoglossum ferreirai	Osteoglossidae	611	

COLLEMBOLA

		MSL	MZUSP
Island Lake			
Tyttobrycon sp.	Characidae	16	20604

DIPLOPODA

		MSL	MZUSP
Flooded Forest			
Astyanax guianensis	Characidae	33	

154

		MSL	MZUSP
DIPTERA			
Beach			
Bryconops caudomaculatus	Characidae	35	29484
Bryconops melanurus	Characidae	33	29473
Bryconops melanurus	Characidae	50	
FORMICIDAE			
Beach			
Bryconops caudomaculatus	Characidae	30	29488
Bryconops melanurus	Characidae	51	29474
Centromochlus sp.	Auchenipteridae	73	
Hemigrammus vorderwinkleri	Characidae	14	29446
Knodus cf. *heterestes*	Characidae	22	29899
Myleus sp. BR	Characidae	158	
Confluence Swamp			
Bryconops melanurus	Characidae	69	29479
Carnegiella marthae	Gasteropelecidae	22	29333
Floating Meadow			
Brycon pesu	Characidae	20	29918
Flooded Forest			
Moenkhausia collettii	Characidae	24	34594
Rhabdolichops longicaudatus	Sternopygidae	235	32245
Island Lake			
Moenkhausia cotinho	Characidae	39	
HYMENOPTERA			
Beach			
Astyanax scologaster	Characidae	37	30251
Lonchogenys ilisha	Characidae	59	29255
INSECT REMAINS			
Beach			
Ageneiosus sp. A	Ageneiosidae	130	34367
Apteronotidae sp. C	Apteronotidae	139	32206
Astyanax guianensis	Characidae	30	29420
Astyanax guianensis	Characidae	31	29418
Astyanax scologaster	Characidae	23	30250
Astyanax scologaster	Characidae	24	30248
Astyanax scologaster	Characidae	31	30249
Astyanax scologaster	Characidae	34	30247
Astyanax scologaster	Characidae	36	30252
Astyanax scologaster	Characidae	37	30251
Bryconamericus sp. n.	Characidae	20	30744
Bryconops alburnoides	Characidae	70	29603
Bryconops caudomaculatus	Characidae	30	29488
Bryconops caudomaculatus	Characidae	34	29485
Bryconops caudomaculatus	Characidae	35	29484
Bryconops caudomaculatus	Characidae	35	29489

		MSL	MZUSP
Bryconops melanurus	Characidae	51	29474
Creagrutus cf caucanus	Characidae	36	29888
Hemigrammus analis *?*	Characidae	29	35052
Hemigrammus analis B	Characidae	21	35042
Hemigrammus mimus	Characidae	23	
Hemigrammus mimus	Characidae	24	
Heterocharax macrolepis	Characidae	28	29228
Knodus sp. 1	Characidae	33	29408
Knodus sp. 1	Characidae	35	
Knodus sp. 1	Characidae	39	29407
Lonchogenys ilisha	Characidae	39	29265
Lonchogenys ilisha	Characidae	45	29264
Lonchogenys ilisha	Characidae	49	29254
Microschemobrycon callops	Characidae	23	
Microschemobrycon callops	Characidae	28	
Microschemobrycon casiquiare	Characidae	21	
Microschemobrycon casiquiare	Characidae	22	
Microschemobrycon casiquiare	Characidae	24	
Moenkhausia collettii	Characidae	26	34608
Moenkhausia lepidura B	Characidae	31	
Moenkhausia lepidura D	Characidae	45	34664
Moenkhausia lepidura D	Characidae	45	34673
Moenkhausia lepidura D	Characidae	46	
Rhinobrycon negrensis	Characidae	31	29386
Myoglanis marmoratus	Pimelodidae	117	30832
Pimelodidae sp. 2	Pimelodidae	38	30631
Pimelodidae sp. 2	Pimelodidae	39	30621
Gymnorhamphichthys rondonii	Rhamphichthyidae	71	30191
Eigenmannia sp. E	Sternopygidae	113	29998
Rhabdolichops longicaudatus	Sternopygidae	123	
Rhabdolichops troscheli	Sternopygidae	118	
Confluence Swamp			
Bryconops caudomaculatus	Characidae	52	29483
Hemigrammus bellottii	Characidae	18	29463
Microschemobrycon casiquiare	Characidae	24	
Moenkhausia lepidura A	Characidae	61	34627
Thayeria obliqua	Characidae	43	29391
Floating Meadow			
Eigenmannia sp. E	Sternopygidae	123	29997
Flooded Forest			
Ageneiosus sp. 2	Ageneiosidae	140	34414
Ageneiosus sp. A	Ageneiosidae	130	34363
Auchenipterichthys sp. 1	Auchenipteridae	128	34687
Auchenipterichthys sp. 1	Auchenipteridae	129	34690
Auchenipterichthys sp. 1	Auchenipteridae	131	34692
Auchenipterichthys sp. 1	Auchenipteridae	139	34694
Bryconops alburnoides	Characidae	114	29602
Hemigrammus analis ?	Characidae	17	35057
Hemigrammus sp.	Characidae	16	30359
Hemigrammus cf. *guyanensis*	Characidae	21	35305
Hyphessobrycon diancistrus	Characidae	20	29844
Triportheus sp. 1	Characidae	194	

APPENDIX 6 CON'T

		MSL	MZUSP
Hypselecara coryphaenoides	Cichlidae	111	32757
Crenicichla johanna	Cichlidae	160	32798
Argonectes longiceps	Hemiodontidae	217	32447
Nannostomus eques	Lebiasinidae	20	29300
Nannostomus marilynae	Lebiasinidae	19	
Island Lake			
Bryconops caudomaculatus	Characidae	52	29482
Gnathocharax steindachneri	Characidae	29	
Hemigrammus analis ?	Characidae	29	35050
Hemigrammus bellottii	Characidae	21	29458
Hemigrammus cf. *guyanensis*	Characidae	23	35034
Heterocharax macrolepis	Characidae	27	29227
Triportheus sp. 1	Characidae	211	
Gymnotus anguillaris	Gymnotidae	107	30068
Gymnotus anguillaris	Gymnotidae	136	
Gymnotus carapo	Gymnotidae	138	30021
Pyrrhulina semifasciata	Lebiasinidae	31	29320
Sternopygus macrurus	Sternopygidae	191	30166
Rocky Pool			
Astyanax cf. *zonatus*	Characidae	32	29468
Astyanax guianensis	Characidae	30	29424
Astyanax sp. A	Characidae	28	
Iguanodectes geisleri	Characidae	39	29618
Moenkhausia collettii	Characidae	35	34597
Myoglanis sp. 1	Pimelodidae	38	30816
Rhabdolichops longicaudatus	Sternopygidae	239	29948
Rhabdolichops troscheli	Sternopygidae	210	32243
Woody Shore			
Astyanax cf. *zonatus*	Characidae	36	
Hemigrammus bellottii	Characidae	22	29455
Hyphessobrycon diancistrus	Characidae	30	29846
Knodus sp. 1	Characidae	36	29413
Serrasalminae sp. GI	Characidae	112	
Thayeria obliqua	Characidae	28	29392
Thayeria obliqua	Characidae	34	
Astronotus ocellatus	Cichlidae	231	32703
Sternopygus macrurus	Sternopygidae	315	32213
Sternopygus macrurus	Sternopygidae	460	32210

ISOPTERA

Flooded Forest			
Leporinus cf. *agassizi*	Anostomidae	303	32422

ORTHOPTERA

Island Lake			
Osteoglossum ferreirai	Osteoglossidae	424	29628
Woody Shore			
Brycon pesu	Characidae	68	29919

SPIDERS

Flooded Forest			
Osteoglossum ferreirai	Osteoglossidae	599	

APPENDIX 7

FRUIT AND SEED SPECIES EATEN OR REPORTED TO BE EATEN BY RIO NEGRO FISHES

All fruit and/or seed species, along with their leaves and often flowers, that Rio Negro fishermen reported as fish food were collected. All fruit and seed species that fishes were observed feeding on were also collected. The plants were identified by specialists listed in the acknowlegments. Only generic names are included here as species of the same genus usually have very similar fruits. The plant collection is registered in the Museu Paraense Emilio Goeldi (MPEG) in Belém, Pará, Brazil.

Seed condition in stomach or intestine contents is indicated as either whole or masticated. Seeds swallowed whole are potentially dispersed (ichthyochory).

Genus	Family	MPEG #	Seed Condition
Guatteria	Annonaceae	87126	whole/masticated
Pseudoxandra	Annonaceae	87113	whole/masticated
Ambelania	Apocynaceae	87144	
Bonafousa	Apocynaceae	87984	
Forsteronia	Apocynaceae	87000	
Himatanthus	Apocynaceae	87039	
Malouetia	Apocynaceae	87062	
Mesechites	Apocynaceae	87083	
Odontadenia	Apocynaceae	87023	
Astrocaryum	Arecaceae		whole/masticated
Bactris	Arecaceae		whole/masticated
Leopoldinia	Arecaceae		whole/masticated
Marsdenia	Asclepiadaceae	87135	
Arrabidaea	Bignoniaceae	87076	
Clytostoma	Bignoniaceae	86379	
Distictella	Bignoniaceae	86356	
Mansoa	Bignoniaceae	87101	
Tabebuia	Bignoniaceae	87082	masticated
Tanaecium	Bignoniaceae	86844	
Cordia	Boraginaceae	86348	
Tournefortia	Boraginaceae	87020	
Couepia	Chrysobalanaceae	87046	whole
Hirtella	Chrysobalanaceae	87136	
Licania	Chrysobalanaceae	87056	whole
Aniseia	Colvolvulaceae	87047	
Buchenavia	Combretaceae	87111	
Combretum	Combretaceae	87096	
Connarus	Connaraceae	86352	
Rourea	Connaraceae	86384	
Dictanostyles	Convolvulaceae	86402	
Cayaponia	Cucurbitaceae	87074	
Gurania	Cucurbitaceae	86455	
Doliocarpus	Dilleniaceae	86302	
Tetracera	Dilleniaceae	86314	
Diospyros	Ebenaceae	87106	
Alchornea	Euphorbiaceae	87060	whole/masticated
Croton	Euphorbiaceae	87107	
Dalechampia	Euphorbiaceae	86409	
Hevea	Euphorbiaceae	87124	masticated
Maprounea	Euphorbiaceae	87140	
Piranhea	Euphorbiaceae	86444	masticated
Laetia	Flacourtiaceae	87009	

158

Genus	Family	MPEG #	Seed Condition
Vismia	Guttiferae	86933	
Nectandra	Lauraceae	87150	whole/masticated
Eschweilera	Lecythidaceae	87058	masticated
Aldina	Leguminosae	87045	
Campsiandra	Leguminosae	86396	masticated
Cassia	Leguminosae	86453	masticated
Crudia	Leguminosae	86457	
Dalbergia	Leguminosae	86440	masticated
Derris	Leguminosae	86367	
Inga	Leguminosae	86437	whole/masticated
Lonchocarpus	Leguminosae	87147	
Macrollobium	Leguminosae	87119	masticated
Melanoxylon?	Leguminosae	87098	
Parkia	Leguminosae	87034	
Peltogyne	Leguminosae	87142	
Pentaclethra	Leguminosae	87043	masticated
Pithecellobium	Leguminosae	86336	masticated
Swartzia	Leguminosae	87006	
Vigna	Leguminosae	87073	masticated
Potalia	Loganiaceae	87158	
Strychnos	Loganiaceae	87063	
Acmanthera	Malpighiaceae	87003	whole/masticated
Burdachia	Malpighiaceae	87033	whole/masticated
Byrsonima	Malpighiaceae	87137	whole/masticated
Heteropterys	Malpighiaceae	87065	
Clidemia	Melastomataceae	87151	whole
Henriettea	Melastomataceae	86332	whole
Toccoca	Melastomataceae	86996	whole
Sciadotenia	Menispermaceae	87134	
Byttneria	Moraceae	86416	
Cecropia	Moraceae	87099	whole
Ficus	Moraceae		whole
Virola	Myristicaceae	87011	whole
Moutabea	Polygalaceae	86388	
Coccoloba	Polygonaceae	87064	whole/masticated
Triplaris	Polygonaceae	87061	
Quiina	Quiinaceae	87007	whole/masticated
Amaioua	Rubiaceae	87146	
Bothriospora	Rubiaceae	87081	
Chomelia	Rubiaceae	86305	
Coussarea	Rubiaceae	87165	
Duroia	Rubiaceae	87035	
Faramea	Rubiaceae	86992	
Palicourea	Rubiaceae	86412	
Posoqueria?	Rubiaceae	87088	
Psychotria	Rubiaceae	86382	whole/masticated
Sphinctanthus	Rubiaceae	86994	
Stachyarrhena	Rubiaceae	87005	
Talisia	Sapindaceae	86392	
Gomphilluma	Sapotaceae	87050	
Simaba	Simarubaceae	87121	whole/masticated
Guazuma	Sterculiaceae	87164	

APPENDIX 8

TERRESTRIAL FRESH PLANT MATTER IN FISH DIETS

Only those fish species whose diet consisted per volume of at least 25% of the indicated food item are listed.

MSL = Mean Standard Length (mm) of the fish population feeding on indicated food item.
MZUSP = Registration number of fish population in the Museu de Zoologia da Universidade de São Paulo.

FRUITS/SEEDS

		MSL	MZUSP
Beach			
Leporinus brunneus	Anostomidae	172	32303
Creagrutus cf. *caucanus*	Characidae	36	29888
Metynnis sp. BR	Characidae	52	35201
Moenkhausia grandisquamis	Characidae	48	30267
Moenkhausia oligolepis	Characidae	48	29837
Myleus cf. *torquatus*	Characidae	178	
Myleus schomburgkii	Characidae	230	
Myleus sp. TH	Characidae	286	
Serrasalminae sp. CH	Characidae	206	
Serrasalminae sp. CH	Characidae	217	
Serrasalminae sp. FU	Characidae	146	
Serrasalminae sp. PA	Characidae	174	
Tetragonopterus chalceus	Characidae	54	29816
Biotodoma wavrini	Cichlidae	71	32725
Crenicara filamentosum	Cichlidae	21	29716
Pimelodidae sp. 2	Pimelodidae	39	
Pimelodidae sp. 2	Pimelodidae	40	30622
Sternopygus macrurus	Sternopygidae	735	32212
Confluence Swamp			
Astyanax cf. *zonatus*	Characidae	34	29471
Floating Meadow			
Astyanax guianensis	Characidae	30	29423
Hyphessobrycon sp. 2	Characidae	27	35023
Moenkhausia collettii	Characidae	35	34606
Moenkhausia lepidura B	Characidae	39	34635
Moenkhausia lepidura B	Characidae	44	34634
Moenkhausia lepidura D	Characidae	25	34660
Moenkhausia lepidura D	Characidae	35	34661
Flooded Forest			
Leporinus brunneus	Anostomidae	270	32304
Leporinus brunneus	Anostomidae	300	32305
Leporinus cf. *agassizi*	Anostomidae	260	32434
Leporinus cf. *agassizi*	Anostomidae	295	32423
Leporinus cf. *agassizi*	Anostomidae	302	32441
Leporinus cf. *agassizi*	Anostomidae	303	32422
Leporinus cf. *agassizi*	Anostomidae	305	32426
Leporinus cf. *friderici*	Anostomidae	290	

APPENDIX 8 CON'T

		MSL	MZUSP
Leporinus fasciatus	Anostomidae		
Leporinus sp. n.	Anostomidae	310	
Auchenipterichthys sp. 1	Auchenipteridae	136	34691
Auchenipterichthys sp. 1	Auchenipteridae	140	34689
Trachycorystes sp. 1	Auchenipteridae	204	34681
Trachycorystes sp. 1	Auchenipteridae	220	34678
Trachycorystes sp. 1	Auchenipteridae	277	34677
Metynnis sp. BR	Characidae	117	
Metynnis sp. BS	Characidae	112	
Myleus cf. *torquatus*	Characidae	142	
Myleus schomburgkii	Characidae	206	
Myleus schomburgkii	Characidae	208	
Myleus schomburgkii	Characidae	239	
Myleus schomburgkii	Characidae	292	
Myleus sp. BR	Characidae	158	
Myleus sp. BR	Characidae	166	
Myleus sp. BR	Characidae	191	
Myleus sp. IR	Characidae	189	
Myleus sp. IR	Characidae	197	
Myleus sp. TH	Characidae	253	
Myleus sp. TH	Characidae	268	
Myleus sp. TH	Characidae	306	
Myleus sp. TH	Characidae	307	
Serrasalminae sp. BU	Characidae	170	
Serrasalminae sp. CH	Characidae	183	
Serrasalminae sp. CH	Characidae	205	
Serrasalminae sp. FU	Characidae	182	
Serrasalminae sp. FU	Characidae	274	
Serrasalminae sp. PA	Characidae	156	
Serrasalminae sp. PA	Characidae	162	
Serrasalminae sp. RH	Characidae	218	
Triportheus sp. 1	Characidae	194	
Triportheus sp. 1	Characidae	196	34030
Triportheus sp. 1	Characidae	200	
Triportheus sp. 1	Characidae	210	34023
Triportheus sp. 1	Characidae	220	34031
Astronotus ocellatus	Cichlidae	241	32707
Heros severus	Cichlidae	164	32948
Heros severus	Cichlidae	183	
Satanoperca jurupari	Cichlidae	142	34894
Megalodoras irwini	Doradidae	500	
Megalodoras irwini	Doradidae	560	35215
Megalodoras irwini	Doradidae	600	
Platydoras costatus	Doradidae	187	32555
Argonectes longiceps	Hemiodontidae	232	32455
Hemiodus cf. *unimaculatus*	Hemiodontidae	185	
Phractocephalus hemioliopterus	Pimelodidae	1150	
Island Lake			
Myleus sp. IR	Characidae	206	
Serrasalminae sp. FU	Characidae	267	
Triportheus sp. 1	Characidae	211	
Heros severus	Cichlidae	209	
Uaru amphiacanthoides JU	Cichlidae	21	33076
Rocky Pool			
Leporinus cf. *agassizi*	Anostomidae	195	32427

		MSL	MZUSP
Woody Shore			
Ageneiosus sp. 2	Ageneiosidae	156	34410
Hemigrammus levis	Characidae	28	29439
Metynnis sp. CO	Characidae	142	
Moenkhausia lepidura B	Characidae	43	34636
Moenkhausia lepidura D	Characidae	34	34659
Myleus schomburgkii	Characidae	184	
Myleus sp. IR	Characidae	181	
Serrasalminae sp. CH	Characidae	153	
Serrasalminae sp. PA	Characidae	165	
Geophagus altifrons	Cichlidae	193	
Platydoras costatus	Doradidae	220	32554

LEAVES/FLOWERS

Beach			
Myleus sp. IR	Characidae	192	
Confluence Swamp			
Ageneiosus sp. A	Ageneiosidae	100	34366
Serrasalminae sp. BU	Characidae	167	
Flooded Forest			
Ageneiosus sp. A	Ageneiosidae	125	34360
Myleus sp. BR	Characidae	158	
Myleus sp. BR	Characidae	166	
Myleus sp. BR	Characidae	191	
Argonectes longiceps	Hemiodontidae	219	
Island Lake			
Leporinus cf. *agassizi*	Anostomidae	254	32428
Myleus sp. IR	Characidae	206	
Rocky Pool			
Dekeyseria scaphirhyncha	Loricariidae	112	35095
Woody Shore			
Myleus cf. *torquatus*	Characidae	135	
Myleus sp. BR	Characidae	175	

APPENDIX 9

AQUATIC PLANTS IN FISH DIETS

Only those fish species whose diet consisted per volume of at least 25% of the indicated food item are listed.

MSL = Mean Standard Length (mm) of the fish population feedin on indicated food item.
MZUSP = Registration number of fish population in the Museu de Zoologia da Universidade de São Paulo.

FILAMENTOUS ALGAE

		MSL	MZUSP
Beach			
Hemigrammus analis ?	Characidae	30	35048
Hemigrammus levis	Characidae	31	29443
Hemigrammus levis	Characidae	32	29437
Knodus sp. 1	Characidae	39	29410
Moenkhausia lepidura D	Characidae	46	
Nannostomus marilynae	Lebiasinidae	17	
Confluence Swamp			
Hemigrammus levis	Characidae	30	29445
Hemigrammus vorderwinkleri	Characidae	17	29453
Iguanodectes adujai	Characidae	52	29619
Metynnis sp. CO	Characidae	142	
Scorpiodoras cf. *heckeli*	Doradidae	101	
Nannostomus marilynae	Lebiasinidae	17	29313
Floating Meadow			
Hemigrammus levis	Characidae	22	29440
Flooded Forest			
Metynnis sp. BR	Characidae	117	
Metynnis sp. CO	Characidae	160	
Uaru amphiacanthoides	Cichlidae	155	
Hemiodus cf. *unimaculatus*	Hemiodontidae	178	32489
Hemiodus cf. *unimaculatus*	Hemiodontidae	213	32490
Hemiodus immaculatus	Hemiodontidae	205	32470
Nannostomus unifasciatus	Lebiasinidae	31	
Island Lake			
Astyanax sp. A	Characidae	27	
Hemigrammus vorderwinkleri	Characidae	15	29449
Iguanodectes cf. *purusi*	Characidae	40	
Apistogramma sp.	Cichlidae	16	29705
Nannostomus marilynae	Lebiasinidae	19	
Rocky Pool			
Laemolyta cf. *taeniatus*	Anostomidae	151	32416
Deuterodon cf. *acanthogaster*	Characidae	20	29907
Hemigrammus analis B	Characidae	23	35045
Moenkhausia cotinho	Characidae	39	29826
Nannostomus marilynae	Lebiasinidae	18	
Woody Shore			
Astyanax cf. *zonatus*	Characidae	36	
Hemigrammus analis ?	Characidae	28	

		MSL	MZUSP
Hemigrammus analis B	Characidae	20	35044
Hemigrammus analis B	Characidae	23	35041
Hemigrammus vorderwinkleri	Characidae	16	29448
Hyphessobrycon cf. *serpae*	Characidae	18	29855
Hyphessobrycon cf. *serpae*	Characidae	21	29856
Iguanodectes spilurus	Characidae	46	
Moenkhausia collettii	Characidae	31	34600
Moenkhausia cotinho	Characidae	45	29829
Thayeria obliqua	Characidae	28	29392
Hemiodus cf. *gracilis*	Hemiodontidae	48	29646
Nannostomus eques	Lebiasinidae	27	29301
Nannostomus trifasciatus	Lebiasinidae	25	29294
Nannostomus unifasciatus	Lebiasinidae	28	29287
Nannostomus unifasciatus	Lebiasinidae	31	29285

MICROALGAE

Beach
Hyphessobrycon sp. 2	Characidae	17	35024
Rhinobrycon negrensis	Characidae	28	29384
Nannostomus marilynae	Lebiasinidae	17	

Confluence Swamp
Iguanodectes spilurus	Characidae	48	29623
Tyttobrycon sp.	Characidae	16	29606
Fluviphylax pygmaeus	Cyprinodontidae	11	29376
Hemiodus cf. *gracilis*	Hemiodontidae	57	29642
Nannostomus eques	Lebiasinidae	25	
Nannostomus marilynae	Lebiasinidae	17	29313
Nannostomus trifasciatus	Lebiasinidae	25	
Acestridium discus	Loricariidae	51	34135

Floating Meadow
Nannostomus trifasciatus	Lebiasinidae	31	
Acestridium discus	Loricariidae	41	34136

Island Lake
Hoplocharax goethei	Characidae	19	29251
Nannostomus eques	Lebiasinidae	26	29304
Nannostomus trifasciatus	Lebiasinidae	25	
Nannostomus trifasciatus	Lebiasinidae	26	29295
Nannostomus unifasciatus	Lebiasinidae	28	29289
Nannostomus unifasciatus	Lebiasinidae	31	29293
Hemiancistrus sp.	Loricariidae	63	35097
Oxyropsis acutirostris	Loricariidae	30	

Rocky Pool
Ancistrus sp. PS	Loricariidae	38	35098

Woody Shore
Leporinus klausewitzi	Anostomidae	60	29195
Hemigrammus analis B	Characidae	23	35039
Iguanodectes spilurus	Characidae	46	
Chilodus punctatus	Chilodontidae	36	29360
Nannostomus marilynae	Lebiasinidae	20	
Nannostomus trifasciatus	Lebiasinidae	25	29294
Nannostomus unifasciatus	Lebiasinidae	31	29285

APPENDIX 9 CON'T

		MSL	MZUSP
Oxyropsis acutirostris	Loricariidae	31	35090

HERBACEOUS PLANT ROOTS

Confluence Swamp
| *Myleus schomburgkii* | Characidae | 233 | |

Flooded Forest
| *Leporinus* cf. *friderici* | Anostomidae | | |
| *Leporinus fasciatus* | Anostomidae | | |

HERBACEOUS STEMS/LEAVES

Beach
| *Hemigrammus analis* ? | Characidae | 27 | 35054 |
| *Hemigrammus analis* ? | Characidae | 30 | 35048 |

Confluence Swamp
| *Hemigrammus analis* ? | Characidae | 26 | 35047 |
| *Hemigrammus analis* B | Characidae | 20 | 35036 |

Flooded Forest
| *Leporinus fasciatus* | Anostomidae | 318 | |
| *Myleus* sp. TH | Characidae | 306 | |

Woody Shore
| *Leporinus* cf. *agassizi* | Anostomidae | 234 | 32424 |
| *Metynnis* sp. BR | Characidae | 118 | |

APPENDIX 10

DETRITUS IN FISH DIETS

Only those fish species whose diet consisted per volume of at least 25% of the indicated food item are listed.

Although not listed here because their stomach contents were not examined microscopically, all species of the families Curimatidae and Prochilodontidae are detritivores [see Appendix 3 for the species in these families].

MSL = Mean Standard Length (mm) of the fish population feeding on indicated food item.
MZUSP = Registration number of fish population in the Museu de Zoologia da Universidade de São Paulo.

FINE DETRITUS

		MSL	MZUSP
Beach			
Apteronotidae sp. C	Apteronotidae	139	32206
Characidium sp. 3	Characidae	30	
Hemigrammus analis ?	Characidae	29	34051
Hemigrammus analis B	Characidae	19	35040
Hemigrammus levis	Characidae	32	29437
Iguanodectes spilurus	Characidae	43	29624
Metynnis sp. BR	Characidae	47	35200
Moenkhausia grandisquamis	Characidae	48	30267
Rhinobrycon negrensis	Characidae	26	29385
Caenotropus labyrinthicus	Chilodontidae	53	29349
Apistogramma sp.	Cichlidae	16	29712
Apistogramma sp,	Cichlidae	15	29707
Apistogramma pertensis	Cichlidae	19	34792
Geophagus surinamensis	Cichlidae	79	32899
Geophagus surinamensis	Cichlidae	163	32900
Geophagus surinamensis	Cichlidae	202	
Micromischodus sugillatus	Hemiodontidae	82	32474
Nannostomus marilynae	Lebiasinidae	17	
Nannostomus marilynae	Lebiasinidae	17	29314
Pimelodidae sp. 4	Pimelodidae	23	
Eigenmannia cf. *humboldtii*	Sternopygidae	113	
Confluence Swamp			
Brittanichthys axelrodi	Characidae	20	29425
Hemigrammus rhodostomus	Characidae	27	29435
Metynnis sp. BS	Characidae	134	
Paracheirodon axelrodi	Characidae	17	29434
Apistogramma sp.	Cichlidae	15	29713
Apistogramma pertensis	Cichlidae	16	
Crenicara filamentosum	Cichlidae	22	29719
Uaru amphiacanthoides JU	Cichlidae	34	33071
Fluviphylax pygmaeus	Poeciliidae	11	29376
Nannostomus eques	Lebiasinidae	25	
Nannostomus marilynae	Lebiasinidae	17	29313
Nannostomus trifasciatus	Lebiasinidae	25	
Nannostomus unifasciatus	Lebiasinidae	29	
Ancistrus sp. 2	Loricariidae	45	35107

166

		MSL	MZUSP
Dekeyseria scaphirhyncha	Loricariidae	69	35096
Floating Meadow			
Nannostomus unifasciatus	Lebiasinidae	31	
Flooded Forest			
Geophagus surinamensis	Cichlidae	188	32903
Heros severus	Cichlidae	183	
Hemiodus cf. *unimaculatus*	Hemiodontidae	250	
Nannostomus trifasciatus	Lebiasinidae	29	
Nannostomus unifasciatus	Lebiasinidae	31	
Hypostomus sp.	Loricariidae	175	
Pterygoplichthys gibbiceps	Loricariidae	240	34782
Pterygoplichthys sp. 1	Loricariidae	270	34789
Rhamphichthys sp. B	Rhamphichthyidae	700	32233
Island Lake			
Laemolyta cf. *taeniatus*	Anostomidae	82	29192
Pseudanos gracilis	Anostomidae	65	29163
Pseudanos gracilis	Anostomidae	65	29168
Astyanax cf. *zonatus*	Characidae	34	29469
Astyanax sp. A	Characidae	27	
Brittanichthys axelrodi	Characidae	20	29426
Hemigrammus analis ?	Characidae	23	35037
Hemigrammus vorderwinkleri	Characidae	15	29449
Hyphessobrycon diancistrus	Characidae	23	29843
Hyphessobrycon erythrostigma	Characidae	28	30214
Hyphessobrycon cf. *serpae*	Characidae	20	29864
Hyphessobrycon sp. 1	Characidae	19	30645
Iguanodectes adujai	Characidae	41	
Iguanodectes spilurus	Characidae	37	29622
Iguanodectes spilurus	Characidae	43	29620
Moenkhausia ceros	Characidae	32	30273
Moenkhausia collettii	Characidae	32	34605
Thayeria obliqua	Characidae	35	29388
Chilodus punctatus	Chilodontidae	36	
Chilodus punctatus	Chilodontidae	43	
Apistogramma sp.	Cichlidae	16	29705
Apistogramma pertensis	Cichlidae	20	29691
Apistogramma pertensis	Cichlidae	23	29687
Geophagus surinamensis	Cichlidae	214	
Fluviphylax pygmaeus	Poeciliidae	11	29370
Fluviphylax pygmaeus	Poeciliidae	12	29372
Hypopygus lepturus	Hypopomidae	45	30168
Copella nattereri	Lebiasinidae	14	29342
Nannostomus eques	Lebiasinidae	27	29303
Nannostomus trifasciatus	Lebiasinidae	25	
Nannostomus trifasciatus	Lebiasinidae	26	29295
Nannostomus unifasciatus	Lebiasinidae	28	29289
Nannostomus unifasciatus	Lebiasinidae	30	29290
Nannostomus unifasciatus	Lebiasinidae	31	29293
Ancistrus sp. 2	Loricariidae	35	35106
Ancistrus sp. 2	Loricariidae	49	35105
Hemiancistrus sp.	Loricariidae	63	35097
Oxyropsis acutirostris	Loricariidae	30	

		MSL	MZUSP
Rocky Pool			
Laemolyta cf. *taeniatus*	Anostomidae	151	32416
Pseudanos gracilis	Anostomidae	69	29164
Apteronotidae sp. A	Apteronotidae	172	32208
Deuterodon cf. *acanthogaster*	Characidae	20	29907
Caenotropus labyrinthicus	Chilodontidae	75	29348
Chilodus punctatus	Chilodontidae	43	29363
Nannostomus marilynae	Lebiasinidae	18	
Ancistrus sp. 1	Loricariidae	42	35111
Ancistrus sp. PS	Loricariidae	38	35098
Dekeyseria scaphirhyncha	Loricariidae	112	35095
Hemiancistrus pulcher	Loricariidae	59	34787
Pterygoplichthys gibbiceps	Loricariidae	146	34780
Woody Shore			
Brittanichthys axelrodi	Characidae	21	29427
Hemigrammus analis B	Characidae	23	35039
Hemigrammus cf. *guyanensis*	Characidae	26	35033
Hemigrammus vorderwinkleri	Characidae	16	29448
Thayeria obliqua	Characidae	34	
Chilodus punctatus	Chilodontidae	36	29360
Apistogramma pertensis	Cichlidae	19	29686
Crenicara filamentosum	Cichlidae	27	29718
Geophagus surinamensis	Cichlidae	217	
Uaru amphiacanthoides	Cichlidae	205	
Nannostomus eques	Lebiasinidae	27	29301
Nannostomus unifasciatus	Lebiasinidae	28	29287
Ancistrus sp. 2	Loricariidae	47	35108
Pterygoplichthys sp. 1	Loricariidae	258	

PLANT REMAINS

		MSL	MZUSP
Beach			
Leporinus sp. n.	Anostomidae	108	
Leporinus sp. n.	Anostomidae	139	
Atopomesus pachyodus	Characidae	26	29609
Bryconops alburnoides	Characidae	70	29603
Iguanodectes spilurus	Characidae	43	29624
Knodus sp. 1	Characidae	33	29408
Knodus sp. 1	Characidae	39	29407
Microschemobrycon sp. MA	Characidae	16	35058
Mesonauta insignis	Cichlidae	100	
Uaru amphiacanthoides	Cichlidae	147	
Uaru amphiacanthoides	Cichlidae	170	33075
Hassar cf. *praelongus*	Doradidae	99	29034
Opsodoras morei	Doradidae	127	32526
Ancistrus sp. 4	Loricariidae	48	35101
Pimelodus cf. *blochii*	Pimelodidae	145	
Pimelodus cf. *blochii*	Pimelodidae	157	
Confluence Swamp			
Iguanodectes adujai	Characidae	52	29619
Aequidens pallidus	Cichlidae	121	29790
Mesonauta insignis	Cichlidae	53	29760
Scorpiodoras cf. *heckeli*	Doradidae	101	

APPENDIX 10 CON'T

		MSL	MZUSP
Floating Meadow			
Nannostomus unifasciatus	Lebiasinidae	31	
Rhamphichthys sp. B	Rhamphichthyidae	412	32230
Flooded Forest			
Leporinus cf. *friderici*	Anostomidae		
Leporinus cf. *friderici*	Anostomidae	290	
Leporinus fasciatus	Anostomidae		
Leporinus sp. n.	Anostomidae	222	32381
Leporinus sp. n.	Anostomidae	264	
Aequidens pallidus	Cichlidae	23	29792
Heros severus	Cichlidae	140	32950
Heros severus	Cichlidae	164	32948
Heros severus	Cichlidae	183	
Satanoperca daemon 2	Cichlidae	230	33011
Uaru amphiacanthoides	Cichlidae	155	
Uaru amphiacanthoides	Cichlidae	215	
Hassar lipophthalmus	Doradidae	220	32518
Opsodoras morei	Doradidae	152	32527
Pimelodus cf. *blochii*	Pimelodidae	182	
Rhamphichthys sp. A	Rhamphichthyidae	710	34921
Sternopygus macrurus	Sternopygidae	450	32211
Island Lake			
Laemolyta cf. *taeniatus*	Anostomidae	82	29192
Leporinus sp. n.	Anostomidae	174	
Hemigrammus analis ?	Characidae	29	35050
Hyphessobrycon stictus	Characidae	28	29850
Iguanodectes geisleri	Characidae	38	29614
Iguanodectes spilurus	Characidae	43	29620
Moenkhausia cotinho	Characidae	39	29827
Moenkhausia oligolepis	Characidae	46	29836
Thayeria obliqua	Characidae	28	29389
Thayeria obliqua	Characidae	38	29390
Acaronia nassa	Cichlidae	121	32666
Mesonauta insignis	Cichlidae	44	
Mesonauta insignis	Cichlidae	72	29766
Uaru amphiacanthoides	Cichlidae	177	
Rocky Pool			
Leporinus cf. *friderici*	Anostomidae	288	
Mesonauta insignis	Cichlidae	80	79759
Woody Shore			
Leporinus cf. *agassizi*	Anostomidae	150	32430
Leporinus klausewitzi	Anostomidae	60	29195
Leporinus sp. n.	Anostomidae	170	29127
Trachycorystes sp. 1	Auchenipteridae	163	34679
Hyphessobrycon stictus	Characidae	26	29851
Iguanodectes geisleri	Characidae	35	29617
Moenkhausia cotinho	Characidae	37	29830
Triportheus sp. 1	Characidae	136	
Heros severus	Cichlidae	148	32949

		MSL	MZUSP
Mesonauta insignis	Cichlidae	111	
Mesonauta insignis	Cichlidae	112	
Uaru amphiacanthoides	Cichlidae	149	33078
Sternopygus macrurus	Sternopygidae	315	32213

COARSE LITTER

Beach

Metynnis sp. BS	Characidae	114	
Acaronia nassa	Cichlidae	70	
Aequidens pallidus	Cichlidae	66	29786
Hoplarchus psittacus	Cichlidae	221	

Confluence Swamp

Ageneiosus sp. A	Ageneiosidae	100	34366

Flooded Forest

Serrasalminae sp. CH	Characidae	153	
Hypostomus carinatus	Loricariidae	217	34770

Island Lake

Leporinus klausewitzi	Anostomidae	67	29193

Rocky Pool

Cochliodon sp.	Loricariidae	140	34604

Woody Shore

Aequidens pallidus	Cichlidae	148	29794
Hypostomus carinatus	Loricariidae	205	34768

APPENDIX 11

PISCIVORES AND IDENTIFIED PREY

The following list is based on fish species from which prey could be identified and whose standard length could be measured or estimated relatively accurately. Prey standard length ranges are given in parentheses following the piscivore.

Ageneiosus sp. **AGENEIOSIDAE** (6-50%)
  Auchenipteridae spp.
  Acestrorhynchus microlepis (Characidae)
  Astyanax sp. (Characidae)
  Microschemobrycon casiquiare (Characidae)
  Serrasalminae sp. (Characidae)
  Tetragonopterinae (Characidae)
  Doradidae spp.
  Hassar sp. (Doradidae)
  Hypophthalmus sp. (Hypophthalmidae)
  Pimelodella sp. (Pimelodidae)
  Synbranchus sp. (Synbranchidae)

Leporinus cf. agassizi **ANOSTOMIDAE** (7-9%)
  Characoidei spp.

Acestrorhynchus falcirostris **CHARACIDAE** (10-64%)
  Leporinus fasciatus (Anostomidae)
  Bryconops sp. (Characidae)
  Tetragonopterinae spp. (Characidae)
  Characoidei spp.
  Chilodus punctatus (Chilodontidae)
  Cichlidae spp.
  Crenicichla sp. *(Cichlidae)*
  Anodus elongatus (Hemiodontidae)
  Monocirrhus polyacanthus (Nandidae)

Acestrorhynchus grandoculis **CHARACIDAE** (38%)
  Tetragonopterinae sp. (Characidae)

Acestrorhynchus microlepis **CHARACIDAE** (24%)
  Unidentified Fish

Acestrorhynchus minimus CHARACIDAE (8-47%)
  Characidae sp.
  Hyphessobrycon sp. (Characidae)
  Tetragonopterinae (Characidae)
  Crenicara filamentosum (Cichlidae)
  Larvae (Cichlidae)
  Larvae (Cynodontidae)
  Engraulidae
  Nannostomus marilynae (Lebiasinidae)
  Unidentified (larvae)

Acestrorhynchus nasutus **CHARACIDAE** (47-48%)
  Characoidei spp.
  Hemigrammus bellottii (Characidae)
  Tetragonopterinae (Characidae)
  Engraulidae spp.

171

Agoniates sp. **CHARACIDAE** (7-29%)
  Astyanax sp. (Characidae)
  Tetragonopterinae spp. (Characidae)
  Characoidei spp.
  Cichla (larvae) (Cichlidae)
  Engraulidae sp.

Astyanax guianensis **CHARACIDAE** (38%)
  Unidentified Fish

Moenkhausia collettii **CHARACIDAE** (29%)
  Characidae?

Moenkhausia cotinho **CHARACIDAE** (34%)
  Tetragonopterinae sp. (Characidae)

Acaronia nassa **CICHLIDAE** (9-20%)
  Bryconinae (Characidae)
  Cichlidae spp.
  Crenicichla sp. (Cichlidae)
  Doradidae spp.
  Gymnotoidei sp.
  Siluriformes spp.

Cichla sp. **CICHLIDAE** (9-31%)
  Anostomidae spp.
  Characidium sp. (Characidae)
  Tetragonopterinae spp. (Characidae)

Cichla monoculus? **CICHLIDAE** (9-31)
  Cichlidae spp.
  Apistogramma sp. (Cichlidae)
  Crenicichla sp. (Cichlidae)

Cichla temensis **CICHLIDAE** (6-43%)
  Leporinus sp. (Anostomidae)
  Characidae sp.
  Acestrorhynchus sp. (Characidae)
  Brycon sp. (Characidae)
  Cichlasoma? (Cichlidae)
  Crenicichla sp. (Cichlidae)
  Larvae (Cichlidae)
  Uaru amphiacanthoides (Cichlidae)

Crenicihla johanna **CICHLIDAE** (6%)
  Apistogramma sp. (Cichlidae)

Crenicichla notophthalmus **CICHLIDAE** (20-33%)
  Hyphessobrycon sp. (Characidae)
  Tetragonopterinae sp. (Characidae)
  Characoidei spp.
  Apistogramma sp. (Cichlidae)
  Fluviphylax pygmaeus (Cyprinodontidae)

Hoplarchus psittacus **CICHLIDAE** (6-20%)
  Centromochlus sp. (Auchenipteridae)
  Cichlidae spp.

APPENDIX 11 CON'T

Apistogramma sp. (Cichlidae)
Larvae (Cichlidae)
Erythrinidae spp.
Gymnotoidei spp.
Loricariidae spp.
Siluriformes spp.
Synbranchus sp. (Symbranchidae)

Boulengerella lateristriga **CTENOLUCIIDAE** (12-29%)
Characoidei spp.
Hyphessobrycon sp. (Characidae)
Characoidei
Chilodus punctatus (Chilodontidae)
Apistogramma sp. (Cichlidae)
Cichla sp. (Cichlidae)
Crenicara filamentosum (Cichlidae)
Curimatidae
Nannostomus sp. (Lebiasinidae)
Nannostomus trifasciatus (Lebiasinidae)
Nannostomus unifasciatus (Lebiasinidae)

Boulengerella maculata **CTENOLUCIIDAE** (13-16%)
Acestrorhynchus sp. (Characidae)
Tetragonopterinae (Characidae)
Characoidei spp.
Cichla spp. (larvae) (Cichlidae)
Larvae (Cichlidae)
Engraulidae spp.
Nannostomus marilynae (Lebiasinidae)
Nannostomus unifasciatus (Lebiasinidae)

Hoplias spp. **ERYTHRINIDAE** (29-46%)
Pseudanos trimaculatus (Anostomidae)
Characidae
Moenkhausia lepidura (Characidae)
Characoidei
Rivulus sp. (Cyprinodontidae)
Doradidae
Hoplias sp. (Erythinidae)
Hypopomus sp. (Hypopomidae)

Brachyplatystoma flavicans **PIMELODIDAE** (35%)
Gymnotoidei sp.

Goeldiella cf. *eques* **PIMELODIDAE** (8-23%)
Tetragonopterinae sp. (Characidae)
Cichla sp. (larvae) (Cichlidae)
Gymnotoidei sp.
Plecostominae sp. (Loricariidae)
Unidentified (larvae)

Pimelodus ornatus **PIMELODIDAE** (33%)
Characidae sp. remains
Tetragonopterinae spp. remains (Characidae)
Siluriformes sp.

APPENDIX 12

FISH IN FISH DIETS

Only those fish species whose diet consisted per volume of at least 25% of the indicated food item are listed.
Fish as a food item is divided into the three following categories:

Fish Flesh
Scales
Fin Rays

MSL = Mean Standard Length of fish population feeding on indicated food item.
MZUSP = Registration number of fish population in the Museu de Zoologia da Universidade de São Paulo.

FISH FLESH = PREDATION

		MSL	MZUSP
Beach			
Ageneiosus sp. 1	Ageneiosidae	230	34396
Ageneiosus sp. 2	Ageneiosidae	130	34407
Ageneiosus sp. 2	Ageneiosidae	140	34413
Ageneiosus sp. 2	Ageneiosidae	147	34409
Acestrocephalus sardina	Characidae	50	
Acestrocephalus sardina	Characidae	53	
Acestrocephalus sardina	Characidae	53	29241
Acestrocephalus sardina	Characidae	55	
Acestrocephalus sardina	Characidae	55	29237
Acestrorhynchus falcirostris	Characidae	186	
Acestrorhynchus falcirostris	Characidae	205	33299
Acestrorhynchus falcirostris	Characidae	249	33303
Acestrorhynchus grandoculis	Characidae	76	29281
Agoniates sp.	Characidae	135	34322
Serrasalminae sp. FU	Characidae	233	
Serrasalminae sp. FU	Characidae	241	
Serrasalminae sp. RH	Characidae	251	
Acaronia nassa	Cichlidae	70	
Aequidens pallidus	Cichlidae	66	29786
Cichla ocellaris	Cichlidae	137	
Cichla ocellaris	Cichlidae	140	
Cichla temensis	Cichlidae	175	
Crenicichla johanna	Cichlidae	203	32797
Crenicichla lenticulata	Cichlidae	150	
Crenicichla lugubris	Cichlidae	218	32832
Geophagus surinamensis	Cichlidae	163	32900
Hoplarchus psittacus	Cichlidae	188	
Hoplarchus psittacus	Cichlidae	221	
Boulengerella maculata	Ctenoluciidae	215	
Boulengerella maculata	Ctenoluciidae	217	
Boulengerella maculata	Ctenoluciidae	231	
Hoplias sp. 1	Erythrinidae	241	34003
Osteoglossum bicirrhosum	Osteoglossidae	550	
Brachyplatystoma flavicans	Pimelodidae	770	
Pimelodus ornatus	Pimelodidae	87	34481
Pseudopimelodus sp. 1	Pimelodidae	142	

		MSL	MZUSP
Rhabdolichops longicaudatus	Sternopygidae	340	
Ochmacanthus cf. *orinoco*	Trichomycteridae	25	30483
Ochmacanthus cf. *orinoco*	Trichomycteridae	31	30476
Ochmacanthus sp. MG	Trichomycteridae	37	30472
Pygidium sp.	Trichomycteridae	12	30354
Confluence Swamp			
Trachelyichthys sp.	Auchenipteridae	28	30600
Acestrorhynchus microlepis	Characidae	117	
Acestrorhynchus minimus	Characidae	59	
Agoniates sp.	Characidae	138	34334
Asiphonichthys condei	Characidae	36	29242
Moenkhausia lepidura A	Characidae	61	34627
Serrasalminae sp. BU	Characidae	167	
Crenicichla johanna	Cichlidae	280	32796
Geophagus surinamensis	Cichlidae	246	
Boulengerella lateristriga	Ctenoluciidae	154	32143
Goeldiella eques	Pimelodidae	119	34488
Flooded Forest			
Ageneiosus sp. 1	Ageneiosidae	240	34393
Ageneiosus sp. 1	Ageneiosidae	277	34394
Ageneiosus sp. 2	Ageneiosidae	140	34416
Ageneiosus sp. 2	Ageneiosidae	164	34415
Ageneiosus sp. A	Ageneiosidae	117	34362
Acestrorhynchus falcirostris	Characidae	357	
Agoniates sp.	Characidae	120	34327
Agoniates sp.	Characidae	135	34326
Serrasalminae sp. FU	Characidae	182	
Serrasalminae sp. GI	Characidae	146	
Serrasalminae sp. PA	Characidae	156	
Serrasalminae sp. RH	Characidae	218	
Cichla ocellaris	Cichlidae	205	
Cichla ocellaris	Cichlidae	255	
Cichla ocellaris	Cichlidae	292	
Cichla temensis	Cichlidae	262	
Cichla temensis	Cichlidae	318	
Cichla temensis	Cichlidae	344	
Cichla temensis	Cichlidae	400	
Crenicichla lugubris	Cichlidae	217	
Hoplarchus psittacus	Cichlidae	181	32968
Hoplarchus psittacus	Cichlidae	245	
Hoplarchus psittacus	Cichlidae	248	
Hoplias sp. 1	Erythrinidae	242	34006
Hoplias sp. 2	Erythrinidae	245	33448
Hoplias sp. 4	Erythrinidae	306	34002
Sternopygus macrurus	Sternopygidae	336	32214
Ochmacanthus sp. MG	Trichomycteridae	43	30474
Island Lake			
Leporinus cf. *agassizi*	Anostomidae	254	32428
Acestrorhynchus falcirostris	Characidae	147	33296
Acestrorhynchus falcirostris	Characidae	200	
Acestrorhynchus microlepis	Characidae	93	29266
Acestrorhynchus microlepis	Characidae	95	
Acestrorhynchus minimus	Characidae	62	29276

		MSL	MZUSP
Acestrorhynchus nasutus	Characidae	56	29270
Acestrorhynchus nasutus	Characidae	61	29268
Agoniates sp.	Characidae	152	34328
Asiphonichthys condei	Characidae	34	29244
Moenkhausia collettii	Characidae	33	34609
Cichla temensis	Cichlidae	301	32704
Crenicichla notophthalmus	Cichlidae	45	33344
Hoplarchus psittacus	Cichlidae	173	29809
Hoplarchus psittacus	Cichlidae	222	32970
Mesonauta insignis	Cichlidae	72	29766
Boulengerella lateristriga	Ctenoluciidae	96	32134
Boulengerella lateristriga	Ctenoluciidae	174	
Hoplias sp. 3	Erythrinidae	182	34012
Hoplias sp. 3	Erythrinidae	225	34010
Osteoglossum ferreirai	Osteoglossidae	424	29628
Rocky Pool			
Hyphessobrycon sp. 2	Characidae	21	35022
Moenkhausia collettii	Characidae	35	34597
Goeldiella eques	Pimelodidae	160	33189
Rhamphichthys sp. B	Rhamphichthyidae	644	32229
Rhabdolichops troscheli	Sternopygidae	210	32243
Woody Shore			
Ageneiosus sp. 1	Ageneiosidae	279	34390
Ageneiosus sp. 1	Ageneiosidae	296	34392
Acestrorhynchus falcirostris	Characidae	186	
Acestrorhynchus falcirostris	Characidae	208	
Acestrorhynchus falcirostris	Characidae	288	
Asiphonichthys condei	Characidae	35	29243
Moenkhausia collettii	Characidae	34	34612
Serrasalminae sp. FU	Characidae	166	
Serrasalminae sp. FU	Characidae	210	
Serrasalminae sp. RH	Characidae	251	
Acaronia nassa	Cichlidae	123	
Aequidens pallidus	Cichlidae	148	29794
Biotodoma wavrini	Cichlidae	105	29735
Crenicichla johanna	Cichlidae	211	32795
Crenicichla lenticulata	Cichlidae	241	32802
Crenicichla lugubris	Cichlidae	213	32823
Crenicichla notophthalmus	Cichlidae	38	33345
Hoplarchus psittacus	Cichlidae	175	
Hoplarchus psittacus	Cichlidae	238	
Hoplarchus psittacus	Cichlidae	240	
Boulengerella lateristriga	Ctenoluciidae	153	32133
Hoplias sp. 2	Erythrinidae	265	33449
Hoplias sp. 3	Erythrinidae	251	34019
Osteoglossum bicirrhosum	Osteoglossidae	460	29662

SCALES

Beach			
Cichlasoma coryphaenoides	Cichlidae	135	
Pimelodus cf. *blochii*	Pimelodidae	73	33321
Confluence Swamp			
Serrabrycon magoi	Characidae	29	29395

APPENDIX 12 CON'T

		MSL	MZUSP
Flooded Forest			
Myleus schomburgkii	Characidae	239	
Serrasalminae sp. RH	Characidae	0	
Aequidens pallidus	Cichlidae	23	29792
Goeldiella eques	Pimelodidae	191	34491
Pimelodus cf. *blochii*	Pimelodidae	182	
Island Lake			
Gymnotus carapo	Gymnotidae	319	30185
Rocky Pool			
Hoplosternum thoracatum	Callichthyidae	104	33397
Woody Shore			
Astronotus ocellatus	Cichlidae	231	32703
Crenicara filamentosum	Cichlidae	27	29718
Platydoras costatus	Doradidae	220	32554
Goeldiella eques	Pimelodidae	200	34493
FIN RAYS			
Beach			
Serrasalminae sp. CH	Characidae	171	
Serrasalminae sp. PA	Characidae	174	
Serrasalminae sp. RH	Characidae	251	
Woody Shore			
Serrasalminae sp. FU	Characidae	210	

REFERENCES

ADIS, J. 1981. Comparative ecological studies of the terrestrial arthropod fauna in central Amazonian inundation forests. *Amazoniana.* 7(2):87-173.

ADIS, J. 1984. Seasonal igapó-forests of Central Amazonian blackwater rivers and their terrestrial arthropod fauna. *In:* H. Sioli (ed.). *The Amazon: Limnology and Landscape Ecology.* Dr W Junk Publishers, Dordrecht:245-268.

ADIS, J., K. FURCH & U. IRMLER. 1979. Litter production of a Central-Amazonian black water inundation forest. *Trop. Ecol.* 20(2):236-245.

AGASSIZ, L. & E. AGASSIZ. 1867. *A Journey in Brazil.* Ticknor & Fields, Boston. 540 pp..

ALMEIDA, R.G. 1984. Biologia alimentar de tres espécies de *Triportheus* (Pisces: Characoidei, Characidae) do Lago Castanho, Amazonas. *Acta Amazonica.* 14(1-2):48-76.

ALVES, L.F. 1983. Estudo sazonal da produção primária e fatores ecológicos num lago de terra firme da Amazônia Central (Lago Verde-Rio Negro). *Master's Thesis.* Instituto Nacional de Pesquisas da Amazônia. 132pp.

ANDERSON, A.B. 1981. White-sand vegetation of Brazilian Amazonia. *Biotropica.* 13(3):199-210.

ANGERMEIER, P.I. & J.R. KARR 1983. Fish communities along environmental gradients in a system of tropical streams. *Environ. Biol. Fish.* 9(2):39-57.

ANON. 1972. Die ionenfracht des Rio Negro, staat Amazonas, Brasilien, nach untersuchungen von Dr. Harald Ungermach. *Amazoniana.* 3(2):175-185.

ARAUJO-LIMA, C.A.R.M. 1984. Distribuição espacial e temporal de larvas de Characiformes em um setor do Rio Solimões-Amazonas, próximo a Manaus, AM. *Master's Thesis.* Instituto Nacional de Pesquisas da Amazônia, Manaus.

ARAUJO-LIMA, C.A.R.M. 1985. Aspectos biológicos de peixes amazonicos. V. Desenvolvimento larval do jaraqui escama grossa, *Semaprochilodus insignis* (Characiformes, Pisces) da Amazônia Central. *Rev. Bras. Biol.* 45(4):1-9.

ARAUJO LIMA, C.A.R.M. & E. HARDY. 1987. Aspectos biológicos de peixes amazônicos. VIII. Alimentação dos alevinos de jaraqui, *Semaprochilodus insignis. Amazoniana,* 10(2):127–136.

ARAUJO-LIMA, C.A.R.M., L.P.S PORTUGAL & E.G. FERREIRA. 1986. Fish-macrophyte relationship in the Anavilhanas Arquipelago, a blackwater system in the Central Amazon. *J. Fish Biol.* 29:1–11.

BACHMANN, A.O. 1977. Heteroptera. *In:* S.H. Hurlbert (ed.). *Biota Acuática de Sudamérica Austral.* San Diego State University, San Diego:189-212.

BATES, H.W. 1863. *The Naturalist on the River Amazons.* John Murray, London, 2 vols.

BAYLEY, P.B. 1973. Studies on the migratory characin, *Prochilodus platensis* Holmberg 1889, (Pisces, Characoidei) in the river Pilcomayo, South America. *J. Fish Biol.* 5:25-40.

BAYLEY, P.B. 1979. The limits of limnological theory and approaches as applied to river-floodplain systems and their fish production. *FAO Tecnichal Paper.* 194:23-26.

BAYLEY, P.B. 1980. The limits of limnological theory and approaches as applied to river-floodplain systems and their fish production. *Trop. Ecol. Dev..* 739-746.

BAYLEY, P.B. 1981. Fish yield from the Amazon in Brazil: comparison with African river yields and management possibilities. *Trans. Amer. Fish. Soc.* 110:251-259.

BAYLEY, P.B. 1982. Central Amazon fish populations: Biomass, production and some dynamic characteristics. *Ph.D. Dissertation.* Dalhousie University.

BAYLEY, P.B. & M. PETRERE. 1986. Amazon fisheries and the aquatic system: current status. *LARS Symposium (Ontario).* 44pp (manuscript).

BEST, R.C. 1984. The aquatic mammals and reptiles of the Amazon. *In:*H. Sioli (ed.). *The Amazon: Limnology and Landscape Ecology.* Dr W Junk Publishers, Dordrecht:371-412.

BOHLKE, J.E., S.H WEITZMAN & N.A. MENEZES. 1978. Estado atual da sistemática de peixes de agua doce da América do Sul. *Acta Amazonica.* 8(4):657-677.

BORGES, G.A. 1986. Ecologia de três espécies do gênero *Brycon* no Rio Negro (Amazonas), com ênfase na caracterização e alimentação. *Master's Thesis*. Instituto Nacional de Pesquisas da Amazônia. 131p.

BOTT, R. 1967. Flusskrabben aus Brasilien und Benachbarter Gebiete, *Potamocarcinus* (Kensley) Ortmann 1897 (Crustacea, Decapoda). *Senck. Biol.*. 48(4):301-312.

BOTT, R. 1969. Die susswasserkrabben Sud-Amerikas und ihre Stammesgeschichte. *Abh. senck. naturf. Ges.* 518:1-94.

BOWEN, S.H. 1984. Detritivory in neotropical fish communities. *In*:T.M. Zaret (ed.). *Evolutionary Ecology of Neotropical Freshwater Fishes*. Dr W. Junk Publishers, The Hague: 59-66.

BOWEN, S.H., A.A. BONETTO & M.O. AHLGREN. 1984. Microorganisms and detritus in the diet of a typical neotropical riverine detritivore, *Prochilodus platensis* (Pisces: Prochilodontidae). *Limnol. Oceanogr.* 29(5):1120-1122.

BRANDORFF, G.O. 1977. Untersuchungen zur Populationsdynamik des Crustaceenplanktons im tropischen Lago Castanho (Amazonas, Brasilien). Ph.D. Dissertation. Kiel.

BROOKS, J.L. 1968. The effects of prey size selection by lake planktivores. *Syst. Zool.* 17:119-127.

CALA, P. 1977. Los Peces de la Orinoquia colombiana. Lista preliminar anotada. *Lozania (Acta zool. Colombiana).* 24:1-21.

CALVALCANTE, P.B. 1978. Contribuição ao conhecimento das Gnetáceas da Amazônia (Gimnospermas). *Acta Amazonica.* 8(2):201-215.

CARBONELL, C.S. 1981. Orthoptera. *Aquatic Biota of Tropical South America. Part 1. Arthropoda. In:* S.H. Hurlbert, G. Rodriquez and N.D. Santos (eds.). San Diego State University, San Diego: 92-99.

CARDENAS, J.D.R. 1981. Aspectos florísticos e fitossociológicos da floresta inundável (Igapó) Praia Grande, Rio Negro, Amazonas, Brasil. *Master's Thesis*. Instituto Nacional de Pesquisas da Amazônia.

CARVALHO, J.C.M. 1983. *Viagem Filosófica pelas Capitanias do Grão Pará, Rio Negro, Matto Grosso e Cuiabá (1783-1793)*. CNPq/Museu Paraense Emilio Goeldi, Belém. 80pp.

CARVALHO, M.L. 1981. Alimentação do tambaqui jovem (*Colossoma macropomum* Cuvier 1818) e sua relação com a comunidade zooplanctônica do lago Grande-Manaquiri, Solimões-AM. *Master's Thesis*. Instituto Nacional de Pesquisas da Amazônia.

CARVALHO, M.L. 1984. Influence of predation by fish and water turbidity on a *Daphnia gessneri* population in an Amazonian floodplain lake, Brazil. *Hydrobiologia*. 113:243-247.

CARVALHO, M.L. & M. GOULDING. 1985. On the feeding ecology of the catfish *Hypophthalmus fimbriatus* in the blackwater Rio Negro of the Amazon Basin. *Revta bras. Zool., S Paulo*. 3(1):33-41.

CHERNELA, J.M. 1983. Hierarchy and economy of the Uanano (Kotiria) speaking peoples of the middle Uaupes basin. *Ph.D. Dissertation*. Columbia Univeristy. 179pp.

COLLETTE, B.B. 1966. A review of the venomous toadfishes, subfamily Thalassophryninae. *Copeia*. 8(4):846-864.

COLLETTE, B.B. 1974. South American freshwater needlefishes (Belonidae) of the genus *Pseudotylosurus*. *Zoologisch. Mededel*. 48(16):169-186.

CONFER, J.L. & P.I. BLADES. 1975. Omnivorous zooplankton and planktivorous fish. *Limn. Ocean.*. 20:571-579.

COOK, D.R. 1981. Acari. *In:* S.H. Hurlbert, G. Rodriquez and N.D. Santos (eds.). *Aquatic Biota of Tropical South America. Part 1. Arthropoda*. San Diego State University, San Diego: 317-323.

COOK, E.F. 1981. Chaoboridae. S.H. Hurlbert, G. Rodriquez and N.D. Santos (eds.). *Aquatic Biota of Tropical South America. Part 1. Arthropoda*. San Diego State University, San Diego: 259-260.

DOYLE, A.C. 1912. *The Lost World*. A.L. Burt Company, New York. 309pp.

DUCKE, A. & G. BLACK. 1953. Phytogeographical notes on the Brazilian Amazon. *Anais Acad. Bras. Cien*. 25(1):1-46.

EDWARDS, A.M.C. & J.B. THORNES. 1970. Observations on the dissolved solids of the Casiquiare and upper Orinoco, April-June, 1968. *Amazoniana*. 2(3):245-256.

EHRLICH, P.R. 1975. The population biology of coral reef fishes. *Ann. Rev. Syst. Ecol*. 6:211-247.

EIGENMANN, C.H. 1917-1929. The American Characidae. *Mem. Mus. Comp. Zool., Harvard* XLIII (5 parts):1-558 (Part V with G.S. Myers).

EMERY, A.R. 1978. The basis of fish community structure: marine and freshwater comparisons. *Envir. Biol. Fish*. 3:33-47.

FERREIRA, A.R. 1972. *Viagem Filosófica pelas Capitanias do Grão-Para, Rio Negro, Mato Grosso e Cuiaba*. Conselho Federal da Cultura, Rio de Janeiro. 246 pp.

FERREIRA, A.R. 1983. *Viagem Filosófica ao Rio Negro*. Conselho Nacional de Desenvolvimento Cientifico e Tecnológico, Brasilia.

FERREIRA, E.J.G. 1981. Alimentação dos adultos de doze espécies de cichlídeos (Perciformes, Cichlidae) do Rio Negro, Brasil. *Master's Thesis*. Instituto Nacional de Pesquisas da Amazônia, Manaus.

FERREIRA, E.J.G. 1984. A ictiofauna da represa hidrelétrica de Curuá-una, Santarém, Pará. II. Alimentação e hábitos alimentares das principais espécies. *Amazoniana 9(1):1-16*.

FISHER, T.R. 1978. Plâncton e produção primária em sistemas aquáticos da bacia da Amazonia Central. *Acta Amazonica*. 8(4):43-54.

FISHER, T.R. 1979. Plankton and primary production in aquatic systems of the Central Amazon basin. *Comp. Biochem. Physiol.* 62:31-38.

FITTKAU, E.J. 1974. Zur okologischen gliederung Amazoniens. I. Die erdgeschichtliche Entwicklung Amazoniens. *Amazoniana*. 5(1):77-134.

FITTKAU, E.J. 1971. Distribution and ecology of Amazonian chironomids (Diptera). *Can. Ent.* 103:407-413.

FLINT, O.F. 1981. Trichoptera. *In:* S.H. Hurlbert, G. Rodriquez and N.D. Santos (eds.). *Aquatic Biota of Tropical South America. Part 1. Arthropoda*. San Diego State University, San Diego: 221-226.

FOLDATS, E. 1962. La concentración de oxigeno disuelta en las aguas negras. *Acta Biologica Venezuelica*. 3(10):149-159.

FONSECA, O.J.M., J.I. SALEM & V.L. GUARIM. 1982. Poluição e autopurificação do Rio Negro nas cercanias de Manaus. *Acta Amazonica*. 12(2):271-278.

FOWLER, H.W. 1954. Os peixes de água doce do Brasil. *Arq. Zool. Estado de São Paulo*. 9(1-9):1-400.

FRANKEN, M., U. IRMLER & KLINGE, H. 1979. Litterfall in inundation, riverine and terra firme forests of Central Amazonia. *Trop. Ecol.* 20(2):225-235.

FRIEBE, B. & J. ADIS. 1983. Entwicklungszyklen von Opiliones (Arachnida) im Schwarzwasser-Uberschwemmungswald (igapó) des Rio Taruma Mirim (Zentralamazonien, Brasilien). *Amazoniana*. 8(1):101-110.

FROST, W.E. 1977. The food of charr, *Salvelinus willughbii* (Gunther) in Windemere. *Jour. Fish Biol.* 11:531-547.

FRYER, G. & T.D. ILES. 1972. *The Cichlid Fishes of the Great Lakes of Africa*. Oliver & Boyd, Edinburgh.

FURCH, K. 1984. Water chemistry of the Amazon basin: the distribution of chemical elements among freshwaters. *In:* H. Sioli (ed.). *The Amazon: Limnology and Landscape Ecology*. Dr W. Junk Publishers, Dordrecht: 167-200.

GALBRAITH, M.G. 1967. Size selective predation on *Daphnia* by rainbow trout and yellow perch. *Trans. Amer. Fish. Soc.* 96(1):1-10.

GARCIA-NOVO, F. & R.M.N. CRAWFORD. 1973. Soil aeration, nitrate reduction and flooding tolerance in higher plants. *New Phytol.* 72:1031-1039.

GEISLER, R. 1969. Untersuchungen uber den Sauerstoffgehalt, den biochemischen Sauerstoffbedarf und den Sauerstoffverbrauch von Fischen in einem tropischen Schwarzwasser (Rio Negro, Amazonien, Brasilien). *Arch. Hydrobiol.* 66(3):307-325.

GERY, J. 1977. *Characoids of the World*. TFH Publications, Neptune City. 672pp.

GESSNER, F. 1958. Relatório provisório de pesquisas limnológicas na região Amazônica. *Publicacões Avulsas do INPA*. 1-29.

GESSNER, F. 1962. O regime de oxigênio do Rio Amazonas. *Bol. Mus. paraense Emilio Goeldi*. 1:43-71.

GESSNER, F. 1968. Zur ökologischen Problematik der Überschwemmungswalder des Amazonas. *Internationale Revue der Gesamten Hydrobiologie*. 53(4):525-547.

GIBBS, R.J. 1967. The geochemistry of the Amazon river system. Part 1. The factors that control the salinity and the compostion of the suspended solids. *Geol. Soc. Amer. Bull.* 78:1203-1232.

GIBBS, R.J. 1971. Amazon river: environmental factors that control its dissolved and suspended load. *Science*. 56:1734-1736.

GIBBS, R.J. 1972. Water chemistry of the Amazon river. *Geochim. Cosmochim. Acta* 36:1061-1066.

GODOI, M.P. 1962. Marcação, migração e transplantação de peixes marcados na bacia do rio Paraná superior. *Arq. Mus. Nac. (Rio de Janeiro)*. 52:105-113.

GODOI, M.P. 1967. Dez anos de observações sobre periodicidade migratória de peixes do rio Mogi Guassu. *Rev. Bras. Biol.* 27(1)1-12.

GODOI, M.P. 1972. Brazilian tagging experiments, fish migration, and upper Paraná river basin ecosystem. *Rev. Bras. Biol.* 32(4):473-484.

GOELDI, E.A. 1895. *Ensaio sobre o Dr. Alexandre R. Ferreira.* Alfredo Silva, Belém.

GOTTSBERGER, G. 1978. Seed dispersal by fish in the inundated regions of Humaitá, Amazonia. *Biotropica.* 10(3):170-183.

GOULDING, M. 1979. *Ecologia da Pesca do Rio Madeira.* Conselho Nacional de Pesquisas e Tecnologia/Instituto Nacional de Pesquisas da Amazônia, Belém. 172pp.

GOULDING, M. 1980. *The Fishes and the Forest: Explorations in Amazonian Natural History.* University of California Press, Berkeley. 280 pp.

GOULDING, M. 1981. *Man and Fisheries on an Amazon Frontier.* Dr W. Junk Publishers, The Hague. 132 pp.

GOULDING, M., 1983a. Amazonian fisheries. *In:* E.F. Moran (ed.). *The Dilemma of Amazonian Development.* Westview Press, Colorado: 189-210.

GOULDING, M. 1983b. The role of fishes in seed dispersal and plant distribution in Amazonian floodplain ecosystems. *In: Dispersal and Distribution.* K. Kubitzki (ed.). *Sonderbd. naturwiss. Verein Hamburg* 7:271-283.

GOULDING, M., 1985. Forest fishes of the Amazon. *In: Amazonia.* Prance, G.T. & T.E. Lovejoy (eds.). Pergamon Press, Oxford 267-276.

GOULDING, M. & M.L. CARVALHO. 1982. Life history and management of the tambaqui (*Colossoma macropomum*, Characidae): An important Amazonian food fish. *Rev. Bras. Zool., S. Paulo.* 1(2):107-133.

GOULDING, M. & M.L. CARVALHO. 1984. Ecology of Amazonian needlefishes. *Revta. bras. Zool., S Paulo.* 2(3):99-111.

GOULDING, M., M.L. CARVALHO & E.J.G. FERREIRA. No date. *First Handbook for Rio Negro Fish Studies.*

GOULDING, M. & E.J.G. FERREIRA. 1984. Shrimp-eating fishes and a case of prey-switching in Amazon rivers. *Revta bras. Zool., S. Paulo.* 2(3):85-97.

GREEN, J. 1967. The distribution and variation of *Daphnia lumholtzi* (Crustacea, Cladocera) in relation to fish predation in Lake Albert, East Africa. *J. Zool.,London.* 151:181-197.

GREENWOOD, P.H., D.E. ROSEN, S.H. WEITZMAN & G.S. MYERS. 1966. Phyletic studies of teleostean fishes, with a provisional classification of living forms. *Bull. Amer. Mus. nat. Hist.* 131(4):339-456.

HARDY, E.R. 1980. Composição do zooplâncton em cinco lagos da Amazônia Central. *Acta Amazonica.* 10(3):577-609.

HASS, F. 1949a. Land- und Süsswassermollusken aus dem Amazonas-Gebiet. *Archiv fur Mollusk.* 78(4/6):149-156.

HASS, F. 1949b. On fresh water mollusks from the Amazonian region. *An. Inst. Biol. (Mexico).* 20(1/2):301-314.

HASS, F. 1950. Some land and freshwater mollusks from Para State, Brazil. *Nautilus.* 64(1):4-6.

HEILINGENBERG, W. & J. BASTIAN. 1980. Species specificity of electric organ discharges in sympatric Gymnotoid fish of the Rio Negro. *Acta Biologica Venezuelica.* 10(2):187-203.

HEILINGENBERG, W. & J. BASTIAN. 1981. Especificidade das descargas do orgão elétrico em espécies de Gimnotoides simpátricos do rio Negro. *Acta Amazonica.* 11(3):429-437.

HORI, M. 1983. Feeding ecology of 13 species of *Lamprologus* (Cichlidae) coexisting at a rocky shore of L. Tanganyika. *Physiology & Ecology, Japan.* 20:129-149.

HORI, M., K. YAMAOKA & K. TAKAMURA. 1983. Abundance and micro-distribution of cichlid fishes on a rocky shore in L. Tanganyika. *African Study Monographs, Kyoto.* 3:25-38.

HUBER, J. 1909. Mattas e madeiras amazônicas. *Bol. Mus. Para. E. Goeldi (Hist. nat. ethnogr.).* 6:91-225.

HUMBOLDT, A. VON. 1852. *Personal Narrative of Travels to the Equinoctial Regions of America,During the Years 1799-1804.* Henry G. Bohn, London, 3 vols.

HYNES, H.B.N. 1950. The food of freshwater stickleback (*Gasterosteus aculeatus*) and *Pygosteus pungitius*), with a review of methods used in studies of the food of fishes. *J. Anim. Ecol.* 19(1):35-58.

HYSLOP, E.J. 1980. Stomach contents analysis – a review methods and their application. *J. Fish. Biol.* 17:411-429.

IRION, G. 1984. Sedimentation and sediments of Amazonian rivers and evolution of the Amazonian landscape since Pliocene times. *In:* H. Sioli (ed.). *The Amazon: Limnology and Landscape Ecology.* Dr W.Junk Publishers, Dordrecht: 201-214.

IRMLER, U. 1973. Population-dynamic and physiological adaptation of *Pentacomia egregia* Chaud. (Col. Cicindelidae) to the Amazonian inundation forest. *Amazoniana*. 4(2):219-227.

IRMLER, U. 1975. Ecological studies of the aquatic soil invertebrates in three inundation forest of Central Amazonia. *Amazoniana*. 5(3):337-409.

IRMLER, U. 1976a. Anpassung von *Eupera simoni* Jousseaume (Bivalvia, Sphaeriidae) an den zentralamazonischen Uberschwemmungswald. *Verh. dtsch. zool. Ges.* 225.

IRMLER, U. 1976b. Zusammensetzung, Besiedlungsdichte und Biomasse der Makrofauna des Bodens in der emersen und submersen Phase dreier zentralamazonischer überschwemmungswalder. *Biogeographica*. 7:79-99.

IRMLER, U. 1977. Inundation-forest types in the vicinity of Manaus. *Biogeographica*. 8:17-29.

IRMLER, U. 1978a. Die Struktur der Carabiden- und Staphylini-dengesellschaften in zentralamazonischen Überschwemmungswäldern. *Amazoniana*. 6(3):301-326.

IRMLER, U. 1978b. Matas de inundação da Amazônia Central em comparação entre águas brancas e pretas. *Ciência e Cultura*. 30(7):813-821.

IRMLER, U. 1979a. Abundance fluctuation and habitat changes of soil beetles in Central Amazonian inundation forest (Coleoptera: Carabidae, Staphylinidae). *Stud. neotrop. Fauna Environ.* 14:1-16.

IRMLER, U. 1979b. Considerations on structure and function of the Central-Amazonian inundation forest ecosystem with particular emphasis soil animals. *Oecologia*. 43:1-18.

IRMLER, U. 1981. Überlebensstrategien von Tieren im saisonal überfluteten amazonischen Überschwemmungswald (Survival strategies of animals in the seazonally flooded Amazonian inundation forest). *Zool. Anz. Jena*. 206(1/2):26-38.

IRMLER, U. 1982. Litterfall and nitrogen turnover in an Amazonian blackwater inundation forest. *Plant and Soil*. 67:355-358.

IRMLER, U. & K. FURCH. 1980. Weight, energy and nutrient changes during the decomposition of leaves in the emersion phase of Central-Amazonian inundation forest. *Pedobiologia*. 20:118-130.

IRMLER, U. & W. J. JUNK. 1982. The inhabitation of artificially exposed leaf samples by aquatic macro-invertebrates at the margin of Amazonian inundation forests. *Trop. Ecol.* 23(1):64-75.

ISBRUCKER, I.J.H. 1980. Classification and catalogue of the mailed Loricariidae (Pisces, Siluriformes. *Verslagen en Technische Gegevens*. 22:1-181.

JANSEN, J. 1976. Feeding modes and prey size selection in the alewife (*Alosa pseudoharengus*). *J. Fish Res. Board Can.* 33:1972-1975.

JANZEN, D.H. 1974. Tropical blackwater rivers, animals, and mast fruiting by the Dipterocarpaceae. *Biotropica*. 6(2):69-103.

JANZEN, D.H. 1976. *The Ecology of Plants in the Tropics*. Edward Arnold, London. 66pp.

JANZEN, D.H. 1978. Complications in interpreting the chemical defenses of trees against tropical arboreal plant-eating vertebrates. *In:* G.G. Montgomery (ed.). *The Ecology of Arboreal Folivores*. Smithsonian Institution Press, Washington: 73-84.

JORDAN, C.F. & J. HEUVELDOP. 1981. The water budget of an Amazonian rain forest. *Acta Amazonica*. 11(1):87-92.

JUNK, W.J. 1970. Investigations on the ecology and production-biology of the floating meadows (Paspalo-Echinochloetum) on the middle Amazon. I. The floating vegetation and its ecology. *Amazoniana*. 2:449-495.

JUNK, W.J. 1973. Investigations on the ecology and production biology of the floating meadows (Paspalo-Echinochloetum) on the middle Amazon. II. The aquatic fauna in the root-zone of floating vegetation. *Amazoniana*. 4(1):9-102.

JUNK, W.J. 1979. Macrófitas aquáticas nas várzeas da Amazônia e possibilidades do seu uso na agropecuária. Conselho Nacional de Desevolvimento Cientifico e Tecnológico. 23pp.

JUNK, W.J. 1980. Aquatic macrophytes: ecology and use in Amazonian agriculture. *Trop. Biol. Dev.* 763-770.

JUNK, W.J. 1983. Aquatic habitats in Amazônia. *The Environmentalist*. 3(5):24-34.

JUNK, W.J.1984. Ecology of the varzea floodplain of Amazonian whitewater rivers. *In:* H. Sioli (ed.). *The Amazon: Limnology and Landscape Ecology*. Dr W. Junk Publishers, Dordrecht: 215-244.

JUNK, W.J., G.M. SOARES & F.M. CARVALHO. 1983. Distribution of fish species in a lake of the Amazon river floodplain near Manaus (Lago Camaleão), with special reference to extreme oxygen conditions. *Amazoniana*. 7(4):397-432.

JUNK, W.J. & C. HOWARD-WILLIAMS. 1984. Ecology of aquatic macrophytes in Amazonia. *In: The Amazon: Limnology and Landscape Ecology of a Mighty Tropical River and Its Basin*. Sioli, H. (ed.). Dr. W. Junk Publishers, Dordrecht: 269-293.

182

KEEL, S.H.K. & G.T. PRANCE. 1979. Studies of the vegetation of a white-sand black-water igapo (Rio Negro, Brazil). *Acta Amazonica.* 9(4):645-655.

KENSLEY, B. & I. WALKER. 1982. Palaemonidae shrimps from the Amazon Basin, Brazil. *Smithsonian Contr. Zool.* 362:1-28.

KIEFER, V.F. 1967. Zewi neue Parastenocaris-Arten (Copepoda, Harpactiocoida) aus dem mittleren Amazonas-Gebiet. *Amazoniana.* 1(2):131-134.

KLAMMER, G. 1984. The relief of extra-Andean Amazon basin. *In:* H. Sioli (ed.). *The Amazon: Limnology and Landscape Ecology.* Dr W. Junk Publishers, Dordrecht: 47-84.

KLINGE, H. 1965. Podzol soils of the Amazon Basin. *J. Soil Sci.* 16:95-103.

KLINGE, H. 1966. Tropische Podsole und Schwarzwasser. *Umschau.* 540.

KLINGE, H. 1967. Podzol soils: a source of black water rivers in Amazonia. *Atas do Simpósio sobre a Biota Amazônica.* 3:117-125.

KLINGE, H. 1976. Nahrstoffe, Wasser und Durchwürzung von Podsolen und Latosolen unter tropischem Regenwald bei Manaus (Amazonien). *Biogeographica.* 7:45-58.

KLINGE, H., W.A. RODRIGUES, E. BRUNIG & E.J. FITTKAU. 1975. Biomass and structure in a Central Amazonian rain forest. *In: Tropical Ecological Systems.* Golley, F.B. & E. Medina (eds.). Springer-Verlag, New York: 115-122.

KNOPPEL, H.A. 1970. Food of central Amazonian fishes. Contribution to the nutrient-ecology of Amazonian rain forest streams. *Amazoniana.* 11(3):257-352.

KOCH-GRUNBERG, T. 1909-1910. *Zwei Jahre unter den Indianern. Reise in Nordwest-Brasilien, 1903-1905.* Berlin, 2 vols.

KOSTE, W. 1972. Rotatorien aus Gewässern Amazoniens. *Amazoniana.* 3(3/4):258-505.

KUBITZKI, K. 1985. Ichthyochory in *Gnetum venosum. An. Acad. brasil. Cien.* 57(4):513-516.

KULLANDER, S.O., 1980. A taxonomical study of the genus *Apistogramma* Regan, with a revision of Brazilian and Peruvian species (Teleostei: Percoidei:Cichlidae). *Bonner Zool. Monograp..* 14:1-152..

KULLANDER, S.O. 1983. Revision of the South American *Cichlasoma.* The Swedish Museum of Natural History, Stockholm. 480pp.

KULLANDER, S.O. 1986. *Cichlid Fishes of the Amazon River Drainage of Peru.* Swedish Museum of Natural History, Stockholm, 431p.

LADIGES, W. & D. VOGT. 1979. *Die Süsswasserfische Europas.* Paul Parey, Hamburg und Berlin. 299pp.

LEENHEER, J.A. 1980. Origin and nature of humic substances in the waters of the Amazon river basin. *Acta Amazonica.* 10(3):513-526.

LEENHEER, J.A. & U.M. SANTOS. 1980. Considerações sobre os processos de sedimentação na água preta ácida do rio Negro (Amazônia Central). *Acta Amazonica.* 10(2):343-355.

LEWIS, R.W. 1970. Fish cutaneous mucus: a new source of skin surface lipids. *Lipids.* 5:947-949.

LOFFLER, H. 1981. Copepoda. S.H. Hurlbert, G. Rodriquez & N.D. Santos (eds.). *Aquatic Biota of Tropical South America. Part 1. Arthropoda.* San Diego State University, San Diego: 14-19.

LOWE-McCONNELL, R.H. 1964. The fishes of the Rupununi savanna district of British Guiana, South America. Part 1. Ecological groupings of fish species and effects of the seasonal cycle on the fish. *Journ. Linn. Soc. Lond. (Zool.).* 45(304):103-144.

LOWE-McCONNELL, R.H. 1967. Some factors affecting fish populations in Amazonian waters. *Atas do Simpósio sobre a Biota Amazônica (Zoologia).* 7:177-186.

LOWE-McCONNELL, R.H. 1969. Speciation in tropical freshwater fishes. *Biol. J. Linn. Soc.* 1:51-57.

LOWE-McC0NNELL, R.H. 1975. *Ecology of Fishes in Tropical Freshwaters: Their Distribution, Ecology and Evolution.* Longman, London.

LOWE-McCONNELL, R.H. 1979. Ecological aspects of seasonality in fishes of tropical waters. *Symp. Zool. Soc. Lond.* 44:219-241.

LOWE-McCONNELL, R.H. 1984. The status of studies on South American freshwater food fishes. *In: Evolutionary Ecology of Neotropical Freshwater Fishes.* Zaret, T.M (ed.). Dr. W. Junk Publishers, The Hague: 139-156.

LOWE-McCONNELL, R.H. 1987. *Ecological Studies in Tropical Fish Communities.* Cambridge University Press, London. 382p.

MACEDO, M. 1975. Dispersão de plantas lenhosas de uma campina Amazônica. *Acta Amazonica (Suplemento).* 7(1):1-69.

MACEDO, M. & G.T. PRANCE. 1978. Notes on the vegetation of Amazonia. II. The dispersal of plants in Amazonian white sand campinas: the campinas as functional islands. *Brittonia.* 30(2):203-215.

183

MAGO-LECCIA,F. 1970. Lista de los peces de Venezuela, incluyendo un estudio preliminar sobre la ictiogeografia del pais. Ministerio de Agricultura e Cria, Caracas. 283pp.

MAGO-LECCIA, F. 1972. La ictiofauna del Casiquiare. *Rev. Def. Nat.* 1(4):5-10.

MAGO-LECCIA, F. 1978. Los peces de agua dulce de Venezuela. *Cuadernos Lagoven, Ecologia.* 35pp.

MAHNERT, V. 1979. Pseudoskorpione (Arachnida) aus dem Amazonasgebiet (Brasilien). *Rev. Suisse Zool.* 86(3):719-810.

MARLIER, G., 1967. Ecological studies on some lakes of the Amazon valley. *Amazoniana.* 1:91-115.

MARLIER, G., 1968. Les poissons du lac Rondo et leur alimentaires trophiques du lac Redondo; les poissons du Rio Preto da Eva. *Cadernos da Amazônia.* 11:21-57.

McNAUGHTON, S.J. 1968. Structure and function in California grasslands. *Ecology.* 49:962-972.

MEADE, R.H., C.F. NORDIN, W.F. CURTIS, F.M. COSTA-RODRIGUES, C.M. VALE & J.M. EDMOND. 1979. Transporte de sedimentos no rio Amazonas. *Acta Amazonica.* 9(3):529-547.

MEDEM, F. 1981. Les Crococylia de sur America. Vol. 1. Les Crocodylia de Colombia. Ministerio Educ. Nac., Bogotá.

MEDINA, J.T. 1934. *The Discovery of the Amazon According to the Account of Friar Gaspar de Carvajal and other Documents.* American Geographical Society, New York. 467pp.

MENEZES, N.A. 1969. Systematics and evolution of the tribe Acestrorhynchini (Pisces, Characidae). *Arq. Zool., S. Paulo.* 18(1-2):1-150.

MENEZES, N.A. & J. GERY. 1983. Seven new Acestrorhynchin Characid species (Osteichthyes, Ostariophysi, Characiformes) with comments on the systematics of the group. *Revue suisse Zool.* 90(3):563-592.

MILL, A.E. 1982. Populações de termitas (Insecta: Isoptera) em quatro habitats no baixo rio Negro. *Acta Amazonica.* 12(1):53-60.

MONTGOMERY, G.G. (ed.). 1978. *The Ecology of Arboreal Folivores.* Smithsonian Institution Press, Washington.

MYERS, G.S. 1944. Two extraordinary new blind nematognath fishes from the Rio Negro, representing a new subfamily of Pygidiidae, with a rearrangement of the genera of the family, and illustrations of some previously described genera and species from Venezuela and Brazil. *Proc. Calif. Acad. Sci.* 23(40):591-602.

MYERS, G.S. & S.H. WEITZMAN. 1966. Two remarkable new trichomycterid catfishes from the Amazon basin in Brazil and Colombia. *J. Zool. Lond.* 149:277-287.

NESSIMIAN, J.L. 1985. Estudo sobre a biologia e a ecologia da fauna invertebrada aquática na liteira submersa das margens de dois lagos do Arquipélago de Anavilhanas (Rio Negro, Amazonas, Brasil). Master's Thesis. Instituto Nacional de Pesquisas da Amazonia. 114pp.

NIESER, N. 1981. Hemiptera. *In:* S.H. Hurlbert, G. Rodriquez and N.D. Santos (eds.). *Aquatic Biota of Tropical South America. Part 1. Arthropoda.* San Diego State University, San Diego: 100-128.

O'BRIEN, W.J. 1979. The predatory-prey interaction of plantivorous fish and zooplankton. *Amer. Nat.* 67:572-581.

PAIXÃO, I.M.P. 1980. Estudo da alimentação e reprodução de *Mylossoma duriventris* Cuvier, 1818 (Pisces, Characoidei) do Lago Janauacá, Am., Brasil. Master's Thesis. Instituto Nacional de Pesquisas da Amazônia. 127pp.

PARENTI, L. 1981. A phylogenetic and biogeographic analysis of cyprinodontiform fishes (Teleostei, Atherinomorpha). *Bull. Amer. Mus. Nat. Hist.* 168(4):341-557.

PARTRIDGE, B.L. 1982. The structure and function of fish schools. *Sci. Amer.* 246(6):90-126.

PATTERSON, C. 1981. The development of the North American fish fauna - a problem of historical biogeography. *In: The Evolving Biosphere.* Forey, P.L. (ed.). Cambridge University Press, London: 265-282.

PEARSON, D.L. & J.A. DERR. 1986. Seasonal patterns of lowland flood forest arthropod abundance in southeastern Peru. *Biotropica.* 18(3):244-256.

PENNY, N.D. 1981. Neuroptera. *In:* S.H. Hurlbert, G. Rodriquez and N.D. Santos (eds.). *Aquatic Biota of Tropical South America.* San Diego State University, San Diego: 89-91.

PENNY, N.D. & J.R. ARIAS. 1982. *Insects of an Amazon Forest.* Columbia University Press, New York. 269pp.

PETRERE, M., 1978. Pesca e esforço de pesca no Estado do Amazonas I. Esforço e captura por unidade de esforço. *Acta Amazonica.* 8(3):439-454.

PETRERE, M. 1985. Migraciones de peces de agua dulce en America Latina; algunos comentários.

Copescal Documento Ocasional, FAO (Rome). 1:1-17.

PETRI, S. & V.J. FULFARO. 1983. Geologia do Brasil. Editora da Universidade de Sao Paulo, Sao Paulo. 631pp.

PIEDADE, M.T.F. 1985. Ecologia e biologia reprodutiva de Astrocaryum jauari Mart. (Palmae) como exemplo de populacão adaptada as áreas inundáveis do rio Negro (igapós). Master's Thesis. Instituto Nacional de Pesquisas da Amazonia. 184pp.

PIMM, S.L. 1982. Food Webs. Chapman and Hall, London & New York. 219pp.

PIMM, S.L. & J.H. LAWTON. 1978. On feeding on more than on trophic level. Nature. 275:542-544.

PIRES, J.M. AND J.S. RODRIGUES. 1964. Sobre a flora das caatingas do rio Negro. Anais do Congresso da Sociedade Botanica do Brasil. 1962:242-262.

PIRES, J.M. & G.T. PRANCE. 1978. The Amazon forest: a natural heritage to be preserved. In: G.T. Prance (ed.). Extinction is Forever. The New York Botanical Garden, New York: 158-194.

POWER, M. 1984a. Depth distribution of armoured catfish: predator-induced resource avoidance?. Ecology. 65:523-528.

POWER, M.E. 1984b. Grazing responses of tropical freshwater fishes to different scales of variation in their food. In: T.M. Zaret (ed). Evolutionary Ecology of Neotropical Freshwater Fishes. Dr W. Junk Publishers, The Hague: 25-37.

POWER, M.E. 1984c. Habitat quality and the distribution of algal-grazing catfish in a Panamanian stream. J. Anim. Ecol. 53:357-374.

PRANCE, G.T. 1978. The origen and evolution of the Amazonian flora. Interciencia. 3(4):207-222.

PRANCE, G.T. 1979. Notes on the vegetation of Amazonia. III. The terminology of Amazoniam forest type subject to inundation. Brittonia. 31(1):26-38.

PRANCE, G.T. 1980. A terminologia dos tipos de florestas amazônicas sujeitas a inundação. Acta Amazonica. 10(3):495-504.

PRANCE, G.T. & H.O.R. SCHUBART. 1977. Nota preliminar sobre a origem das campinas abertas de areia branca do baixo Rio Negro. Acta Amazonica. 7(4):567-569.

PRETZMANN, G. 1972. Die Pseudothelphusidae (Crustacea, Brachyura). Zoologica (Stuttgart). 1:201-182.

RADAM. 1976-1978. Projeto Radambrasil. Ministério das Minas e Energia and Departamento Nacional da Produção Mineral, Rio de Janeiro.

RAI, H. 1978. Distribution of carbon, chlorophyll-a and pheo-pigments in the black water lake ecosystem of Central Amazon Region. Arch. Hydrobiol.. 82(1/4):74-87.

RAI, H. 1979. Microbiology of Central Amazon lakes. Amazoniana. 6(4):583-599.

RAI, H. & G. HILL. 1980. Classification of central Amazon lakes on the basis of their microbiological and physicochemical characteristics. Hydrobiologia. 72:85-99.

RAI, H. & G. HILL. 1981a. Physical and chemical studies of Lago Tupé; a Central Amazon black water ria lake. Int. Revue. Ges. Hydrobiol. 66(1):37-82.

RAI, H. & G. HILL. 1981b. Bacterial biodynamics in Lago Tupé, a Central Amazonian black water ria lake. Arch. Hydrobiol. 58(4):420-468.

RAI, H. & G. HILL. 1984. Primary production in the Amazonian aquatic ecosystem. The Amazon: Limnology and Landscape Ecology of a Mighty Tropical River and Its Basin. Sioli, H. (ed.). Dr. W. Junk Publishers, Dordrecht: 311-336.

REISS, F. 1977. Qualitative and quantitative investigations on the macrobenthic fauna of Central Amazon lakes. I. Lago Tupé, a black water on the lower Rio Negro. Amazoniana. 6(2):203-235.

RIBEIRO, M.C.L.B. 1983. As migracões dos jaraquis (Pisces, Prochilodontidae), no rio Negro, Amazonas, Brasil. Master's Thesis. Instituto Nacional de Pesquisas da Amazonia, Manaus. 192pp.

RIBEIRO, M.C.L.B. 1985. A natural hybrid between two tropical fishes: Semaprochilodus insignus X Semaprochilodus taeniurus (Teleostei, Characoidei, Prochilodontidae). Revta bras. Zool., S Paulo. 2(7):419-421.

RIEMANNN, F. 1981. Nematoda (free living forms). In: S.H. Hurlbert, G. Rodriquez and N.D. Santos (eds.). Aquatic Biota of Tropical South America. San Diego State University, San Diego: 133-135.

ROBERTS, T.R. 1970. Description, osteology and relationships of the Amazonian cyprinodont fish Fluviphylax pygmaeus (Myers and Carvalho). Breviora. (247):1-28.

ROBERTS, T.R. 1970. Scale-eating American characoid fishes, with special reference to Probolodus heterostomus. Proc. Calif. Acad. Sci. 20:383-390.

ROBERTS, T.R. 1972. Ecology of fishes in the Amazon and Congo basins. Bull. Mus. Comp. Zool., Harvard. 143(2):117-147.

ROBERTS, T.R. 1974. Osteology and classification of the Neotropical Characoid fishes of the families Hemiodontidae (including Anodontinae) and Parodontidae. *Bull. Mus. Comp. Zool, Harvard.* 146(9):411-472.

ROBERTS, T.R. 1984. *Amazonsprattus scintilla*, new genus and species from the Rio Negro, Brazil, the smallest known clupeopmorph fish. *Proc. Calif. Acad. Sci.* 43(20):317-321.

ROBERTSON, B.A. & E.R. HARDY. 1984. Zooplankton of Amazonian lakes and rivers. *In:* H. Sioli (ed.). *The Amazon: Limnology and Landscape Ecology.* Dr W. Junk Publishers, Dordrecht: 337-352.

RODRIGUES, W.A. 1960. Aspectos fitosociológicos das caatingas do rio Negro. *Ciência e Cultura.*

RODRIQUEZ, G. 1981. Decapoda. *In:* S.H. Hurlbert, G. Rodriquez and N.D. Santos (eds.). *Aquatic Biota of Tropical South America. Part 1. Arthropoda.* San Diego State University, San Diego.

SALATI, E, J. MARQUES & L.C.B. MOLION. 1978. Origem e distribuição das chuvas na Amazônia. *Interciencia.* 3:200-206.

SALATI, E. & J. MARQUES. 1984. Climatology of the Amazon region. *In:* H. Sioli (ed.). *The Amazon: Limnology and Landscape Ecology.* Dr W. Junk Publishers, Dordrecht: 85-126.

SALE, P.F. 1977. Maintenance of high diversity in coral reef fish communities. *Amer. Nat.* 111:337-359.

SALE, P.F. 1980a. The ecology of fishes on coral reefs. *Oceanography and Mar. Biol.* 18:367-421.

SALE, P.F. 1980b. Assemblages of fish on pathy reefs – predictable or unpredictable? *Envir. Biol. Fish.* 5:243-249.

SANTOS, G.M. 1981. Estudo de alimentação e hábitos alimentares de *Schizodon fasciatus* Agassiz 1829, *Rhytiodus microlepis* Kner 1859 e *Rhytiodos argenteofuscus* Kner 1859 do Lago Janauacá - Am. (Osteichthyes, Characoidei, Anostomidae). *Acta Amazonica.* 10(2):267-283.

SANTOS, G.M., M. JEGU & B. MERONA. 1984. Catálogo de peixes comerciais do baixo Rio Tocantins. Eletronorte/CNPq/INPA, Manaus. 83pp.

SANTOS, N.D. 1981. Odonata. *In:* S.H. Hurlbert, G. Rodriquez and N.D. Santos (eds.). *Aquatic Biota of Tropical South America. Part 1. Arthropoda.* San Diego State University, San Diego: 64-85.

SANTOS, U.M., S.R.B. BRINGEL, H.B. FILHO. 1984. Rios da bacia amazônica. I. Afluentes do Rio Negro. *Acta Amazonica.* 14(12):222-237.

SATTLER, V.W. 1963. Uber den Korperbau, die Ökologie und Ethologie der Larve und Puppe von *Macronema* Pict. (Hydropsychidae), ein als Larve sich von Mikro-Drift ernahrendes Trichopter aus dem Amazonasgebiet. *Arch. Hydrobiol.* 59(1):26-60.

SATTLER, V.W. 1968. Weitere Mitteilungen über die Okeethologie einer neotropischen *Macronema*-larve (Hydropsychidae, Trichoptera). *Amazoniana.* 1(3):211-229.

SAUL, W.G. 1975. A study of fishes at a site in upper Amazonian Ecuador. *Proc. Acad. nat. Sci., Philadelphia.* 127:93-134.

SAZIMA, I. 1977. Possible case of aggressive mimicry in a Neotropical scale-eating fish. *Nature.* 270: 510-512.

SAZIMA, I. 1984. Scale-eating in characoids and other fishes. *In:* T.M. Zaret (ed.). *Evolutionary Ecology of Neotropical Freshwater Fishes.* Dr W. Junk Publishers, The Hague: 9-23.

SAZIMA, I. & F.A. MACHADO. 1982. Hábitos e comportamento de *Roeboides prognathus*, um peixe lepidófago (Osteichthyes, Characoidei). *Bolm. Zool. Univ. S. Paulo.* 7: 35-56.

SCHMIDT, G.W. 1976. Primary production of phytoplankton in the three types of Amazonian waters. IV. On the primary productivity of phytoplankton in a bay of the lower Rio Negro (Amazonas, Brazil). *Amazoniana.* 4(4):517-528.

SCHMIDT, G.W. & G. UHERKOVICH. 1973. Zur Artenfulle des Phytoplanktons im Amazonien. *Amazoniana.* 4(3):243-252.

SCHOBBENHAUS, C. (ed.). 1984. *Geologia do Brasil.* Departamento Nacional de Produçao Mineral, Brasilia.

SCHOLANDER, P.F. & M. OLIVEIRA PEREZ. 1968. Sap tension in flooded trees and bushes of the Amazon. *Plant Physiol.* 43:1870-1873.

SCULTHORPE, C.D. 1971. *The Biology of Aquatic Vascular Plants.* E. Arnold Ltd, London. 610 pp.

SILVA, M.F., P.L.B. LISBOA & R.C.L. LISBOA. 1977. *Nomes Vulgares das Plantas Amazônicas.* Conselho Nacional de Desenvolvimento Científico e Tecnológico, Manaus.

SILVA, V.M.F. 1983. Ecologia alimentar dos golfinhos da Amazonia. *Master's Thesis.* Instituto Nacional de Pesquisas da Amazonia. 110pp.

SINGER, R. 1978. Origins of deficiency of Amazonian soils – a new approach. *Acta Amazonica.* 8:315-316.

SINGER, R. 1979. Litter decomposition and ectomycorrhizae in Amazonian forests. 1. A comparison of litter decomposition and ectomycorrhizal Basidiomycetes in latosol-terra-firme rainforest and white podzol campinarana. *Acta Amazonica.* 9:25-41.

SINGER, R. 1984. The role of fungi in Amazonian forests and in reforestation. *In*: H. Sioli (ed.). *The Amazon: Limnology and Landscape Ecology*. Dr W. Junk Publishers, Dordrecht: 603-614.

SINGER, R. & I. ARAUJO. 1979. Litter decomposition and ectomycorrhyzae in Amazonian forest. *Acta Amazonica*. 9(1):25-41.

SIOLI, H. 1951. Zum Alterungsprozess von Flussen und Flusstypen im Amazonas Gebiet. *Archiv fur Hydrobiologie*. 45(3):267-284.

SIOLI, H. 1955. Beiträge zur regionalen Limnologie des Amazonasgebietes. III. Über einige Gewässer des oberen Rio Negro-Gebietes. *Archiv für Hydrobiologie*. 50(1):1-32.

SIOLI, H. 1956. As aguas da região do alto rio Negro. *Bol Tec.Inst. Agron. Norte, Belem*. 32:117-155.

SIOLI, H. 1957. Valores de pH de águas amazônicas. *Bol. Mus. paraense E. Goeldi (Geologia)*. 1:1-37.

SIOLI, H. 1964. General features of the limnology of Amazônia. *Verh. Internat. Verein. Limnol.* 15:1053-1058.

SIOLI, H. 1967. Studies in Amazonian waters. *Atas do Simpósio sobre a Biota Amazônica (Limnologia)*. 39-50.

SIOLI, H. 1968. Hydrochemistry and geology in the Brazilian Amazon region. *Amazoniana*. 1(3):267-277.

SIOLI, H. 1975.. Amazon tributaries and drainage basins. Hasler, A.D. (ed.). *Coupling of Land and Water Systems*. Springer Verlag, New York: 199-213.

SIOLI, H. & H. KLINGE. 1961. Über Gewässer und Boden des brasilianischen Amazonasgebietes. *Erde*. 91:205-219.

SIOLI, H. & H. KLINGE. 1962. Solos, tipos da vegetação e águas na Amazônia. *Bol. Mus. paraense E. Goeldi*. 1:27-41.

SIOLI, H. & H. KLINGE. 1965. Sobre águas e solos da Amazônia brasileira. *Bol. Geogr. (Rio de Janeiro)*. 24(185):195-205.

SMITH, N.J.H. 1979. *Pesca no Rio Amazonas*. INPA/CNPq, Manaus.

SMITH, N.J.H. 1981. *Man, Fishes and the Amazon*. Columbia University Press, New York. 180pp.

SOARES, M.G.M. 1979. Aspectos ecológicos (alimentação e reprodução) dos peixes do Igarapé do Porto, Aripuanã, MT. *Acta Amazonica*. 9:325-352.

SPIX, J.B. and K.F.P. MARTIUS. 1823. *Reise in Brasilien auf Befehl Sr. Majestät Maximilian Joseph 1, Königs von Baiern in den Jahren 1817 bis 1820 . . . .* M. Lindauer, München. 3 vols.

SPRUCE, R. 1908. *In*: *Notes of a Botanist on the Amazon and Andes*. MacMillan, London. 2 vols. (Wallace, A.R. ed.).

ST. JOHN, T.V. & A.B. ANDERSON. 1982. A re-examination of plant phenolics as a source of tropical black water rivers. *Trop. Ecol*. 23(1):151-154.

STARK, N. & C. HOLLEY. 1975. Final report on studies of nutrient cycling on white and black water areas in Amazonia. *Acta Amazonica*. 5:51-76.

STATON, M.A. & J.R. DIXON. 1975. Studies on the dry season biology of *Caiman crocodilus crocodilus* from the Venezuelan Llanos. *Mem. Soc. Cienc. Nat. L Salle*. 101:237-264.

STERN, K.M. 1970. Der Casiquiare-Kanal, einst und jetzt. *Amazoniana 2(4):401-416*.

STERNBERG, H. O'R. 1950. Vales tectônicos na planície amazônica. *Rev. Bras. Geogr*. 12:513-533.

STERNBERG, H. O'R. 1953. Sismicidade e morfologia na Amazônia brasileira. *An. Acad. Bras. Ciencias*. 25:443-453.

SUDAM. 1984. *Atlas Climatológico da Amazônia Brasileira*. Sudam, Belém.

SWEET, D. 1974. A rich realm of nature destroyed: the middle Amazon valley, 1640-1750. *Ph.D. Dissertation*. University of Wisconsin, Madison.

TAKEUCHI, M. 1961a. The structure of the Amazonian vegetation II. Tropical rain forest. *Jour. Fac. Sci. Univ. Tokyo*. 8(1/3):1-26.

TAKEUCHI, M. 1961b. The structure of the Amazonian vegetation. III. Campina forest in the Rio Negro region. *Journ. Fac. Sci. Univ. Tokyo*. 8(2):27-35.

TAKEUCHI, M. 1962a. The structure of the Amazonian vegetation. IV. High Campina forest in the upper rio Negro. *Jour. Fac. Sci. Univ. Tokyo*. 8(5):279-288.

TAKEUCHI, M. 1962b. The structure of the Amazonian vegetation. V. Tropical rain forest near Uaupés. *Jour. Fac. Sci. Univ. Tokyo*. 8(6):289-296.

TAKEUCHI, M. 1962c. The structure of the Amazonian vegetation. VI. Igapo. *Jour. FAc. Sci. Univ. Tokyo*. 8(7):297-304.

THORNES, J.B. 1969. Variability in specific conductance and pH in the Casiquiare − Upper Orinoco. *Nature*. 221:461-462.

187

THORSON, T.B. 1972. The status of the bull shark, *Carcharhinus leucas*, in the Amazon river. *Copeia*. 3(8):601-605.

THORSON, T.B. 1974. Occurrence of the sawfish, *Pristis perotteti*, in the Amazon river, with notes on P. pectinatus. *Copeia*. 2:560-564.

UHERKOVICH. G. 1976. Algen aus den Flussen Rio Negro und Rio Tapajos. *Amazoniana*. 5:465-515.

UHERKOVICH, G. 1984. Phytoplankton. *In:* H. Sioli (ed.). *The Amazon: Limnology and Landscape Ecology*. Dr W. Junk Publishers, Dordrecht: 295-310.

UHERKOVICH, G. & G.W. SCHMIDT. 1974. Phytoplanktontaxa in dem zentralamazonischen Schwemmlandsee. *Amazoniana*. 5(2):243-283.

UHERKOVICH, G. & H. RAI. 1979. Algen aus dem Rio Negro und seinen nebenflussen. *Amazoniana*. 6(4):611-638.

UNGEMACH, H. 1967. Sobre o balanco metabólico de iônios inorgânicos da área do sistema do Rio Negro. *Atas do Simpósio sobre a Biota Amazônica (Limnologia)*. 3:221-226.

VAN der PIJL, L. 1982. *Principles of Dispersal in Higher Plants*. Springer-Verlag, Berlin. 215pp..

VAN OOSTEN, J. 1957. The skin and scales. *In*: M. E. Brown (ed.). *The Physiology of Fishes*. Academic Press, New York: 207-224.

VANZOLINI, P.E. 1977. A brief biometrical note on the reproductive biology of some South American *Podocnemis* (Testudines, Pelomedusidae). *Papeis Avulsos Zool., S. Paulo*. 31(5):79-102.

VANZOLINI, P.E. & N. GOMES. 1979. Notes on the ecology and growth of Amazonian caimans (Crocodylia, Alligatoridae). *Papeis Avulsos Zool. Sao Paulo*. 32:205-216.

VARI, R.P. 1982. Systematics of the Neotropical characoid genus *Curimatopsis* (Pisces: Characoidei). *Smith. Contr. Zool.* 373:1-28.

VARI, R.P. 1983. Phylogenetic relationships of the families Curimatidae, Prochilodontidae, Anostomidae, and Chilodontidae (Pisces: Characiformes). *Smith. Contr. Zool.* 378:1-60.

VARI, R.P. 1984. Systematics of the Neotropical characiform genus *Potamorhina* (Pisces: Characiformes). *Smith. Contr. Zool.* 400:1-36.

VARI, R.P. 1986. Serrabrycon magoi, a new genus and species of scale-eating characid (Pisces: Characiformes) from the upper Rio Negro. *Proc. Biol. Soc. Wash.*. 99(2):328-324.

VARI, R.P. & H. ORTEGA. 1986. The catfishes of the Neotropical family Helogenidae (Ostariophysi: Siluroidei). *Smith. Contr. Zool.* 442:1-20.

VIEIRA, L.S. & J.P.S. FILHO. 1962. As caatingas do rio Negro. *Bol. Tec. Inst. Agron. Norte*. 42:1-32.

VIERA, I. & J. GERY. 1979. Crescimento diferencial e nutrição em *Catoprion mento* (Characoidei). Peixe lepidófago da Amazônia. *Acta Amazonica*. 9:143-146.

VOLKMER-RIBEIRO, C. 1981. Porifera. S.H. Hurlbert, G. Rodriquez and N.D. Santos (eds.). *Aquatic Biota of Tropical South America. Part 2. Anarthropoda*. San Diego State University, San Diego: 86-95.

WALKER, I. 1978. Rede de alimentação de invertebrados das águas pretas do sistema do Rio Negro. I: Observações sobre a predação de uma ameba do tipo *Amoeba discoides*. *Acta Amazonica*. 8:423-438.

WALKER, I. 1985. On the structure and ecology of the micro-fauna in the Central Amazonian forest stream Igarapé da Cachoeira. *Hydrobiologia*. 122:137-152.

WALKER, I. & M.J.N. FERREIRA. 1985. On the population dynamics and ecology of the shrimp species (Crustacea, Decapoda, Natantia) in the Central Amazonian river Tarumã-Mirim. *Oecologia*. 66:264-270.

WALKER, I. & FRANKEN, W. 1983. Ecossistemas frágeis: a floresta da terra firme da Amazônia Central. *Ciencia Interamericana*. 23:9-21.

WALLACE, A.R. 1853. *Narrative of Travels on the Amazon and Rio Negro*. Reeve and Co., London. 363p.

WALLACE, A.R. 1905. *My Life: A Record of Events and Opinions*. Dood, Mead & Company, New York. 435 and 464pp.

WARD, R.A. 1981. Culicidae. *In*: S.H. Hurlbert, G. Rodriquez and N.D. Santos (eds.). *Aquatic Biota of Tropical South America. Part 1. Arthropoda*. San Diego State University, San Diego: 245.

WEITZMAN, S.H. 1960. Further notes on the relationships and classification of the South American characid fishes of the subfamily Gasteropelecinae. *Stanford Ichthyol. Bull.*. 7(4):217-239.

WEITZMAN, S.H. 1978. Three new species of fishes of the genus *Nannostomus* from the Brazilian states of Pará and Amazonas (Teleostei: Lebiasinidae). *Smithsonian Contr. Zool.* 263:1-14.

WEITZMAN, S.H. & J.S. COBB. 1975. A revision of the South American fishes of the genus *Nannostomus* Gunther (Family Lebiasinidae). *Smith. Contr. Zool.* 186:1-36.

WEITZMAN, S.H. & W.L. FINK. 1983. Relationships of the neon tetras, a group of South American freshwater fishes (Teleostei, Characidae), with comments on the phylogeny of new world Characiformes. *Bull. Mus. Comp. Zool., Harvard*. 150(6):339-395.

WEITZMAN, S.H. & R.P. VARI. 1988. Miniaturization in South American freshwater fishes: overview and discussion. *Proc. Biol. Soc., Washington* 101(2):444–465.

WEITZMAN, S.H. & M. WEITZMAN. 1982. Biogeography and evolutionary diversification in Neotropical freshwater fishes, with comments on the refugium theory. *In: Biological Diversification in the Tropics*. Prance, G.T. (ed.). Columbia University Press, New York: 403-422..

WELCOMME, R.L. 1979. *Fisheries Ecology of Floodplain Rivers*. Longman, London. 317p.

WELCOMME, R.L. 1985. River fisheries. *FAO Fisheries Technical Paper*. 262:1-330.

WESSLER, E. & I. WERNER. 1957. On the chemical composition of some mucuous substances of fish. *Acta Chem. Scand.* 2:1240-1247.

WIEBACH, V.F. 1967. Amazonische Moostiere (Bryozoa). *Amazoniana.* 1(2):173-187.

WIEBACH, V.F. 1970. Amazonische Moostiere (Bryozoa). *Amazoniana.* 11(3):235-243.

WILLIAMS, C.M., R.S. LOOMIS & P.T. ALVIM. 1967. Insectical properties of the waters of the Rio Negro. *Progress Report, R-V Alpha Helix Amazon Expedition (La Jolla).* C14:1-5.

WILLIAMS, W.A. 1971. Environments of evergreen rain forest on the lower rio Negro, Brazil. *Trop. Ecol.* 13(1):65-78.

WISSMAR, R.C., J.E. RICHEY, R.F. STALLARD & J.M. EDMOND. 1981. Plankton metabolism and carbon processes in the Amazon river, its tributaires, and floodplain waters, Peru-Brazil. *Ecology.* 62(6):1622-1633.

ZARET, T.M. 1975. Strategies for existence of zooplankton prey in homogeneous environments. *Verh. Internat. Verein. Limnol.* 10:1484-1489.

ZARET, T.M. 1976. Vertical migration in zooplankton as a predator avoidance mechanism. *Limn. Ocean.* 21(6):804-813.

ZARET, T.M. 1980. *Predation and Freshwater Communities*. Yale University Press, New Haven. 187pp.

ZARET, T.M. & S. RAND. 1971. Competition in tropical stream fishes: support for the competitive exclusion principle. *Ecology.* 52(2):336-342.

INDEX